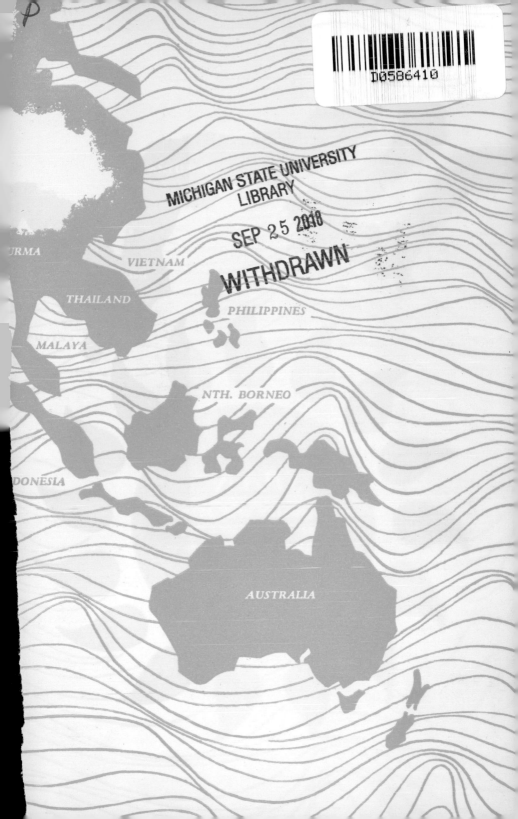

URMA

VIETNAM

THAILAND

PHILIPPINES

MALAYA

NTH. BORNEO

DONESIA

AUSTRALIA

SPAN

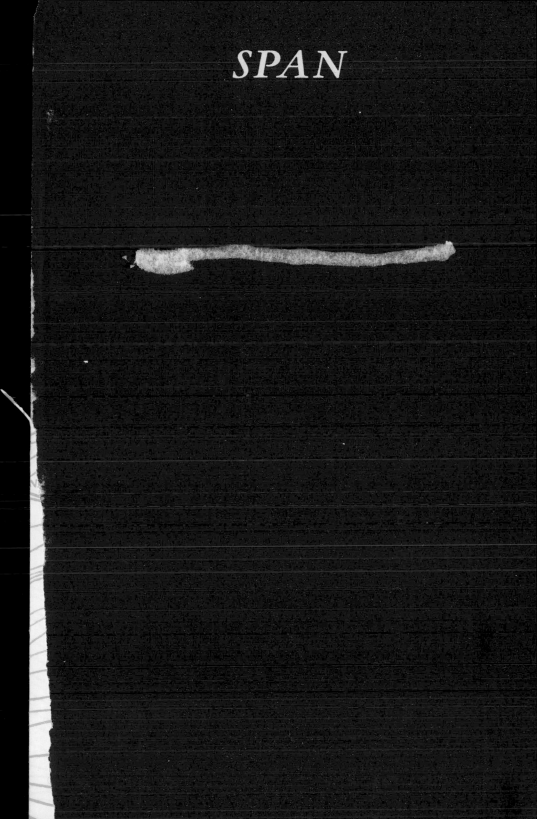

AN ADVENTURE
IN ASIAN AND AUSTRALIAN WRITING

SPAN

EDITED FOR THE CANBERRA FELLOWSHIP OF AUSTRALIAN WRITERS

Lionel Wigmore

F. W. CHESHIRE

First published 1958
by F. W. CHESHIRE PTY. LTD.
338 Little Collins Street,
Melbourne, C.1, Victoria

❊

ARTWORK AND TYPOGRAPHY
by Arthur Leydin

❊

PRINTED AND BOUND BY HALSTEAD PRESS, SYDNEY
Registered in Australia for transmission by post as a book

OUR REGION

SEVENTY-TWO writers, in a dozen countries, have helped to weave the pattern of people, place and circumstance in this book. It is a venture in spanning the distances and differences —distances between countries, differences in race, religion, language and outlook—which exist in that part of the world known today as South and South-east Asia, and Australia.

The people of Australia other than its aborigines are, of course, the most newly arrived in this region. Australian literature reflected less than a century ago the feeling of exile which existed among the early settlers in this country. Today it reflects a keen sense of having become at one with the environment they found so strange; of having become Australians.

Among the other people of the region, any such process occurred a very long time ago. Nearly all the Asian countries represented have, however, like Australia, achieved nationhood in the present century, and this has brought with it a keener national consciousness.

There are signs that they and Australians are now undergoing a still newer process. This is a process of becoming naturalised, as it were, to the whole intensely interesting and richly productive region in which they are neighbours; of awakening to each other's viewpoints, aims and resources, and to the possibilities of co-operation for their mutual and common good. In this process, creative writers are a powerful influence, for it is they above all who give expression to the innermost thoughts of the people around them, who best portray their lives and who thereby become interpreters of the life and spirit of their countries.

Whether this widening of outlook and deepening of understanding will go on over the whole region or only part of it, and how much it will enlighten and enrich the lives of its people,

v

remains hidden. It can be hoped, however, that as well as pleasing and profiting its readers, this book will aid the process; thus helping people to live peacefully and pleasantly together rather than being haunted by the current fears of dying horribly or surviving no less horribly amid the distorted remnants of life on earth.

Span is the third book which the Canberra Fellowship of Australian Writers has produced since it came into existence in 1950. Both the earlier books consisted wholly of Australian prose and poetry. Their success—both have now sold out—led to the present venture into a wider field. This was an ambitious move in the sense that it required a far greater amount of work than the Fellowship is geared to undertake (the correspondence involved would far more than fill this volume). However, the task of organising the venture, obtaining and selecting the material, and editing and otherwise preparing it for publication was eventually performed, on a wholly honorary, spare-time basis.

The Fellowship does not possess funds beyond those necessary to keep it alive, but its publishers have on each occasion undertaken the outlay necessary for production. In keeping with a principle agreed upon between the Fellowship and the publishers, payment to writers of the contents has been made as a first charge to production costs.

In choosing the contents the prime concern was to select from what became available that which would contribute most to the quality, interest and balance of the book, and would convey most about the countries and the circumstances at the time it was written. We were not hamstrung by having to consider whether any writer or his contribution was right, left, centre or elsewhere on the political chart. As a means of safeguarding our freedom of choice on the merits of what was offered, financial aid in the selection stage was neither sought nor accepted. It need surprise no one, therefore, if some who are regarded as rebels or revolutionaries, and some who rate as reactionaries, rub shoulders on these pages.

Short stories were selected in preference to other prose, because their quality and interest were greater in most instances, and they seemed to fulfil most fruitfully the purposes of the book.

Translation problems greatly restricted the choice of poetry, for of course poems usually need the services of a poet to breathe their music and meaning from one language into another. It seems reasonable to hope that in the translations of both prose and poetry which appear in this book, the tone and spirit of the originals have been preserved to a satisfying extent.

Many problems were encountered in selecting the Asian contents. Bearing in mind the many national, racial, religious and other groups from which material came, how could the task be performed with the necessary insight and discrimination?

It would have been parochial and churlish to apply a purely Australian standard and outlook to the task. In generous response to requests, representatives of Asian writers, and others in the countries concerned, co-operated in procuring and sifting material, and sending to Canberra what they considered most worthy of further consideration. This was then read by the Editor, and two or more members of the Editorial Board whose judgment came from broad experience and well-informed minds. Final determination of the contents had to be made by the Editor in keeping with the aims of the book and within the practical limits of its size.

A boundary in time, taking in only the period since 1945, was drawn so that the book might reflect the Asian-Australian neighbourhood while the enormously powerful effects of World War II were in their dawn. It is now evident, however, that the stream of events has seeped into literature at different speeds in different countries according to circumstances. These circumstances include, of course, the facilities available for literary expression, and the degree of freedom with which it may be exercised, but also the stage reached in the evolution of ideas. For these and other reasons, including the relatively small choice available in the material received from a few of the countries, not all the contents relate to the period in which they were written. Again, three attractive contributions *The Golden Goby, The Mandarin and the Flower Festival,* and *The Old-Man and Marrgon the Lightning* have been included in the sense that though they are old legends in substance, they have been recreated or revived by the authors as current literature, in collections from which they were chosen.

As the work of selection progressed, it became evident that a broad survey of each country's literature as a preface to a section of the book containing its contributions would be impracticable. Furthermore, the idea of marshalling the contents according to national boundaries gave way to a conviction that letting them mingle would produce a far happier, gayer effect. To avoid intrusion between reader and writer, editorial notes and explanations have been inserted only where they seemed to be essential.

In short, this is a book presented with conviction that, despite its unusual span, it is better to let the contents speak for themselves than to make what could only be inadequate attempts to speak for them. If it sharpens interest in the countries represented, and serves as a base for further such neighbourly publications, it will have done its job.

LIONEL WIGMORE

ACKNOWLEDGMENTS

THE co-operation of many people in Asian countries and in Australia was necessary in bringing this book into existence, because of the wide area it covers and the extent of organisation and overseas representation consequently required. This invaluable assistance is gratefully acknowledged. In the upshot, far more material was procured than could be used. The sifting undertaken by some of the helpers in Asia, however, kept the amount received in Canberra to manageable proportions yet left a wide range of choice to the Editorial Board. The contents are in the main, therefore, the result of joint endeavour by the many thus concerned in the countries represented, though not all the items were received in this way. (For instance, the inclusion of a story drawn from Han Suyin's novel, ". . . and the rain my drink" resulted from Professor Manning Clark, of the Editorial Board, meeting her during a flight from Rangoon to New Delhi.) Those organisations and individuals whom it is possible to acknowledge by name as having helped overseas in this preparatory stage include the following (the positions mentioned are those they held at the time):

BURMA: Burma Translation Society (and, in Australia, the former Ambassador for Burma, U. Sain Bwa, and the former First Secretary of the Embassy, U. Htoon Shein).

CEYLON: Mr J. Padmanabha, of the Ceylon *Daily News*, and Mr S. Muttiah, of the *Times of Ceylon*; (and Mr H. O. Wijegoonawardena, Secretary of the Ceylon High Commission in Australia).

INDIA: Mr H. R. K. Kripalani, Secretary of the Sahitya Akademi; Professor Humayun Kabir, Vice President of the Council of Cultural Relations; Mr K. G. Saiyidain, Secretary of the Ministry of Education; Dr K. Shridharani (see biography, p. 378); Mrs Muriel Wasi, of the Ministry of Education, Mr U. Bhaskar Rao, Editor of the *Indian Express* newspaper, Mr R. Mitchell, of the Australian News and Information Bureau, and Mrs Mitchell. Thanks are due especially to the three last mentioned for reading a very large number of manuscripts. (In Australia, aid and encouragement were given by the former High Commissioner for India, General K. M. Cariappa, and the former Official Secretary, Mr K. R. P. Singh.)

INDONESIA: Mr Achdiat K. Mihardja and Mr Oentoeng Soebroto (see biographies, pp. 375, 379), who were studying in Australia under the Colombo Plan; Mr R. Supangkat, Cultural Attaché, and Mr Tjuk Atmadi, Press Attaché, of the Embassy of Indonesia in Australia.

MALAYA: Che Hawa, writer and broadcaster; Inche Mohd. Ali, of the Selangor Department of Education; Messrs Yap Bun Pho, of the Government Chinese Language School, K. S. Chang, of *Sin Chew Jit Poh* newspaper, G. Alagirisami, Editor of *Tamil Nesan* newspaper, Patrick Keith, of Radio Malaya, and W. Emslie, of the British Council (who acted as Chairman of this group).

PAKISTAN: Mr Jalaluddin Ahmad, Department of Advertising, Films and Publications, Government of Pakistan; Mr Hadi Husain, of the Pakistan High Commission, Bangkok; Mr M. M. Taqi, Deputy Director, United Nations Information Centre, Karachi, and Mr Agha Abdul Hamid, Joint Secretary of the Cabinet Secretariat, Karachi.

PHILIPPINES: Mrs Pura Santillan Castrence, Chief of the Division of Cultural Activities; Professor Cristino Jamias, Mr N. V. M. Gonzalez, both of the University of the Philippines.

SINGAPORE: Mr Lee Siow Mong, President of the China Society, historian and author; Mr S. Fraser, of the Teachers' Training College, lecturer and author; Inche Yusof bin Ishak, manager of *Utusan Melayu* newspaper; Mr G. Sarangapany, Editor of *Tamil Murasu* newspaper; Mr M. Baker, the University of Malaya (Chairman) and Mr Hugh Savage, journalist and author (Deputy Chairman).

Acknowledgments

THAILAND: Mr Norman Bartlett, Australian author and officer of the News and Information Bureau, stationed in Bangkok. He characteristically undertook practically all the work involved in obtaining Thai contributions, and overcame many difficulties.

VIETNAM: Professor Nguyen Cuong Cuu, Dean of the Faculty of Letters at the National University.

The problem of translating stories and poems from the many languages used in South and South-east Asia naturally restricted the choice that could be made. It was, however, possible to include a number of selections as a result of translations by the following:

Mr A. Anjad Ali (*Defeat*).

Mr A. Brotherton (*Born Before the Dawn*).

Mr Robert MacQuaid (*Hamid*).

Mr K. Filshie (*The Mandarin and the Flower Festival*).

Mr Hamid Jalal (*The Black Shalwar*).

U. Kaung (*The Beda Flower*).

Mr Victor Kiernam (*Freedom's Dawn* and *A Prison Nightfall*).

Nai K. Kitiyakara (*The Good Citizen*).

Mr S. K. Mukherjee (*The Birds* and *Alaka*).

Prince Prem Purachatra (*Shoot to Kill*).

Mr Oentoeng Soebroto (*Mother's Pilgrimage to Paradise* and, with Robert Chapman, *The False*).

U. Win Pe (*His Spouse*).

Mr Ian Hamilton, of the News and Information Bureau at the time, and stationed in Singapore, initiated the formation of the co-operating committees in Singapore and Malaya and gave other aid.

The Editorial Board on whose advice and assistance the Editor drew especially for the reading and assessing of the material available, consisted originally of the following:

Mr T. A. G. Hungerford, 1955-56 President of the Fellowship; author of *The Ridge and the River*, *Riverslake* and *Sowers of the Wind*.

Mr David Campbell (see biography, p. 370).

Professor C. Manning Clark, Professor of History, Canberra University College, author of *Documents in Australian History* (two volumes) and *Sources of Australian History*.

Acknowledgments

Professor C. P. FitzGerald, Professor of Far Eastern Studies, Australian National University, author of books including *China— A Cultural History* (1935), *Revolution in China* (1952) and *The Empress Wu* (1955).

Mr L. F. Fitzhardinge, Reader in Australian History, Australian National University; author of historical and literary studies.

Mr John D. Keating, formerly an officer of the Australian News and Information Bureau stationed in New Delhi.

Mr T. Inglis Moore (see biography, p. 375).

Mrs L. F. H. Rees, as Secretary of the Canberra Fellowship of Australian Writers (from its inception).

Dr Russel Ward, Scholar in History at the Australian National University, and authority on Australian bush ballads, author of *The Australian Legend* (now lecturer in Ancient History, University of New England).

Mr Lionel Wigmore, whose special interest is in the development of understanding and goodwill between Asians and Australians. He was elected to the task of organising the project and editing the volume.

Of these, more than half were overseas for lengthy periods while the book was being prepared. Thus, the board does not, as a whole, share fully the responsibility for the choice of contents. The Editor is especially grateful to Messrs Campbell and Moore for having selected the poems. The exacting task of preparing the biographical notes about contributors to *Span* was performed in the main by Miss Patricia Croft of the Australian National University, whose experience was of great value. Others whose services were co-opted as occasion arose included Mr John Tregenza, Scholar in Australian History, Australian National University; Mr Oentoeng Soebroto, Mr Brian Johns, Treasurer of the Fellowship. Mrs C. P. FitzGerald gave valuable aid in registering and circulating material as it was received.

Mrs Rees not only acted as a member of the board, but provided it with a meeting place and generous hospitality.

Most of the material for *Span* was received in manuscript. In respect of items which have already appeared in print, thanks are extended to the following:

ANGUS & ROBERTSON LTD for "Nationality" from *Fourteen Men* by Mary Gilmore, "Josie" from *Let the Birds Fly* by Vance Palmer, "The Pepper-Tree" from *The Scholarly Mouse and Other Tales* by Dal Stivens, and for "Sandy Swamp" from *The Gateway* and "The Hand" from "Flesh" in *The Two Fires*, both by Judith Wright.

APNI NAGARIA for "Defeat" by Mumtaz Shireen.

THE ATLANTIC MONTHLY and INTERCULTURAL PUBLICATIONS INC. for "The Lotteries of Haji Zakaria" by Mochtar Lubis, "Hamid" by Achdiat K. Mihardja, and "Born Before the Dawn" by Pramoedya Ananta Toer.

AUSTRALIAN LETTERS No. 2 for "When Out of Love" by David Campbell.

AUSTRALIAN POETRY 1957 for "Cock-Crow" by Rosemary Dobson and "Align your Act" by T. Inglis Moore.

THE AUSTRALASIAN BOOK SOCIETY for "Going Through" from *Black Cargo and Other Stories* by John Morrison.

THE BULLETIN for "The Time of the Peacock" by Mena Abdullah and Ray Mathew, "Embarkation" by Robert D. Fitz-Gerald, "For My Daughter" by Vivian Smith, and "The Sun Made" from *Socrates* by Francis Webb.

BURMESE NEW WRITING for "His Spouse" by Zawgyi.

JONATHAN CAPE LTD for "Big Dog Tsou" from . . . *and the rain my drink* by Han Suyin.

CEYLON ANNUAL for "The Horror of Mahahena" by S. W. R. D. Bandaranaike.

F. W. CHESHIRE PTY LTD for "My Bird" from *How's Andy Going?* by Alan Marshall.

THE DILIMAN REVIEW for "The Ambitious Failure" by Ricaredo Demetillo and "Rowena, Playing in the Sun" by Edith L. Tiempo.

GEOFFREY DUTTON for his short story "The Wedge-Tailed Eagle".

EDWARDS & SHAW for "The Old-Man and Marrgon the Lightning" from *The Feathered Serpent* and "Tumult of the Swans" from *Tumult of the Swans*, both by Roland Robinson.

Acknowledgments

GONGOTRI for "On a Small Death" by Umashankar Joshi.

THE GRAPHIC PRESS, Manila, for "May Day Eve" and "Verde Yo Te Quiero Verde" from *Prose and Poems* by Nick Joaquin.

THE ILLUSTRATED WEEKLY OF INDIA for Margaret Chatterjee's poem "In a Young Year" and for "The Power of Darkness" by Mulkraj Anand.

THE INDONESIAN REPUBLIC SOCIETY for "Because of You" by an anonymous author, "Story for a Girl, Dien Tamaela" and "To Gadis", both by Chairil Anwar, "The Wanderer" by Rivai Apin, and "Pemuda" by J. Moeljono, all taken from *The Flaming Earth*.

THE LYRE-BIRD WRITERS for "Present" from *Song and Dance* by Ray Mathew.

OVERLAND for "The Keeper of the Night" by David Forrest.

POEMS FROM CHINA for "Having been Attacked for Speaking the Truth . . ." by Ahmed Ali.

QUADRANT for "Meditation on a Bone" by A. D. Hope, "Secret Song" by James McAuley, and "The Silkworms" by Douglas Stewart.

THE SUNDAY STANDARD, Bombay, for "Achha Dood" by Sri Thandaveswara.

THE WOUNDED STAG for "Cautery" by Bienvenido N. Santos.

When the time for printing *Span* came round, the publication sources of some of the Asian stories and poems had not been finally established; nevertheless, just as much thanks is due to those whose names arrived too late for inclusion here.

CONTENTS

IN THE TABLE OF CONTENTS *the names of contributors are grouped into countries and then arranged alphabetically.* IN THE BOOK *the contributions from each country have been scattered.*

The titles of poems are printed in italics.

Contents

BURMA

CEYLON

INDIA

INDONESIA

xvi

Contents

INDONESIA—*continued*

xvii

B

Contents

N. J. Dalal

THE SILVER ANKLETS

*B*HIMA swung her hips gracefully as she walked, and every male within a hundred yards turned his head to stare. The men were working in the sugar-cane fields, cutting the tall slender canes with their curved knives in smooth, even strokes. As the women came into view with their mid-day food, there was a stir and a ripple of excitement.

Bhima felt their eyes on her and her eyelashes fluttered as she jingled the bells on her silver anklets. She was bubbling with vitality and her skin was flushed and her eyes brilliant.

There was a cold wind blowing but the sun was warm—a typical North Indian winter's day. In spite of the cold the men were stripped to the waist, their sweat-polished skins glistening in the sun. They worked with a movement so rhythmic that it had in it something of the perfected grace of a ballet. The sweet smell of the sugar-cane filled the air as the women settled themselves in the shade of the trees, waiting for the men to lay down their knives.

Bhima glanced around at the other women. They were all old and worn out before their time, their figures coarsened and made thick by incessant child-bearing. Only Sita was young and rounded like herself, still scarcely more than a bride, with the bloom of childhood like dew upon her skin. From the very first moment that Bhima had come to the village as Madhu's bride, there had been an unspoken feud between her and Sita. Sita was looking at her now with that mixture of envy and hatred to which Bhima had grown accustomed.

The corners of her mouth twitched irrepressibly as she thought of what they would say if they knew about Kapil. Married less than six months and she had a lover! Bhima smiled again to herself, a slow satisfied smile and her young figure strained at

1

the tight clothes, the breasts showing clearly through the thin stuff of her bodice.

From where she sat she could see both Madhu and Kapil. Both of them had strong athletic bodies and though intensely conscious of her kept their heads turned carefully away. The other men sent furtive glances at the provocative figure, half-lying, half sitting under the tree, and the women, noticing the glances, muttered angrily among themselves.

Bhima allowed her thoughts to wander idly. She thought of the night Madhu had come back from the town, bringing with him the silver anklets, fashioned like snakes, their tails curled round into their mouths. Such a scene they had caused! Madhu's mother had been furious.

"To spend good money," she had spluttered, "on that good-for-nothing slut, who does little all day except bathe and oil herself, instead of working. The money would have bought new utensils and warm blankets for the winter. Oh my son, what has come over you? You are bewitched by her."

Madhu had shifted uneasily, since the words struck home. It was a needless extravagance, and he knew it. Impossible to explain the sudden impulse to buy, with his money, not something useful, but the pretty circlets of silver—to wait for the lighting up of velvety brown eyes, and the quick brilliant intimacy of a smile meant only for him. Bhima saw the indecision in his face and acted at once. She gave a half-stifled sob, and big tears gathered in her eyes and trickled slowly down the soft brown cheek. It was exquisitely done. She held the heavy silver ornaments for a moment, slipping her fingers caressingly over them, and then she stretched out her palm in surrender.

"Take them back," she said softly, "take them back and buy the blankets and the cooking utensils. These are beautiful, but I do not need them." She attempted a smile, which broke off half-way and the corners of her mouth drooped as she pulled her sari forward to hide her face.

Madhu's face had grown a dull red.

"Be quiet," he said furiously to his mother, "I have bought the anklets for my wife, and she shall keep them."

He went down on his knees and with his own hands slipped the anklets over the small feet. They were a bit loose but they looked enchanting, and the bells tinkled with each movement. With her eyes still demurely cast down Bhima shot a triumphant look at her mother-in-law.

The next day at the well she displayed them to the other women. They were all loud in admiration and envy, only Sita had stood speechless. Her own jewels, thin silver bangles and ear-rings, of which she had been so proud, were completely eclipsed by the rich silver anklets. For a moment it seemed to the watching women that Sita would tear the ornaments from Bhima's slender ankles, but instead she turned and ran back home, anger and frustration in every line of her body.

The sun was overhead now, and one by one the men laid down their knives and stretched their aching muscles. The women began to unwrap the food. There were chappatties (cakes of unleavened bread) and vegetables for Madhu, and a bottle of "lassi". Bhima spread out the handkerchief and arranged everything neatly for her lord and master. The role of obedient submissive wife appealed to her sense of humour, and she stood well back as Madhu began to eat, avoiding his eyes which sought hers constantly.

Kapil stood a little apart from the rest, with the two other young men who had come in from the town to help with the harvesting. No women had brought any food for them, and they stood smoking and talking, their eyes sliding cautiously towards the women. Since they did not live in the village, the glamour of strangeness clung about them like a perfume, and their cautious glances were returned, for the most, by appraising stares.

Madhu had finished eating, and Bhima bent to take the empty plate, but his fingers closed at once about her wrist. He knew the other men were looking at him and laughing, but he was long past caring. The women too, glanced up with a mixture of envy and disapproval.

"Well," he whispered softly.

"Let me go," Bhima murmured. "The others are looking, and mother will be angry if I don't return soon." She lifted her eyes and looked at him and Madhu tightened his fingers till she winced.

"Wait for me," he said, "I will be home early." Then suddenly his face fell. "I had almost forgotten—we are taking the cane to the market tonight. Come with me?"

Bhima shook her head. "The cart makes my back ache," she said. "I shall wait here till you return." She smiled again to take the sting out of her words, and Madhu released her reluctantly. All the women had gone by this time, and the men lay under the trees in a cloud of cigarette smoke, exchanging ribald remarks.

Bhima walked sedately until she was lost from sight, and then she began to run, laughing and turning her face up to the sun. On her left was a small stream, shallow and hidden almost entirely by thick thorn bushes. She hesitated for scarcely a moment and then dropping her bundle, let herself lightly over the edge. She found a flat rock, still warm from the sun, and sat down, dangling her toes in the icy water. She pulled her sari above her knees and tilted her head, looking with pleasure at the anklets glinting in the sun.

A low laugh behind her made her turn quickly. Kapil stood there, still stripped to the waist and chewing a piece of sugar-cane. He ran his eyes slowly, and with a sort of caressing insolence over her. Bhima felt the blood rush to her cheeks and throat, but she did not move as he came and sat down beside her on the stone. There was an animal splendour about his lean tanned body, and his eyes were neither dog-like nor devoted when he looked at her. Already he was beginning to lose the hard line of his jaw, and Bhima knew that they said many things about him, and that few of them were good.

He split the sugar-cane in two and gave her one. She took it, bending her head over the juicy stalk.

"Madhu is taking the cane to the market tonight," she said without lifting her dark head.

Kapil looked up quickly. "So," he said softly, his full lips smiling. "And you, will you not go with him?"

She did not answer, and still smiling he turned and slid his hand down her arm. It was quite late when she reached home.

Madhu's mother was sitting in front of the hut, waiting.

"Where have you been, you worthless wife of my only son," she shrilled. "It is two hours since you took his food, and the other women have returned long ago."

Bhima shrugged her shoulders indifferently, and would have

4

continued on her way to her own hut. Even the two huts had been a source of contention between the old woman and herself. She had wanted her son and his bride to share her hut with her, but Bhima had refused firmly. Madhu had planted a hedge of thorny twigs around it giving it a certain amount of privacy. Now as she walked past, the old woman caught at her sari and jerked her to a stop.

"Answer," she screamed, panting with fury.

Bhima loosened herself calmly. "Your son would not let me go," she said enjoying the old woman's look of envy. "He kept me talking to him."

Madhu's mother was aware that this might quite easily be the case, and she let Bhima go, hearing the latch of her hut click shut behind her.

When Madhu returned Bhima greeted him gaily. She helped him load the cart and oil the big roughly-hewn wheels. With the other women she stood and watched as the procession of bullock carts creaked down the road, the drivers cracking their whips and the big white bulls straining at the yokes.

One by one the women disappeared into their huts and only Sita remained. She looked at Bhima with narrowed eyes.

"Will you sleep in your own hut tonight?"

Bhima laughed. "Where else; with you?"

Sita said slowly, "No, not with me," and turned away.

In her own hut Bhima pondered over Sita's words. Could she have meant anything? Anyway she was too excited to care.

The village slept and even the yellow pariah dogs lay down with their heads on their paws. A shadow crept softly out of the silence in the direction of Bhima's hut. A latch was lifted from inside and then everything was quiet again.

Dawn was creeping up from over the plains, and all the light had gone from the stars, leaving them pale shadows. Kapil pushed the door half open and leaned against it, sniffing the freshness of the morning. He was rolling a cigarette lazily when a sound made him stiffen. Unmistakably from down the road came the creaking of cart wheels, and the sing-song tinkle of the bullocks' bells. Bhima too heard the sound and sprang to the door. Together they watched the cart come into sight, lit by the swinging hurricane lamp underneath.

5

Bhima let out a long breath. "It is Madhu," she said with certainty. "No one else would return so quickly."

Kapil swore softly, cursing himself for a fool. Already the cart was turning into the low-walled courtyard surrounding the huts. Bhima leaned over and wrenched off her silver anklets.

"Here," she gasped. "Take them quick. You can give them back later. I shall pretend they were stolen. Quick," she urged. He took them silently and without a backward glance ran swiftly across the courtyard.

Already, doors were opening all along the huts, and heads looked out enquiringly. Bhima saw Kapil reach the wall and she began screaming, "Thief, thief," with hysterical abandon.

It was indeed Madhu in the bullock cart, and he was the first to reach her. The others crowded around asking questions. Bhima sobbed and wailed so loudly that it was some time before they could make any sense of what she was saying.

The women had little sympathy for her. They said that if she must sleep alone these things would happen, and she was lucky not to have had her throat slit. Madhu looked worried. Thieves were rare in the village, but it was harvest time, and there were many strangers.

Bhima, who hated the feel of her denuded ankles, wished she had never seen Kapil at all. She sobbed loudly, and now it was genuine grief at the loss of her beautiful anklets. Madhu soothed her as best he could, but he was uneasy.

There was no sign of Kapil, and Bhima had lost all her verve. Even the old woman was worried, and in time suggested a trip to town.

"Buy her some glass bangles," she said aside to Madhu, "the girl is fretting for the anklets."

So Madhu got out the cart and harnessed the big white bulls. Bhima lay quietly at the back till they reached the town. The jolting of the cart did not produce a single grumble, but when they reached the town and smelt the unfamiliar smells, she brightened a bit. Her eyes widened at the stalls piled high with goods—the coloured silks spilling out on to the pavement in shining heaps, and the flower stalls piled high with mogra and jasmine and sweet-smelling pink roses.

6

Madhu smiled indulgently at her excitement. Such a child she was! Perhaps she would cheer up when he bought her a few bangles. He began to bargain for them while Bhima looked around idly. Suddenly she felt her flesh creep with the awareness of danger.

Standing in front of one of the many stalls was Kapil. Between his fingers he held a flower which he dangled laughingly out of reach of the girl beside him. Bhima's eyes were turned in fascination on the girl. She was slender, with heavy blackened eyes and a loose red-lipped mouth. Her hair hung in a dark cloud around her face and she was smiling up at Kapil. Bhima's eyes, however, were glued to the girl's ankles. Falling loosely around each ankle were the silver snakes, with the tiny jingling bells. The intensity of her stare made Kapil turn.

He saw her at once and his bold eyes ran over her in the remembered look. Then he turned, and putting his arm around the girl whispered into her ear. They both threw their heads back and laughed, the girl derisively, and Kapil with frank enjoyment of the joke.

Bhima's fingers curled. Oh, if she could only scratch those eyes out, tear her nails across that smooth brown face. But she was helpless. She dare not say a word, and any minute now, Madhu would turn and see them.

She moved away, dragging Madhu with her, his hands full of the trashy glass ornaments. Behind them she could hear the echoes of laughter, following them all the way down the road.

Umashankar Joshi

❧❦❧❦❧❦❧❦❧❦❧❦❧❦❧❦

ON A SMALL DEATH

AH, what is there to weep for you, a little girl, that dies too soon?
Yet they all wept, with reasons each his own:
The grand-mother wept conventional tears,
Though glad at heart to be rid of a girl from a burdened house;
Mother—ah, poor woman—shed her sorrow secretly, though it
     did not reach you;
And the good neighbours, who always join to help the dead to
     their final rest,
Why should they weep for what to them is a second-hand sorrow?
I could have wept, but thought why weep for a death so small?
And thus all mourned, as men must at a death,
Convention-wise, resting their foreheads on their hands.

At last we lifted you, a tiny burden, from the sorrowing home,
Walking a little, at the corner turned to the cremation ground.
And there she was, your small playmate, on a window-ledge;
Intently she looked, watching this new game of yours
To mount like that and sleep on the shoulders of grown-ups like
     that.
And she also stretched her hands to mount somewhere, somehow,
     on the shoulders of someone.

Uncaring we the mournful marched on—and suddenly it dawned
     on her—
This cruel game—your grim departure, and rang out her loud
     lament.
Stamping her tiny feet, outstretching her flowery hands,
She moaned miserably, the only one in the wide world to feel
     your loss.
And I, who never meant to weep, could not hold the tears that
     flooded out.

8

Krishnalal Shridharani

THE MILKMAID'S SONG

I'M the milkmaid of the cowherd!
He's the cowherd of this milkmaid!
Like a mango he grows skyward;
I'm the soil-bed with love laid.

Vermilion lines my parted hair;
It's longing, not kohl, that clouds my eye.
Like a dancing peahen I seek to pair
With my peacock in tthe-tthetha-tthai.*

I come to the grassland at noon;
On my head is a pitcher of curd;
Under a banyan I wait, and soon
His eye walks but not his word.

His fatigue speeds away with the cow.
Let thieves get into my shack!
With us it's here and now!
Such now can never come back.

I'm the milkmaid of the cowherd!
He's the cowherd of this milkmaid!

* Time-beats of Kathak dance.

Alan Marshall

꧁꧂꧁꧂꧁꧂꧁꧂꧁꧂꧁꧂꧁꧂꧁꧂꧁꧂

MY BIRD

*I*T was not a silent darkness. Away out over the flat swamp water came rustles, splashes, quacks and the quick flap of wings being stretched and folded again.

Swans cried out and were answered, and plovers, flying low over the water, called to birds standing on the sandhills that divided the swamp from the bay.

The smell of water weeds and reeds and thrusting roots hung over the swamp and the tall marram grass growing on the bank.

It was just after midnight, the morning of the opening of the duck season. The day before, Dan Lucey, an inspector of the Fisheries and Game Department, had arrived at Werribee in a utility truck. He had gone into the swamp lands during the afternoon and carried out an inspection before preparing for the arrival of the shooters that night.

The swamp lands were divided into two areas, one of which was a sanctuary for native birds.

Shooters were forbidden to enter the sanctuary, and here the water birds were allowed to breed and live in peace.

What was left of the swamp lands was known as the Main Swamp. This section was thrown open to shooters for three months of the year, a period known to sportsmen as "The Duck Season".

The main swamp was divided from the sanctuary by a levee. During the open season, shooters could roam the main swamp as they pleased but beyond the levee they must not go. This wall of earth was a boundary between two countries, one of which was given to war and the other to peace.

It was Dan Lucey's task, on this opening day, to keep shooters off the sanctuary and to prevent the slaughter of protected birds. During the close season all ducks were protected but when, by official proclamation from the Office of the Director of Fisheries and Game, the duck season opened, those birds that were losing the struggle to survive were still forbidden game and men who shot them were open to fines and the confiscation of their guns.

Dan Lucey stood beside his truck watching the headlights of cars coming in to the turn-around beside the swamp where shooting was allowed.

For almost a year he had guarded these ducks against men with guns.

He had patrolled the swamp lands on moonlight nights, listening and watching, sometimes running in a crouch from shadow to shadow towards the report of a forbidden gun.

He had waded waist-deep through tangled places where the nests were, had drawn aside the reeds and seen the eggs warm from birds he had startled. He had watched the wild ducks leading flotillas of quick-paddling ducklings across smooth patches of water and had seen their first heavy, ungainly flight.

"It's good to look at ducks flying," he had once said. "I like to see them coming in to land at sunset.

"It's great to hear the whistle of their wings then look up and see them swerve away from the movement of you. Ducks are good, you get to love them."

Dan Lucey had been born on the Murrumbidgee and here, where the slow river flowed between high clay banks, and gnarled red gums leaned over the water, he had spent his childhood. As a man he was tall with a blackfellow's grace of movement and a face that was at peace with the bush, but, as a child, barefooted and brown, he had not yet come to terms with his surroundings. He had been restless and questioning and pursued some illusive revelation, some answer, some final discovery that he felt awaited him around each river bend, behind each tree or beyond each rise.

He was a searcher, lifting pieces of dry bark where centipedes shrank back from the light, thrusting his hand into hollow limbs where possums slept or parrots nested and wading through lignum swamps, parting branches and peering or standing silent with his face turned to the sky where the whistle of a driving wing still lingered.

Had there been, in his home, books in which poets sang the

11

truth of things, or great writers wrote inspiringly, he would have sat cross-legged beneath the belah-tree in his back yard, and the book upon his knee would have been as wings to him.

But there were no books, and, in the flight of birds his need of beauty found its answer, in the strength and power of scarred red gum trunks, deep-rooted in the earth, he felt the lift of spirit that comes to the man of books when he reads great literature. The drama and poetry he knew passed through no interpretative pen before enchanting him; it came to him from its source, pure and clear like a bullock bell.

He knew the river birds well. He had gazed on the egg, the splintering shell, the powder-puff young ones, the fat squeakers still unable to fly. He had watched the close-plumaged, grown ducks coming down wind with the long sun of evening upon them. They had come in with swerve and bank and flash of jewel and he had held his breath to the singing within him.

Yet, he had, with other boys, fired shanghai stones at resting birds, but his shots were wide. It was the twang of rubber and the soaring stone that delighted him.

Later, proud with the responsibilities of a new manhood, he had carried his birthday-present gun through the swamps, and had slain ducks as he went. He had tied the necks of bleeding birds to his belt and had come home with tales of marvellous shots he had made.

But he couldn't kill without a feeling of shame. With a draggled bundle of dead ducks at his belt the flight of those still living was always a withdrawal from him. He was left earth-bound and solitary, weighed down by his betrayal.

He had put away his gun, only taking it out to clean it or to feel the satisfaction of squinting down its gleaming barrel before returning it to its brackets on the wall.

When he finally came to the city looking for work he went straight to the Fisheries and Game Department, where he was engaged as an inspector. He was eager and enthusiastic, inspired by a vision.

Now he stood in the darkness thinking of these things, his vision gone.

The drone of engines, like a requiem, moved with the cars that stretched in a broken line from Werribee to Melbourne.

The cars thrust out feelers of light towards those ahead of them. They lurched over ruts of swamp lands, and the dust-laden beams shot up and fell again, illuminating tussocks of grass and striking glitters from the chromium bumpers of vehicles rocking ahead.

On a circular area flattened in the grass on the bank of the swamp, they came to rest. They crowded together in dark clusters divided by passageways along which those arriving nosed their way with whining gears, searching for a space in which to park. They moved into these places then stopped, their blazing eyes flicked out, their engines became silent.

More came, and more. Men carrying torches or hurricane lanterns jumped back and stood aside while groups moved past. In all those hours of darkness the sound of engines never ceased. A thousand cars came in that night, three thousand shooters stepped from them and moved off into the dark, their gun barrels gleaming in the headlights of the cars still seeking a resting place.

Legs moved in the light of swinging lanterns, passing and re-passing each other while their shadows made frantic sweeps over the grass. Silhouetted men swore softly, called to companions, asked questions, proffered information.

"Where's Jack? . . . Have you got my gun? . . . I've been here before; we'll go this way. . . . Where's the best place?"

They stepped high over tussocks, they walked with bent heads, watching the uneven ground, they stooped and pushed their way through brush.

"Over here. This way. I can hear them quacking."

Men hurried for positions of vantage. The swamp was ringed with men. They were shoulder to shoulder on spits of land where the ducks swept low for a landing. They stood side by side on the hillocks. They crouched like waiting soldiers in the hollows.

"We start at six."

"We're into them at six."

"We'll let them have it at six."

The uneasy birds on the dark water moved towards the centre of the swamp. There was a pale sky in the east.

Shells were thumbed from belts, locks clicked and snapped. Guns were shouldered and lowered, swept round and back, tested and thumbed and gripped.

13

"Don't swing over my area."

"I never swing over any man's area."

Dan Lucey drove the utility truck along the swamp bank and into the sanctuary. He left the truck near a patch of scrub and walked to the swamp's edge from where the water lay stretched beneath the dark in a pale light of its own.

He paced the bank, restless, feeling, in all that was around him, the existence of an intense awareness, an emotion of his own creating. The very air was listening, the trees were expectant and still.

He waited while the sky grew lighter and the darkness retreated to the shelter of the banks. Patches of darkness lay netted in grass and hollows where the tea-tree grew, but birds could be faintly seen on the water.

Dan slowly rolled a cigarette.

That teal with the one leg. A cod had probably taken the other one when she was a duckling. Or maybe a trap. Some men set rabbit traps on sandbanks to catch ducks, spread wheat around them. By hell, she was tame! Maybe she won't leave the water when they start. She'll be safe in the sanctuary. But the noise will start the lot off. If she's with a flock she'll go but she might be in the reeds. No, she'll take off with the rest. She'll rise with them. Having one leg won't affect her flying, anyway. You never know, though.

She may not be able to swerve as quickly. But she'll go high. They always do. She might get above it.

He looked up at the paling sky, seeing, in his imagination, the sanctuary it seemed to offer streaked with screaming pellets. He turned away.

It was half past five when the first gun was fired. In the stricken moment that followed, men's voices shouting a protest came from different parts of the swamp. A double report drowned their cries. Rosebuds of flame quivered above clumps of reed. Single reports followed each other rapidly. They made a staccato of sound that merged and grew till it became a thunderous volume of sound that pressed on Dan like a weight.

The air above the swamp, torn apart by the explosive roar, eddied across the still water, leaving a quivering surface and the smell of smoke behind it.

There were no gaps of silence in the sound. It was continuous and violent and controlled. Yet, within it and apart from it, could be heard the thrash of wings, the splash of falling bodies, quick, terrified quacks and the whish of speeding flocks hurtling by like companies of projectiles.

The thin, whispering whistle of shot, torn out of shape by pitted barrels, threaded the din and sent speeding birds into swerves and dives of terror.

Piercing the rumble in stabs of sharper sound, two hollow cracks came at intervals from the far side of the swamp.

Dan raised his head and listened.

Home made cartridges? There they go again! No. Poley chokes on their guns. That American idea for greater range. They'll get the high ones.

One more . . . Two . . . Three . . . Struth! That finishes the high ones. That pulls them down. No hope up on top now.

He suddenly took off his hat and shook some pellets of shot from the crown.

They must be as thick as rain up there.

When the firing began in the swamp, a panic swept across the birds on the waters of the sanctuary. Some swam swiftly to and fro while others took to the air in a flurry of wings. Those leaving infected the undecided ones with fear and in a moment they were all leaving the water, some in silence, others with quick cries of alarm.

Black duck, the first to leave, rose sharply, shooting upwards, their wings drumming. They held their wings low down, flying with short, swift chops, straining for speed. They banked in a sweeping turn at the sanctuary's edge and came round over the head of the watching man, the whistle of their speed trailing just behind them.

Dan's head jerked round to follow them.

By the hell, they're hiking! They'll circle twice before they beat it.

The flock swung off the sanctuary at the second spiral and the guns reached up for them in a bay of sound that rose above the steady roar of the continuous shooting.

They're for it. Dan drew a deep breath.

A hail of shot broke the formation and scattered the ducks

like leaves in the wind. One bird, a broken wing raised above it like a sail, came down in a tight spin, its uninjured wing thrashing desperately. It struck the levee bank between the sanctuary and the open swamp with a thud. A dozen men rushed towards it yelling, "My bird!"

A flock of grey teal, flying in line, followed the black duck up from the water then shot out over the open swamp on their first circle. A blast from a group of shooters broke their line into two groups, the centre birds tumbling from the sky like stones.

Pelicans and swans circled in a slow climb. The pelicans beat their giant wings with slow, deliberate strokes, their heads tucked back, their heavy bills resting on curved necks. With them were cranes, herons and avocets.

Ducks rising from the water, passed through and over this layer of heavy birds, circling on a different level before shooting out over the bay to safety.

Shot, whistling upwards to the high ducks, sometimes struck the heavy birds screening those above them, and they faltered in their slow climb, became agitated, called to each other or plummeted earthwards in silence.

The protected widgeon, slower than the grey teal or black duck, circled the sanctuary in jerky, uneasy flight, swerving unnecessarily when the gunfire from the swamp suddenly sharpened. They chattered as they flew, their voices like the sound of rusty hinges, continuing even when, in sweeps over the open swamp, they fell singly and in twos to the guns of men out to kill every bird that passed.

Dan swore in a sudden anger.

Half these bastards don't know their birds. They don't know a widgeon from a black duck. I'll pick them up. I'll get them on their way out.

"You damn fools," he shouted.

He watched each flock as it passed and when, against the dawn sky, he saw the wide shovel-bills, the heavy heads, the set-back wings of the widgeon as they banked and turned for the open swamp, he cupped his hand to his mouth and yelled "Widgeon!" across the water to where the first line of shooters were blazing at all that went over.

Some lowered their guns at the yell, others went on shooting.

A pair of grey teal came hurtling across the open swamp making for the sanctuary. A wave of sound followed them, its peak just beneath them as they moved. They were flying high and fast but a crack shot blasted the rear bird sideways in its flight and it began to drop. Five shots struck its falling body before it reached the water where it floated without movement.

The leader faltered in its flight when its mate was hit. Then it gathered itself and flew on till the sanctuary lay beneath it.

It came in as if to land but rose again and returned for its mate.

Dan gestured hopelessly. He's a gonner. He'll cop the lot. He's finished.

When the shot struck it, it didn't fold up and fall uncontrolled from the sky. It came down in a swift, steep glide, its body still in the position of normal flight. When it struck the ground it bounced and rolled like a football.

The last birds to leave the water of the sanctuary were eight wood duck. They had been sheltering in some rushes, but fear drove them out and they took off in a ragged group, their wings almost touching. As they gained height a drake moved forward and took the lead. The others fell naturally into the V formation behind him.

He led them down the water of the sanctuary, their necks undulating as they put power into their climb. They circled over the far end of the reserve then came back, their speed increasing with every chop of their wings. They banked above Dan Lucey, their mottled breasts bright in the dawn light, then turned for another round.

When they again reached the limits of the sanctuary, the drake, leading them in a steep climb, banked and lost height in a short, steep dive, then flattened out and brought them back towards where Dan was standing. Dan saw the manoeuvre and was puzzled.

Hell! he came down. Must be a heavy wind on top. No. He's building up speed. That's the stuff! Give it all you've got! Into it!

The drake, as if seeking a gap of silence through which to pass, kept turning his head from side to side as he flew.

Dan suddenly saw him as a symbol. The things that he stood for and in which he believed made a continued preoccupation

17

with the killing around him intolerable. This bird lived and was free. A strong heart beat within him and blood flowed through his veins. His survival became important to Dan. If he lived, a thousand slaughtered ducks lived on in him, if he died there was nothing but death upon the swamp.

"Round again, round again," Dan muttered aloud as he watched him. "Bring them around again, damn you!"

But the drake had made his decision: he led them on towards the open swamp. They passed over Dan's head at ninety feet or so, their wings whistling.

They're for it now, he thought. There they go—the suicide squad.

He watched them, standing in a slight crouch, his hands clenched. He *must* make it. He *must*. He *must*. He took a deep breath and stood still.

The ducks crossed the first line of shooters into the open swamp in a perfect V. The crest of a roaring sound-wave leapt up towards them as they went over and the drake led the group in a swerve as it struck them.

Now with the light of the morning full on them, the eight wood duck were a target for every gun. Barrels like black reeds fringed the open water along which they flew, reeds that exploded then jerked down in the recoil.

Dan, watching the birds, stood in a crouching attitude as if he were facing enemies.

One gone!

The duck to the left, and just behind the drake, changed from something firm and hard and full of power to a soft and shapeless bundle of feathers that fell without resistance towards the water.

Dan was up there with them now. He swung and lifted to their wings. He made each downward plunge to earth.

The V closed up and the gap was filled. The drake led the remaining six in quick swerves and dives. Every turn and twist he made, each violent, evasive movement was followed by the six ducks behind him.

Their every action was born of his, they had no mind but his.

The whisper of shot drove him to more desperate turns and his followers repeated them. But, in the centre of the swamp,

18

one of the rear ducks suddenly lost height. It fluttered, fell, then flew again. It followed the V at a lower height for a few yards then its wings went limp and it fell loosely to the water.

"My bird!" cried splashing men holding guns aloft.

A third bird was plucked from the formation before they reached the last line of shooters beyond which was safety.

The drake, leading his four companions across this last barrier where the shooters were side by side, suddenly banked steeply as shot whistled past them. He flew a moment in indecision then, as another duck fell, he brought the remnant of his flock round and made down the swamp once more.

Dan, watching him through his field glasses, cursed softly.

A shout rose from the shooters as the ducks turned. Again the wave of sound moved beneath the birds.

The drake dropped all evasive tactics now. He was dazed with noise.

He flew straight ahead with the remaining three birds in line behind him.

He led them down in a shallow dive to increase their speed but rose steeply as two of his companions fell together, a puff of feathers left floating behind them.

There was only one duck following him now. With a quick chop of her wings she closed up, moving a little to one side till her head was level with his body. But she began to flag and he drew away from her.

The shot that hit her threw her violently upwards and she turned over on her back before crashing at the feet of the shooters on the levee.

The drake was alone now. He swept out over the sanctuary to a last burst of sound then turned and made out over the bay.

To the man this speeding bird, like some winged vessel, bore in its seed the life wrenched from a thousand slaughtered ducks upon the swamp. He felt the lift of victory, the faith, the elation. As, against bright clouds the drake rose to an upward swing of air, twinkled and was gone, he flung his arms up in an acclaiming gesture, then turned and faced the shooters on the levee.

"*My* bird!" he yelled. "*My* bird, damn you! *My* bird!"

A. D. Hope

MEDITATION ON A BONE

WORDS scored upon a bone,
Scratched in despair or rage—
Nine hundred years have gone;
Now, in another age
They burn with passion on
A scholar's tranquil page.

The scholar takes his pen
And turns the bone about,
And writes those words again.
Once more they seethe and shout,
And through a human brain
Undying hate rings out.

"I loved her when a maid;
I loathe and love the wife
That warms another's bed:
Let him beware his life!"
The scholar's hand is stayed;
His pen becomes a knife

To grave in living bone
The fierce archaic cry.
He sits and reads his own
Dull sum of misery.
A thousand years have flown
Before that ink is dry.

And, in a foreign tongue,
A man, who is not he,
Reads and his heart is wrung
This ancient grief to see,
And thinks: When I am dung,
What bone shall speak of me?

Roland Robinson

TUMULT OF THE SWANS

WHAT else had I come to find,
driven by that travail's needs,
but the black swans sailing out
beyond the shaking spears of reeds?
Looking back from where I climbed,
secret lay the still lagoon
holding double tree and cloud,
swans and the solitary moon.
If the land I crossed was dumb,
ravaged, stark with fire's scars,
sudden, in green flames of scrub,
rose the blood-proud waratahs.
Savage was the place where night
cried in winds about my ears,
where the honey-eaters still
sang clinging to the grass-tree spears:
blending song with song where day
died behind the ridge's stones,
leaving earth and sky for one
wind-torn tumult of the swans.

"Zawgyi"

HIS SPOUSE

I

MARKET-WOMAN Ma Paw was the wife of Ko Hsin. Each morning she walked a mile to town with greens on a tray. If business was brisk she returned early, otherwise only when the sun had declined. Whenever she reached the bamboo bridge that crossed the stream beside the village on her return, thoughts of her husband and children arose in her mind.

She was tall with reddish hair and slightly protruding teeth, but it could not be said that she was ugly. Her husband Ko Hsin was a man of leisure who sat and ate at home. It was not wholly true that he did nothing. He had to cook the rice and look after the children.

Ko Hsin had been a novice in the Buddhist Monastic Order for nine years and had some learning. He was good natured, fond of laughter and was the prime mover at charities and weddings. He was not as tall as his wife, was small-chested, had a fine crop of hair and a thin strip of moustache. He was tattooed to his knees.

When they were married and after they had a son, Ma Paw kept shop and ministered to Ko Hsin's needs. When the second son was born she could only keep shop. After the birth of their daughter Ma Paw often became very tired. Once when she was hard hit by a business loss her state was pitiable. But she did not complain.

She was heartened when one of her friends told her: "You should listen to your husband read the awbasa [eulogy and blessing] at a wedding in the village. Magnificent. He is a learned man." She was heartened when her fourteen-year-old son sometimes met her at the bamboo bridge and relieved her of her tray and basket. At these times her thoughts turned in gratitude to her husband.

Once when she and her children were talking on the raised platform of their house a tipsy drinker of toddy appeared on the road and made insulting eyes at them. The children ran into the house in fear. Ko Hsin hurriedly appeared from within the house and stood with arms akimbo on the platform. The drunkard's eyes turned and whirled, leading away his tottering feet. Ma Paw was thankful. Were it not for my man we would have suffered great indignities, she thought.

Ma Paw was now in her thirty-seventh year. Ko Hsin was six years older.

Ko Hsin, for all his years, had never really worked. When people said of him that he supported himself by clutching the hem of a skirt he would reply jokingly: "Even Wethandaya[1] had to live on what Maddi[2] could get for him." He would add: "I am able to live in leisure as I live now because of my past meritorious deeds. Don't be jealous." Though he said this, in his heart he was hurt. But the pain was almost forgotten in pride of his brilliant repartee. Because of his replies the others frowned on him or thrust their chins at him in derision. In time these acts of his neighbours spurred him to action. He borrowed money from a cousin and entered the bamboo business. He lost heavily. The next rains he went down to the fields to plough. He returned home with blood dripping from his foot where he had run in the plough-share. It took fifteen days for the wound to heal.

II

He was forty-three on the day he got well. The wound of the flesh had healed but the wound of the heart had swollen.

Ma Paw had set off to market as usual, the elder son had gone on to the monastery-school. The other two children were playing beneath the tamarind tree in front of the house. As Ko Hsin sat drinking a pot of green tea he saw the carpenter father of six

[1] Wethandaya: The famous charitable prince from the Birth Stories of the Buddha who lived in exile in a forest with his wife and two children.

[2] Maddi: The devoted wife who fed her family by gathering fruits and berries.

from a neighbour's house set out with his box of tools. The man from next door crossed the stream to cut dani-leaves on the other bank. Even the old man from the opposite house whittled a piece of wood to make a puddling stick.

At first Ko Hsin was filled with a sense of ease and pleasure as he drank cup after cup of tea and watched his children at play. But when his neighbours began to stir to work his pleasure faded, and he remembered that he had yet to get the pot of rice on the fire. He suddenly recalled the taunts of his neighbours and the procession of his past passed before his eyes. His foppishness since leaving the monastery, his marriage to Ma Paw, his business failure, his hurt foot. He became sad and ashamed. He desired to break out of this way of life. He thought it would be good to become a monk. Then he would not have to boil rice. He would be able to turn his eyes towards Nibban.[3] His wife and children would gain merit by him. He felt certain that the time for his release from the sorrows of samsara[4] was at hand. He would endeavour to become a small god. Thus did he think. But he remembered again that he must prepare the rice or he would have nothing to eat and that the children would cry. He arose and entered the kitchen.

Meanwhile in the market, Ma Paw was adding water to her greens to make them heavier whereby she might earn more. With what more she earned she intended to buy some nice cheroots for her husband.

Ko Hsin was skilled at preparing boiled rice. He called the children and gave them the rice with the remains of yesterday's curry. When the children had gone back to their play he sat with his feet dangling from the raised platform and returned to his thoughts. When he became a monk he would come with his begging bowl to Ma Paw's house every morning and get a chance to meet Ma Paw and the children. But Ma Paw was illiterate and ignorant of the Law. When she died she would pass to the lower worlds. For this he pitied her. He wanted to open her eyes to the Law.

The quarrel of his children returned him to realities. The

3 Nibban: The supreme good.

4 Samsara: Buddhism's chain of births, deaths, and rebirths.

sister had scratched the brother's face, in retaliation he had pulled her hair. Now both were crying.

Ko Hsin called the children into the house and made them sit in different corners. He then tried to return to his reverie but could not pick up the chain of thought. He glanced at his children and saw their little heads nodding into sleep. He felt a yawn rise in him.

"Don't move," he commanded the children and laid himself down for a nap.

The moment his eyes were closed the children opened theirs. They threw speaking glances at each other and at their father. They agreed to run down to play as soon as he fell asleep.

Ko Hsin awoke to Ma Paw's voice calling to her son in the tamarind tree.

"Get down from there at once, you'll fall. Where is your sister?"

"At the streamside," the boy replied.

"Woe betide us," Ma Paw cried. "Ko Hsin, do you leave your children unattended like that. A good father you are!"

The daughter appeared with muddy hands and the boy climbed down from the tree.

Ko Hsin looked daggers at his children. They hid behind the mother.

"Here're cheroots for you," said Ma Paw and thrusting them on him she headed the children into the kitchen. Ko Hsin's eyes followed them. Ma Paw washed her daughter's hands and gave the children pea-cakes to eat. Then sitting down, Ma Paw spread her legs on the floor, untied her hair, bent forward and let the hair hang above her legs.

"Massage my back with your elbows," she told her son. He did so while keeping his cake between his teeth. The quacking of the back under the pressure of the elbows and the swing of the spreading hair as her head swayed made Ma Paw appear as though possessed by the devil.

Ko Hsin looked and heaved a deep sigh of disgust. I must adorn the yellow robes, he thought.

However, he did not dare to tell his wife till the year had turned.

III

It was now three months though Ko Hsin had said that he would wear the yellow robes for only a month. Ma Paw's aunt who had come over to help look after the children began to yearn for her own in her village.

"When will the Upazin[5] return to lay life," she had asked the monk one day.

The monk had not replied. Instead he had quoted sacred verses extolling the life of a monk. The sacred verses did not enter the aunt's ears. Only anger rose in her because she felt that she was being kept here unfairly. When the monk had departed she called Ma Paw to her.

"Ma Paw. I want to go back. Tell your Upazin to cast off the robes. I cannot stay on longer as a servant in your house," she threatened.

Ma Paw too wanted her husband to return home: She had alluded to the matter once or twice only to have been turned back with sermons. Now Wazo[6] was near when the monks would go into Retreat for three months. Not knowing what to do she conferred with a friend. After some talk they burst into laughter.

IV

The morning was gold with sunlight. Doves cooed in the tamarind tree. Ma Paw did not go to market. Instead, she fried and cooked at home. Then she bathed and made herself fragrant with thanakha[7] down to her toes. She smeared it lightly on her face. She gathered her straying strands and tied them in a knot to suit her features. The meagre hair on her forehead was collected into a "dove's-wing". She pencilled her eyebrows in a wide sweep and made red her lips by chewing betel. She put on a jacket of fine white cloth and a new skirt of printed red flowers. The children too were dressed in clean clothes and the household things were packed. A bullock cart waited in readiness in the yard.

[5] Upazin: Form of address to a Buddhist monk. The Burmese monk leads a celibate life.

[6] Wazo: The fourth month of the Burmese calendar and the first of Buddhist Lent.

[7] Thanakha: The fragrant powder of the bark of the Kurraya Exotica.

At ten o'clock the monk appeared accompanied by his eldest son who was in his monastery-school. As he approached he thought with apprehension, they will ask me again to forsake the life of a monk. He drew near the house and saw the cart. He entered the house and saw the packed household things. He sat on the mat the aunt had rolled out for him in the place of reverence in the house and searched in vain for Ma Paw.

After some time Ma Paw appeared with a tray of food. With sad eyes and movements she offered the food. The monk took a quick glance at her. He noticed how dressed up she was. He took another glance. He was puzzled by her behaviour but his thoughts were occupied in steeling himself to refuse the request to return to lay life which he knew Ma Paw would surely make.

After the meal Ma Paw took away the tray and sat reverently at a distance. As the monk made to preach the sermon Ma Paw spoke to her aunt.

"Aunt. Hasn't the cartman arrived yet?"

The monk, unable to begin his sermon, looked towards the waiting cart.

"Ma Paw. What's going on here?" he asked.

"I will reveal all to the Upazin," Ma Paw addressed the monk without raising her head. "Aunt wants to return to her village. If she returns I will be unable to keep shop and look after the children at the same time. That is why I beg permission of the Upazin to allow me and the two children to go live with aunt in her village. The eldest son will be left in the Upazin's care."

She turned to her eldest son, "Son, stay behind with the Upazin," she said and wiped away a tear from her downcast face.

The monk remained silently thoughtful.

"The Upazin may continue to be a monk throughout his life if that is his wish. His humble lay woman will try to make a living somehow. The Upazin's world and hers are different worlds; there is a vast gap between them. Henceforth there can only be the relationship of monk and lay devotee between them. Since she still has two children, if she can find someone to depend upon somewhere else she desires to accept him. That is why she wishes to make things clear now so that complications may not arise later."

The monk uttered a cry of amazement. Ma Paw raised her

27

eyes slightly. The monk's hands fluttered about his robes. He looked at Ma Paw.

Ma Paw continued: "This is said for the benefit of both. The Upazin will be able to follow the Law in freedom, and his humble devotee will be able, should she find someone . . ."

"There are too many toddy drunkards in your aunt's village," the monk said. "I will return to the lay life."

Ma Paw became Ko Hsin's wife again.

Burma

"Zawgyi"

THE BEDA FLOWER

STRUNG along the creek the Beda flowers
float—close friends of the water.
They bend when the creek bends
They stretch when the creek stretches
Though no wind strikes, they float along
ever-lastingly.

A boy with reed pipe rivals the coucal bird,
sitting on the bank
The coucal leads, the piper follows,
"Beda, you come with flow-tide and you
go with ebb.
Miss Beda of ebb and flow
How I shall miss you when you go.

"You float up-stream and down-stream.
Whence have you come?
Where do you go?
And when the sun sets,
By which mud-bank
Will you rest?"

Alejandro R. Roces

OF COCKS AND KINGS

"*T*HIS rooster cannot lose."

I had heard my brother Kiko make that allegation many times. And each time it had cost me a lot of money. There was a time, for instance, when he had his so-called invulnerable rooster. A constabulary soldier had an *anting-anting* that he had obtained from a captured Moro outlaw. It was guaranteed to make the skin of its carrier immune to all forms of violent harm. Kiko bought the talisman for his fighting fowl. He told me that he had paid such a fabulous amount for the amulet that he had no money left to bet on his bird. So he asked me to be his partner. He supplies the gamecock and amulet; I furnish the cash. I still don't know why, but I agreed to the proposition. That Sunday, I couldn't go with Kiko to the cockpit. Mother was sick and I had to keep her company. So Kiko went off by himself with his combat cock and my money. Anxiously, I awaited his return. The minute he arrived, I asked:

"What happened?"

"Well," Kiko said, scratching his head, "it's a long story."

"Did we win? Did the charm work?"

"Oh, yes, the *anting-anting* worked."

"Good!" I said. "I'm so glad! How much did we win?"

"Look, partner," Kiko then told me, "I think I had better tell you the story from the beginning."

"Go ahead," I said. "I'm dying to hear it."

"Well, first of all, I got to town and made the rooster swallow the charm. True enough, it made our rooster invulnerable. Just as I said it would. During the fight, all the offensive efforts of its opponent proved futile."

"Yes, yes, go on. Go on."

"As I was saying, the other rooster couldn't harm ours."

29

"And then?"

"Then our rooster took the offensive. It struck at its adversary and its thrust was so powerful that—believe it or not, partner—it chopped the other cock in two!"

"Yippee! So that's how it won!"

"No, partner. That is how it lost."

"Now, wait a minute, wait a minute, I don't get this. You said that our rooster slashed the other in two. Right?"

"Right."

"That is what I thought you said. Then we won."

"No, partner. We lost."

"Lost? How?"

"That's just what I'm trying to tell you. We lost because when our rooster saw its opponent torn in two, it ran, thinking that it had two opponents."

"Then it was a tie."

"No, partner, we lost. I told you we lost."

"Why?"

"Because when the birds were billed, the other rooster managed to display that it had died with its hackles up. You know the rules of the pit in instances like that. Runaway rooster loses."

"You mean to tell me that the other cock managed to make the two necessary pecks?"

"Yes, partner."

"But how can a cleaved cock do that?"

"Reflex action, partner. If you think that is amazing, you should see a snake. I have seen snakes bite and wriggle hours after being severed."

"Yes, but those were snakes. This was a rooster. And how can a cock's thrust cut another in two? A rooster's leg doesn't carry that kind of power."

"The *anting-anting* supplied the power, partner. I told you that was a potent charm. It not only made our rooster impregnable, it also made it strong. Too strong, in fact, for its own good. They call that the point of diminishing returns. You will know all about that after you take economics in school."

"Look, Kiko: if our rooster lost, it is all right. But why do you have to add bull to a cock story?"

30

"What do you mean?"

"I mean: why do you have to tell me that our rooster was invulnerable?"

"Because it was."

"Then how can an invulnerable rooster lose?"

"I just told you how, partner. After all I told you that it was invulnerable—not invincible. There is a big difference, you know. I think you have things confused, partner."

"I see. Well, where is the rooster? I want to see the rooster."

"Rooster? What rooster? Oh, the rooster. Yes, the rooster. That's another thing I wanted to tell you. I—I killed it."

"Killed it! Why?"

"I was so disgusted at its having turned tail and making us lose all that money that I killed it."

"How? You said it was invulnerable."

"Sure, it was invulnerable. But I drowned it in the river on my way home. An *anting-anting* makes your skin impenetrable, but it cannot protect you from drowning. I am sure you know that, partner."

"But where is it? Where is the drowned rooster? Why don't you have it with you? You always bring your dead cocks home for mother to cook."

"Not this one, partner. Not even mother could cook this one. It wouldn't be good even for *talunan*. The *anting-anting* has made its flesh too tough. So how can mother cook it? Besides, mother is too sick to cook. By the way, how is mother? Is she feeling any better?"

"Never mind mother. Look, could it be possible that the rooster was not invulnerable? And that you didn't take it home because it has certain wounds that you don't want me to see?"

"Of course not. I don't know what you mean."

"Oh yes, you know what I mean. This is not the first time that you make me lose my money in the cockpit. Remember that cock with seven odd scales? You told me it couldn't lose because the seven scales signified the seven holy virtues. And it lost."

"I told you: it lost because there are also seven deadly sins."

"Well, why did you tell me to bet for it then? And how about that one with twelve odd scales? You said that one was unbeatable too because there were twelve apostles."

"Sure, there were twelve apostles. But only eleven were loyal to our Lord. So we really should have looked for a rooster with eleven—and not twelve—odd scales. The science of numerology is not as simple as you would like to make it out. Numerology is a complex thing. Everything should be taken into consideration. And above all, nothing—but nothing!—should be taken for granted."

"Well, why didn't you tell me all that before the fight? And, oh, yes. By the way, just for the record: which half of the opponent managed to make the two decisive pecks?"

"The half with the beak," Kiko said.

That did it. After that, I resolved to have nothing to do with Kiko's gamefowls. For months I stayed clear from the cockpits. More important still I made no more bets in absentia. In fact, I made it a point not even to discuss roosters. The only chickens that I had anything to do with, were those that I ate. Kiko, of course, tried extremely hard to get me interested in cocks again. And he wasted no opportunity in injecting chickens in all our conversations. Once, for instance, we were talking about the graft and corruption in the government. Suddenly Kiko interrupted the conversation saying:

"Did you hear a rooster crow?"

"No," I said.

I was damned positive that no rooster had crowed.

"Well, speaking of roosters," Kiko said, "did you see my new red roos——"

"Now, stop it!" I said, cutting him short. "I told you I don't want to hear any more about roosters. I am sick and tired of it. Gad dehmet!"

When Kiko saw that I was really determined to cease cocking, he changed his technique. He tried a psychological approach. He came to me one day and admitted that the *anting-anting* proved inefficacious. But he claimed good faith and blamed everything on the soldier who had sold him the amulet. He even threatened to punch the constable the next time he saw him in town. But even this failed to revive my interest in cockfighting. It took the King of Roosters to entice me back into the pit.

The King of Roosters was partly my creation. For one day, our teacher asked us to submit a legend gathered from the barrio. I went to see Lakay Kardo regarding this class project, and Lakay Kardo favoured me with a folk tale regarding the origin of roosters.

Here is the legend the way I wrote it for teacher:

"Chiliads before the conquest, there lived a kind, powerful King who had twin sons. When this King died, both twins claimed to be the rightful heir to the throne and they grappled for the King's crown. This so incensed Bathala that he cursed them. And upon being damned, their bodies burst with bright feathers. Then their arms changed to wings and their legs shrivelled as their knees shifted to their backs. Scales encrusted their legs and their feet turned to claws. Their noses and chins met into a hard beak and their eyes slipped over to where their ears had been. And as the ultimate punishment, they were crowned with their own flesh. Bathala had transformed them into the first roosters!

"But so potent was the power of this old King that up to the present time, we feel his great influence. For when roosters crow, everybody—from the president down—has to get up from bed. And to this day, the descendants of this King are still trying to peck the crowns from each other's heads."

Kiko read my theme and then said:

"Very interesting. You know I think you should take up writing seriously. Who knows? You may be another Rotor. Or another Arguilla."

Now if Kiko's reaction to my composition had stopped with that comment, chances are that I might never have exposed myself anew to the contingencies of cocking. But, unbeknown to me, the legend on the genesis of gamecocks had given my brother ideas. So much so that a few months later, he came to me and said:

"Come with me. I want to show you something."

We went down the house, and in the yard, tethered to the ground, was a capital cock.

"There," Kiko said, "is the King of Roosters. I have been searching for it high and low ever since I read your story. And now I have found it."

"Nice-looking bird," I said. "But I don't see what it has to do with my story."

"Don't you see?" Kiko said indicating the rooster.

"No."

"Remember what you said about a cock's comb?"

"Yah."

"Well, look at the comb of that chicken."

I picked up the rooster and looked at its crest. It was different from that of other roosters. A cock's comb is flat and palmate. This one was round and shaped like a crown. But I still didn't see what that peculiarity had to do with my story.

"Don't you see?" Kiko said on the verge of exasperation. "This is the King of Roosters. All roosters have combs. But this is the only one that has a crest that looks like a crown. Why? Because it is the real King of Roosters. It is the true heir to the King's crown."

"So?"

"So it cannot lose. How can the King of Roosters lose?"

"Look, why are you telling me all this?"

"Because this fowl is just as much your discovery as it is mine. If I had never read your paper, I never would have known of the existence of this bird. So, actually you and I are co-discoverers of this cock. Do you remember that hermaphrodite chicken that we pitted in a main?"

"Yah, I remember."

"Well, both discovered that rooster, you and I. And that rooster won. It slaughtered its opponent with one blow."

"It won because its opponent thought it was a hen. And by the time it learned the truth, it was too late."

"Don't be silly. It won because you and I found it together in the cornfields. It was our mutual cock. Just like this rooster. It is our discovery—yours and mine."

"All right, now what do you want me to do?"

"I want you to help me get this royal rooster ready for battle. This is our chance to clean up. O.K.?"

Getting the King ready for combat was no problem. Particularly because Kiko had decided against the usual prerequisites for gamefowls. My brother did not bother to stub its spurs. Nor did he trim its feathers or divest it of its comb, wattles and earlobes. "That stuff is for common gamecocks," Kiko said, "but not for regal roosters. The crown is the *sine qua non* of a King.

Our rooster must enter the ring in all its grandeur." So all we had to do was to get the King in condition. This meant toughening its muscles and getting rid of fat deposits—particularly around the internal organs—as these induce excessive heat and premature fatigue. Our work comprised merely in proper feeding and diurnal exercitations. The ration and exertion wore off the fowl's fat and made its muscle corky. In less than a month, the rooster was in prime physical condition.

Brother and I got up at dawn on that morning of battle. Kiko took the King from its coop and tossed it to the ground. The King flapped its wings majestically and then crowed as if the sun had risen to hear its voice. There was no question that it was ready for action. Its nerves were vibrant and it was demanding opponents to vanquish. In fact, I had never seen it looking so fit. With its crown perched on its head, it looked regal as a pineapple. Kiko picked up the King and we headed for the battle pit. But first we made a stop at the house of Don Vicente Valenzuela to borrow an old cock-spur. This spur was a relic of the coffee boom of the eighties, when roosters were reputedly pitted with solid gold gaffs. Its blade was made of Toledo steel and its forked flange was inlaid with gold. It was a beautiful work of art. "No other gaff will do for the King of Cocks," Kiko said. Don Vicente gladly granted us the use of his gaff. From there Kiko and I proceeded to the arena.

We had not been in the matching place for more than a minute when a man carrying a Jolo rooster challenged our cock. Even if we had tried, I don't think that Kiko and I could have found a less worthy-looking opponent for the King. The Jolo had exiguous neck-feathers. It looked half-naked and half-starved. Kiko and I readily accepted the challenge.

After the usual pre-fight preparations, the two birds were freed for the fray. The Jolo showed absolutely no regard for royalty. As soon as it touched ground, it charged and catapulted itself at the King. The King ducked neatly and the Jolo whizzed overhead with its legs pumping the empty air. Then they turned again and stood fronting each other.

The King then tried to peck the Jolo's head. But there was little to peck. The Jolo's head was dubbed clean. There were no fleshy appendages to hold on to. On the other hand, the King's

35

crown served only to provide the opponent with an ideal place for a bill-hold. The Jolo managed to get several good beak-grips on the King and this placed our rooster at a tremendous disadvantage. For each time the Jolo had a nib-hold, he belted the King almost at will. Luckily, it never connected with its steel.

The two roosters now began feinting each other with leaps. Both were trying to catch each other in an off-position. Then the Jolo jumped. The King instinctively crouched low. For an instant our rooster was in a vantage position. For the Jolo had its heart and vitals exposed while the King had only its head and back as target. The King, however, failed to follow up this advantage. Instead the Jolo descended and delivered a brain-blow. The head is easy to withdraw from danger. But by now, the excess weight of the crown had begun to tell on our rooster. It could no longer bob its head with the celerity that it displayed at the outset. So when the blow came, the King failed to weave its head on time. The gaff went right through the crown into its royal head. Heavy, indeed, is the head that wears a crown.

For a while I was too stunned to say anything. Then one of the handlers approached me and handed me our dead rooster. The cock's head was hanging like a plumb bob. I took it by the tail, then I accosted Kiko, saying:

"I thought you said that this was the King of Cocks."

"It was," Kiko said.

"Then why did it lose?"

"For God's sake," Kiko said angrily, "don't tell me that you still believe in divine rights of kings. This is already the century of the common man. The era of royalty is over. Haven't you heard of the revolt of the masses? Why don't you study your history more?"

Nick Joaquin

❧❧❧❧❧❧❧❧❧❧❧❧❧❧❧❧

VERDE YO TE QUIERO VERDE

COLOUR of Green: I love you: Green:
(Red
    scorches; White
        has whips; Blue
            bites.)

the river-cool sea-serpent skin
of your deep arms enfolds my flesh in silence.

Red assaults; rains fire, blood; excites,
devours. Red, our terror aloud,
cried out, of death. (Green is the night's
luxuriant waters jewelled thick with islands.)

White is wisdom, the scourge of God.
Insanity, her nudeness. Pain,
her blinding deserts. Noon, her shroud.
(O moss-grown wells, raw fruits, slopes hung with
    curtains!)

Blue is thought, despair; the ink-stain
time prints on all matter; the cold
vague melancholy, eyes retain
of voyages long perished from importance ...

Red,
    ripeness, then; White,
            age; Blue,
               mould.

Yet from these senses, though in their
decadence, still rises fourfold
a hunger for that other colour, virgin, girlish!

That abrupt, sharp waking up, bare
of blankets, of all dreams—with dawn
on the grasses: all water, air
and earth caught for an instant clean and careless!

Have I built of such moments one
more sanctuary? Have enthralled
stupid the flesh as swine that none
may interrupt these ears turned to the siren ...

Deep the jungle. Here have I walled
me stranded from the rainbow; in
this leaf-wooed shrine the emerald
stone-unripe guavas pack their smell of iron.

Yea, this my world—spun, sped between
fire branching under, fire above: you
are its whisper of Eden, Queen
crowned over colour:
                    Colour of Green: I love you!

Eknath Easwaran

❧❦❧❦❧❦❧❦❧❦❧❦❧❦❧❦❧❦

THE POSTMASTER

"Two postcards and one pound of sugar."

"One envelope and half a bottle of coconut oil."

Menon listens to his customers with a cheerful smile, and notes them down in two separate exercise books. The postcards and the envelope go into the red one, and the pound of sugar and the half-bottle of coconut oil into the blue. The table at which Menon sits has two drawers; the left belongs to the government, and the right to the grocery store.

Menon is an incongruous mixture of the Postmaster and the shopkeeper, and reminds one of an ill-suited married couple. They are often at loggerheads and get on each other's nerves, but they jog on together without their home and hearth flying to pieces. The Postmaster is the flower of courtesy, and has a warm smile for every visitor to his office. On the other hand, the shopkeeper looks askance at every customer as one who has come to get the better of him in a bargain.

The shop is a comfortable room with a carved ceiling and wide wooden shelves on three sides. On the shelves are green-painted tins neatly labelled Cashewnuts, Pepper or Asafoetida. Half the floor space is occupied by wooden boxes with open covers containing black gram, green gram, red chillies, ground-nut or beaten rice. In the corner gleams a tin of coconut oil with a pump and a funnel on it ready to go into action at a moment's notice. On the walls hang coloured calendars of soap and tea and vegetable oil. Over all this presides the Goddess of Wealth, rising from an outsize lotus, with a garland of fresh marigolds around her auspicious picture every day.

The red letter-box is fixed with a huge nail on the trunk of a tamarind tree outside. It has become one of the sights in the village since the day an unsuspecting correspondent pushed his

39

fingers too far inside and frightened out of its skin a little snake that was resting peacefully among the covers and cards inside. In an awful panic the little snake jumped out of the red box and darted into a crab-hole nearby, where it had to fight for its life against the rightful occupants. Ever since then the red letter-box is known to every man, woman and child as the Snake Box. There is neither fear nor fun in this appellation.

On the veranda hangs the Notice Board with its picturesque appeals to the literate members of the public to Write Legibly and Address Correctly. The board also volunteers information on postal charges, air or surface mail, to far-off lands across the seven seas, and pleads with the peasant to invest his savings in National Certificates instead of burying them in his yam patch at the back of the house. But no one ever bothers to decipher these departmental communications because the Postmaster is there to give you all the information you need and, if necessary, to Write Clearly and Address Correctly into the bargain. He has all the data at his finger-tips, and can tell the weight of a parcel by the feel of it in his palm.

But the man of the hour is not the Postmaster. He is the Postman. He may not be the glass of fashion and the mould of form, but the observed of all observers he certainly is as he arrives on the scene in his khaki coat and white dhoti. The khaki coat is worn neither for personal style nor to follow sartorial regulations, but to provide a very convenient hold-all for letters and money orders, cash and stamp-pad for taking thumb impressions. The Postman carries on him a few covers and cards for sale to distant farmers, and takes it upon himself to carry their letters to be despatched from the Post Office. In short, he is Postmaster, Postman and Post Box for all in outlying farms around the village.

The mail is brought from the town on a red cycle, often in the pockets of the cyclist himself. There is a sharp and sudden excitement that turns the grocery store into a tense theatre. The Postmaster breaks off the seal of the bag with a fierce tug, and empties the contents on the floor to be sorted out by the Postman.

It is almost like sleight-of-hand to watch the Postman putting the seal on the letters arranged in a neat cascade. The big brass seal in his right hand flies between the ink pad and the letters with such rapidity that the spectator feels his head swimming as he watches the lightning operation. Then the addresses are read out one by one in a sing-song chant to soothe the tremor of expectation. Anxious necks are craned and anxious hands outstretched from among the crowd; young men looking for jobs, older people prospecting for sons-in-law. Postcards are passed from hand to hand and studied carefully by all those who can read. What does it matter to whom it is addressed? Isn't the whole village one big family?

Money Orders come in few and far between, and they are ever welcome because a Money Order blesseth him who receives and him who delivers it. The Postal Department is, of course, tooth and nail against any of their employees accepting any sum, however small, from the addressee. But the Postman can't be taken officially to task for the long arm of coincidence on such occasions. He may be asked to join the family for a couple of *dosas* (pancakes) and coconut chutney and a cup or two of strong tea; or he may be given a crisp packet of sugared banana chips for his many children. When the *zamindar* (landlord) received a huge Money Order from one of his tenants, he waited patiently for months to attend the Postman's sister's marriage and gave her a silver rose-water sprinkler as a wedding present. But it did not fool any one in the village at all.

The Postmaster may rank higher in the official hierarchy, but he does not enjoy the warm fellowship in which the Postman is held in every home. Even on the question of salary—an important factor in deciding social status—the Postman is at an advantage because he is a wholetime official whereas the other is only a part-time one. But these niceties of social ranking are not allowed to come in the way of their friendly relations, and their pleasant sallies at each other never fail to draw hearty laughter from the crowd every day. They address each other as man of letters and master of letters!

Look out! There is a snake in the grass! A sinister telegram amongst the innocent covers and cards. The Postman picks it up gingerly and holds it as far from him as possible. It is for the village schoolmaster.

"Poor man! And his wife in bed with raging Hill Fever!"

"No good can ever come of a cursed wire! Let us be glad we don't have a telegraph office in our village."

This was too much for the Postmaster. It was a wicked reflection on the Government Postal and Telegraph Department. As if a telegram, he patiently explained to the apprehensive audience, could bring only bad news! Were there only bad omens? Were there not good ones also? If it was bad to see an oncoming buffalo, was it not very good to set eyes on a milk-white cow?

Was it not by a telegram that the Snake Doctor had learnt of the birth of a son in his despairing old age? Was it not by a telegram that the Temple Priest had come to know of the signal success of his in the Matriculation Examination? Was it not . . .

"Here is another telegram!" gasps the Postman, "it is, let me make sure, yes, it is for the Postmaster!"

"Oh, no! Not for me!" screams the Postmaster springing back as if to ward off a physical blow. "Say it is not for me. Say it is not. What have I done to receive this blow?"

The audience look on in fear and trembling at the telegram on the table as if it were a cobra, with its hood up, ready to strike.

India

Margaret Chatterjee

IN A YOUNG YEAR

As travellers on the edge of a dark country
We stand—against the haunted hinterland
Of yesterdays, for the year is young
And there are many days to come.

Fears, like the shadows of birds' wings
In sunny places, disturb our noon,
And in the clamour of the market
There are too many voices.

Our nights are sleepless
With the memory of the withered blade
And where the earth knew evil;
And we conjure up in images
The presence of those to whom
We never said good-bye.

The prejudices of our fathers
Dog us, and in the green avenues of hope
We tread falteringly.
In the tabernacles of peace
We dwell uncertainly
For there is no peace in us.
Only by hardening ourselves
Can we bear the whine of the beggar,
The limp of the cripple, and the eyes of the
        poor.
For we are not in high places—
Principalities and powers
Busy themselves with such matters—
And so we hide our guilt
And so we look away.

For we are neither very young
Nor very old, that we can wish to live
With all the eagerness in us.
For we are tired men, and our eyes
Are worldly wise, all wonder lost
In the littlenesses that clutter up our day.

Yet of these broken vessels
Build Thou a world, a year,
And in these winter fields, in time,
The corn shall ripple like a golden flag,
For somewhere in the trees' dark sap
Bloom next spring's flowers.

S. Rajaratnam

THE TIGER

*F*ATIMA felt the cool yellow waters of the river—a sheet of burnished gold in the dying sunglow—flow sluggishly around her. She clung to the bank and moved further along until she stood waist-deep in a shallower part of the river. The wet sarong clung to her plump, brown figure, and accentuated the full breasts and womb of a pregnant woman. The round, high-cheekboned face, so typical of the Malays, had been drained of its dark sensuality, and instead an ethereal melancholy in the black oblique eyes gave her the expression of one brooding over some pulsating vision within herself.

With a quick toss of her head she unloosed her black, glossy hair, and let the wind whisper gently through it. From where she stood she could neither hear nor see the village obscured by the creepers and trees at the bend of the river. In front of her stretched an unbroken expanse of lalang grass, tall trees, and a bewildering luxuriance of foliage. The languid stillness of the evening was occasionally disturbed by the cry of a lonely water fowl, or the sinister flap, flap of night birds stirring from their sleep. Now and then a rat dived with a gentle splash into the river, whilst timid, nervous animals rustled their way through the tall grass and creepers. The air was full of the scent of wild flowers and mud and grass. A feeling of loneliness and desolation came over her, as though she had stumbled into a world still in the dawn of creation, when the earth was an oozing swamp in which wallowed a host of hideous monsters.

Hence when she heard the low, vibrant growl of the tiger it only heightened the illusion, until the tiger broke into a dull angry roar and convinced her that it was not a creature of her imagination but the real thing.

Framed by the lalang and low to the ground were the massive

head and shoulders of the tiger, not more than twenty yards from her. The sun imparted a wicked glint to its staring, yellow eyes, and its ears were drawn back warningly. It turned its head and snarled, revealing its red tongue, and the yellow fangs looked like tree stumps.

Fatima was hypnotized into a helpless fear by the glaring eyes of the tiger, and the sudden stillness that fell around her numbed her mind. She dared not move or take her eyes away from the watching animal, which too was still as if it had been rendered motionless by the unexpected meeting with a human being.

Fatima and the animal watched one another, she frightened and it suspicious. Except for occasional growls, which became less menacing each time, the tiger showed no signs of really wanting to attack her. Instead, after a while the animal took a diminishing interest in her. Its huge paws, stretched out in front, now and then dug its claws into the damp grass. Except when she moved the animal's attention seemed to be nowhere in particular. The glare of its eyes had changed into a sullen and frequently bored expression, so that Fatima noticed the surprising changes of mood in the animal's eyes.

Meanwhile the dusk which had crept from over the hills had obliterated the colourful scene of a moment ago, and replaced it with grey shadows which drifted imperceptibly into darkness. A faint mist had risen from the river, and had spread itself over the land. The shrill scream of a cicada and the distant hoot of an owl signalled the transition of the day into night.

Now that she had only a quiet fear of the tiger, she felt exhaustion creep over her. She shivered with the cold, and as the tiger showed no signs of going away she grew desperate. Her hands wandered over her stomach, and the realization that she was a being of two lives engendered in her a fierce determination to escape. She could still discern the shadowy form of the tiger by the failing light. Fatima had studied the animal very carefully and could sense when it would turn its eyes away from her. She waited, her body tense in the water and radiating a feeling of fearful strength. Then with a desperate movement she dived under water so that she scraped the river-bed as she swam.

Fatima made for the opposite bank and in the direction of the village, coming to the surface only when she felt that her lungs would burst for air. She felt bewildered and lost in the middle of the river, but when she heard the far-away growl, a fear which she had not felt even in the presence of the tiger seized her.

She swam frantically towards the shore until she saw the twinkling oil-lamps of the village.

The village was in a panic by the time Fatima's mother had spread an exaggerated version of the story her daughter had told her. The women, clucking like hens at the sight of a wheeling hawk, gathered the children into their arms, and having bolted their flimsy doors called out to the men to do something about the marauding tiger. The men rushed around anxious about their cattle and goats, while the old men munched betel-nut and demanded what the fuss was all about.

Fatima lay exhausted on a straw mat when the village headman and a crowd came to question her as to the whereabouts of the tiger. Fatima's mother proceeded to give a graphic and noisy tale of her daughter's encounter with the "hairy one" until the headman with an impatient gesture commanded the old lady to hold her peace for a while. He then turned to question Fatima. There was impatience in her voice as she answered his questions. For some reason, unlike the anxious villagers around her, she was averse to having the tiger hunted and killed. The headman, noting the reluctant manner in which she answered his questions, frowned.

"Allah!" exclaimed the old lady, wishing to be the centre of interest once more. "It was the providence of Allah which snatched my daughter away from the jaws of the 'hairy one'."

She threw up her skinny brown hands in a gesture of thanks to Allah. The headman shrugged his shoulders.

"Perhaps it was," he said, "but the next time Allah will not be as merciful. A tiger, perhaps by now drunk with the scent of human flesh, is not a pleasant thing to have roving near our village. For the peace and safety of the women and children the beast must be hunted down and destroyed without delay."

He scanned the faces of the men, silent and nervous. They were fully alive to the dangers of tracking down a tiger in the

46

night, especially when the dense, shadowy lalang afforded it an advantageous position from which to strike quickly and silently.

"Well!" said the headman.

The men regarded the floor in silence. The headman's face twitched and he was about to upbraid them for their cowardice, when Mamood, his youthful face afire with excitement, came in with a gun slung across his shoulders.

"What is this I hear?" he asked eagerly. "The women told me that a tiger has attacked our Fatima. Is it true?"

While the headman told him the facts, briefly and accurately, Mamood fingered his new, double-barrelled gun with all the impatience of one whose hunting spirit had been aroused. He was all for hunting the tiger at once, simply because he loved hunting. The fact that his quarry was a tiger made him all the more eager.

"That's true," said Mamood, when the headman had finished. "We have to think of the women and children. The poor creatures will never move an inch out of their houses until they know that the tiger is dead. It is the duty of the menfolk to protect them. Now who will come with Mamood and help him slay the tiger? As surely as I am the son of my mother I shall drag home the carcass of the beast before sunrise, if you will help me."

After some hesitation, a dozen men volunteered, encouraged by the words of Mamood and the knowledge that he was a good shot.

"Good!" exclaimed Mamood, running his fingers along the gun-barrel, "I knew I could rely on you."

Then he and the men left.

"Believe me, daughter," said Fatima's mother, as she bolted the door after the men, "that boy Mamood is a wild tiger himself."

Fatima rose up from her mat and looked out of the narrow window. The moon cast a mellow radiance over everything it touched, and she could see the moon, broken like molten silver, through the rustling coconut fronds. Men moved about calling out to one another in stifled, excited voices as they prepared for the hunt. Fatima stared gloomily at the men.

Then the men left until at last there was only the grey garbed trees and the whisper of the fretful wind. Straining her ears she heard the faraway chuckle of the river.

E

Somewhere, she reflected, was the tiger about which she had wondered the whole evening. She hoped that it was far out of the men's reach.

"O Allah!" wailed her mother, pounding some areca-nut in a wooden vessel, "tonight is the night for death. Think of those men groping for a beast as cunning as a hundred foxes and which can measure its distance in the darkness. Sure enough there will be the cry of mourning before the night is over."

"They should have left the tiger alone," said Fatima, still looking out of the window.

"That's a crazy thing to say," said the woman. "Somebody has to kill the tiger before it kills us. That's sense."

"Perhaps it would have gone away of its own accord."

"A tiger which comes near a village does not go back until its purpose is accomplished," croaked the old woman. "They are generally killers which venture near a village."

"But this one didn't look like a killer," protested Fatima.

The old woman snorted contemptuously, but said nothing.

"The tiger was not more than twenty yards away from me and it could have jumped on me easily," said Fatima, "but it didn't. Why? Can you explain that, mother? It kept watching me it's true, but then I was watching it too. At first its eyes glared at me but later they were gentle and bored. There was nothing fierce or murderous about it. . . ."

"Now you are talking the crazy way your father used to," said her mother fiercely pounding the areca-nut. "He used to say that the wind sang songs to him. Heaven forgive me that I should talk so of your dead father, but he was a crazy man sometimes."

Fatima scowled out of the window and listened. There was an unearthly silence over the village as though enveloped in a funeral shroud. Her hands, swollen and fleshy, were clenched tightly as she strained the silence for some revealing sound. The pound, pound of her heart kept pace with the jabs her mother made into the areca-nut vessel. Then a sharp pain shot through her. Her hands went over her stomach.

"What is it, Fatima?" said her mother looking up.

"Nothing," answered Fatima between pressed lips.

"Come away from that draught and lie down," cautioned her mother.

Fatima stood by the window and felt the pain rise and fall. She closed her eyes and pictured the tiger crouching in the lalang, its eyes now red and glaring, now bored and gentle.

Then she heard the faraway crack of a rifle. Then another shot followed. Fatima quivered as if the shots had been aimed at her. Then came the roar of the tiger; not the mild growl she had heard that evening, but full of pain and defiance. For a few seconds the cry of the animal, long drawn out in its agony, seemed to fill up her heart and ears. She wanted to re-echo the cry. Her face was tight with pain and her body glistened with sweat. A moan broke between her shut lips.

"Allamah! allamah!" cried out the old woman. "You look ill. What is it? Come and lie down. Is it . . . ?"

"I've got the pains, mother," gasped Fatima.

The old woman led the girl towards the mat and made her lie down.

"Oi, oi, it's a fine time to have a baby!" cried her mother, a little frightened. "You lie down here while I get you some hot water to drink. I'll have to wait till the men return before I go for the midwife. Ay, this is a fine night for a poor old woman!"

Fatima lay on the mat, her eyes shut tight while her mother boiled the water and muttered.

"Listen," said the old woman, "the men are returning. I can hear their voices."

The air suddenly was filled with the excited voices of men and women outside.

The old lady opened the door cautiously and called out to someone.

"Hurrah for Mamood, auntie," cried a youth rushing in. "He's shot the tiger and they have dragged the beast home. It's a big animal. No wonder it put up a good fight before it was killed. After it was shot twice they had to spear it before it was really killed. And then what do you think happened?"

Fatima looked attentively at the youth. The old lady turned her tiny shrivelled head impatiently towards the youth.

"Well, what happened?"

"They said," explained the youth, lisping slightly, "that after they had killed the animal they heard noises. Then by the light of the hurricane lamps they saw three of the tiniest tiger-cubs.

49

Their eyes were scarcely open and Mamood says that they could not be more than a few hours old. No wonder the beast fought like one possessed. Mamood says that he could sell the tiger-cubs for a good price."

Fatima moaned in pain. The sweat glistened like yellow pearls on her forehead.

"Mother!" she cried.

The old woman pushed the astonished youth towards the door.

"Get the midwife, boy," she shouted. "Quick! Go! The mid-wife."

The youth stared, gasped and then ran for the midwife.

Singapore

Margaret Leong

JAPANESE CEMETERY—SINGAPORE

OVER their graves with naked feet
Only the keeper and his children go,
No mourners come to brood the fate
Of warriors buried not so long ago;

Above their graves, a Shinto sign
Blurred red, still points the north
For those who lie forever in
This unlikely tropic earth;

The firs engulf the leading roads
With memorial shade; while deep
In the locked earth, the conqueror
And the conquered sleep.

Mochtar Lubis

THE LOTTERIES OF HAJI ZAKARIA

I T was on the bus going to Kerinchi that I began thinking about Haji Zakaria. I had not seen him for more than fourteen years. My father had recently died in our little village in Sumatra, and I had had to return home to console my mother and look after all the affairs that need handling when one's father dies. One of them was this trip I had to make to Kerinchi, where he had a little rubber estate. And there I was to stay in the house of Haji Zakaria.

At first there was no chance to think of anyone or anything except the bus. I had not liked the idea of this trip, because I knew that the motor road from Padang to Sungai Penuh, its terminus in Kerinchi, was in the worst possible condition. Many big rivers must still be crossed by pontoons, and the road goes through dense wild jungles, up and down great mountains. I could not refuse my mother's request. But the trip from the beginning proved to be everything I had expected.

Not that we had grave accidents, though twice the axle of the bus broke, and we skidded to a stop a few feet from the gaping mouths of deep ravines. But the driver seemed to be used to this, and indeed had quite a supply of new axles in the back of the bus. Still, such incidents kept one a little tense.

The near-murder was even more distracting. From the very beginning of the trip a young man returning from a religious school in Pariaman had been loudly chanting Koran verses. The passenger beside him, already distressed enough by the heat and by the bus's speedy swings round the hairpin mountain bends, was made quite ill by the loud chanting, and asked the young religious fanatic to stop. But he only chanted the louder. The sick man suddenly lost his temper and angrily shouted to the singer to stop that noise, to shut his mouth.

"Cursed infidel!" the young fanatic shrieked back, clapping his hand to the long knife inside his belt. "How dare you order me to stop chanting the sacred verses of the Holy Koran?"

He thereupon let loose a stream of Arabic sentences, then switched back to his local dialect, cursing the sick man with Hell's fire, God's wrath, and Black Death for seven generations. This done he looked at each of us in turn. Seeing that nobody wanted to challenge him, he quieted down, forgot his intention to murder the sick passenger, and again started to chant his verses louder than ever.

But one finally gets used even to broken axles, chasm brinks, and chanting fanatics, and my mind went back to Haji Zakaria. It was when my father was district commissioner in Kerinchi, a long time ago. I was only a small boy then, but I always remember Haji Zakaria as one of the kindest men I have ever known.

At harvest time, he never forgot to send Mother rice, still young and green, from which to make sweet cookies for us. Returned from a hunt, he always sent her dried well-seasoned strips of tender deer meat. And at the Lebaran, the great day after the month of fasting, we children were overwhelmed by his gifts. Fireworks were best, and once Father, on opening a case of them was shocked to see that each was as big as a stick of dynamite. We therefore regarded Haji Zakaria as part of the family, as the kindest, most generous uncle that ever was.

He was a very rich man. He had acres of rice fields. And, in those years when coffee prices were high, he had huge coffee plantations, with the best Robusta and Arabica types.

My father also had a coffee plot, but much smaller. When rubber began to bring higher prices in the markets, my father decided to cut down his coffee trees and plant rubber instead. Haji Zakaria advised against this, but Father feared the coffee market would crash, and then rubber would be the thing. Haji Zakaria laughed at Father's idea as crazy. People would always drink coffee, he said, but who would eat rubber?

Every New Year he and Father and Mother would make a promise to go together on the pilgrimage to Mecca. But Haji Zakaria always had to go alone. Father and Mother could never make the pilgrimage to Mecca; and it was only later I knew that it was because they did not have the money. Each year Haji Zakaria tried to get them to accept the money from him, and said to Father:

"Oh my friend the district commissioner, why are you so cruel to me? Is not my money your money? Is not my house your house? If you will not accept money as a gift, regard it then as a loan, which you can pay back whenever you wish."

But my father would laugh and refuse the offer, and Haji Zakaria would leave our house angrily. And when the day came, it was once more alone that he would set out on the pilgrimage. But when he returned from the Holy Land of Mecca, he never forgot to bring Mother the red coral stones of the Red Sea, small branches from certain holy trees in Mecca which were used as toothbrushes, and the *zam-zam* water in a bottle from the holy springs.

And then I remembered also how fond Haji Zakaria was of lotteries. Every month he would spend large sums on lottery tickets from Padang—four hundred to five hundred *rupiahs*-worth. And in those days that meant almost three hundred dollars. As far as I could recall, he had never won anything. Yet he never threw away the old tickets, but kept them carefully as a collection. I remember that on the night of a new Lebaran Father and Mother took us to visit him, and he began to tell us about the lotteries.

"Oh, my good friend," he said, "last month I almost won the big prize. The winning number was 567889, and one of my tickets was 567888. Now I am getting close to winning; next month I shall buy more tickets."

Father, who thought lotteries as great an evil as gambling, disagreed with Haji Zakaria, and they often fought about it. This time a naughty twinkle came into my father's eye, and he asked:

"Ah, Haji, how much have you wasted on these lotteries without getting a single cent back?"

Haji Zakaria left the room and returned with a big tin case. Inside it were lottery tickets stacked thick upon each other.

"There are about ten thousand *rupiahs*-worth there," he said, banging the case with his palm. "It is just the play of fortune. If you win, you get great profit; if you lose, well, what do some five hundred, or eight hundred, *rupiahs* a month matter?"

53

My father shook his head, and then said:

"What use are these paper tickets to you? I strongly advise you to throw them away. They are evil, and will bring sorrow to your heart later."

Haji Zakaria laughed aloud:

"No," he explained, "the pleasure of lotteries lies in realizing how close you have sometimes been to winning the big prize. Only one or two numbers make all the difference."

It was just at this point in my reminiscences that the bus stopped at Haji Zakaria's house, and I jumped out. Haji Zakaria was already waiting out front, and he hugged me to him as if I were still a child. Inside, his wife, sons, and daughters welcomed me. And food was ready too. Only after dinner did I begin to feel that the big house had changed and now seemed somehow empty. I missed the thick Smyrna carpets on the floor, and the noise the children used to make.

They too had grown. He had six children, and now only one girl, Maryam, remained at home, still unmarried. She used to play with us as a child, but now she had become a beautiful young girl. I kept looking at her.

Haji Zakaria talked and talked, remembering the old days, and repeating how wonderful it was to see me again, and how sad that my father had died. Later, when the married sons and daughters had left, and Maryam and her mother had gone back to the kitchen, Haji Zakaria suddenly said:

"We are poor now, son. When the coffee market crashed, many years ago, I followed your father's example, cut down my coffee trees and planted rubber. But just when the rubber trees had grown, that market crashed too. And I stupidly cut them down and replanted coffee. But coffee prices stayed down. Your father was lucky: he stuck to rubber during its slump, and when the Korean War made rubber boom, it paid off. He asked me to take care of his plantation, and that has helped us much. But now rubber is down again," he concluded, "and I do not know what will happen."

I told him my mission: Mother asked him to continue to care for the rubber plantation, but now that Father was gone, to regard it as his own.

Later in the evening, he went to the mosque, and Maryam came in to talk. It seemed that, when coffee crashed, her father had not taken it too seriously. He still went to Mecca each year, and bought his lottery tickets, just as usual. Later on, he had to sell some rice fields each year to pay for his pilgrimage.

But the biggest blow had come after the Japanese military occupation. Haji Zakaria was a patriot, with his sons in the revolutionary army, and he had sold many of his rice fields to buy Republican National Loan Bonds. Not that it was only patriotism, either: the Republican government guaranteed the interest on the bonds, and full payment of the principal within three or four years. But when Indonesia had won her freedom, the government failed to redeem the bonds. Then came the Korean War, however, and fortunately my father had asked Haji Zakaria to oversee his rubber plantation, for one half the profits.

From Maryam's story, I considered Haji Zakaria still well-off by ordinary standards. All his sons were working, and helping him. And he still had a few rice fields, so he did not need to buy rice.

"But," said Maryam, "he can no longer afford to play the lottery or to make his annual pilgrimage to Mecca, and that saddens him."

When, later, Haji Zakaria came home from the mosque, an impish impulse caused me to ask him about his lotteries. His face lit up, and he brought from his bedroom the big tin case, which he opened:

"Do you remember how I used to buy lottery tickets every month? And how often I was very close to winning? Please, try to estimate what all this is worth."

"Oh, it must be thousands of *rupiahs*," I said.

"No, not just thousands, son. I know exactly how much I paid for them: fifty-six thousand *rupiahs*, no more, no less. And they were good *rupiahs*, mind you, not our present *rupiahs*."

"And yet you never won?" I asked with amazement.

"And I never won," he answered. He laughed, shut the case, and started towards his bedroom. "Sleep well, son," he said.

Then I exclaimed: "Fifty-six thousand *rupiahs*, the old good *rupiahs*! Don't you realize that means more than a million and a half today? What could you not buy with so much money, even at today's prices. Why, you would be rich today!"

Haji Zakaria paused and laughed; then suddenly he stopped laughing, a cloud crossed his face, and he looked strangely at me. Then he muttered:

"You talk nonsense. Sleep well. You must be tired from your journey."

My room was between that of the old couple and Maryam's. I heard her being restless, and in my heart I hoped that if she could not sleep it was because of me.

I was back in Jakarta only a month when I received a letter from Maryam. She wrote that she felt uneasy about her father ever since my visit. He often shut himself in his room, and once they saw that he was busy counting his lottery tickets. He had become very quiet, and for hours and even days did not talk to anyone. And once, when he took his gun to go hunting, he had come back empty-handed, refusing to say where he had been or what had happened. And the lakes were so full of wild ducks just then that he couldn't have missed them.

I wrote back, telling Maryam not to worry, and saying, as young people do, that old people have their own problems but they blow over.

A week later, a telegram from Maryam informed me that her father was dead. A letter following the wire explained that Haji Zakaria had committed suicide in his locked bedroom by blowing out his brains with a gun. When they forced the door, they found him lying in the middle of the room, his blood spattered over all his lottery tickets and Republican National Bonds spread around him on the floor. "My mother," Maryam ended, "has fallen ill, and I do not know what to do."

So this is now my problem. What am I to do? For nights now, I have not been able to sleep. I feel guilty. I murdered Haji Zakaria by reminding him of his lottery tickets: in sorrow he killed himself because I reminded him of his folly.

I love Maryam. But can the murderer of the father marry the daughter?

With what great happiness would I make Maryam my wife, if I could only feel the certainty and assurance that it was not because of the lotteries that Haji Zakaria killed himself. If only I could believe that what led him to suicide was his sorrow over the unpaid Republican National Bonds!

M. Nurdin Abd

THE FALSE

EVER since the settlement was deserted:
A place for dust carried by the wind,
For green flies coming together in the foul air,
Air uncut by even the call of a lad minding goats.
Instead a corruption and lassitude hang there
Like a poison which, working silently, can kill at any time.

Prayers ascending with needy palms open and up
And the tears falling clean and clear.
Slowly insight grows
Demanding we promise ourselves again, regret our past—
The seconds tumbling over themselves to take our years,
Grass in the garden of the village mosque growing taller,
And . . . the scale is not yet in balance.

Our lamps are almost out for lack of oil,
The wick of man's short life is dry and cracked.
Is this the way things must be, that power
To create is from love and after a time of sorrow only?

These are shadows thrown by rays
Played on living skeletons.
The faces are already wrinkled, are stark questions.
Drums of ceremony used to fill and measure empty time
Shudder stiff on the air, tense for flight,
Because again . . . neglect
Passion's force shelters behind the lids of the eyes.

The leaves of old writings that now lie scattered beside
    the paths
Are sufficient evidence: man did exist long ago,
Moving about in the settlement,
Doing what he ought, devoutly serving,
Remembering that life will go on and judgment come.

There remains man, the maker of history,
Carrying out his vows, staking his life.
Shrieks meet the growling thunder.
Memories pass, still embracing on the heavy death bed,
Beckoning day on to follow day.
So it began, so it will end.

A thousand words
A thousand promises of obedience
Taking a thousand years—
In a muddle of dust and deceit.

Mumtaz Shireen

DEFEAT

IT is drizzling outside. A cold wind is blowing and an old man sits shivering in a hut. His mind is overcast with sadness—a deep melancholy. The dampness and darkness of the hut add to the gloom. The roof is dripping and the walls are wet; so is the floor, and it is all so lonely.

There was a time when such cold evenings were spent delightfully. They both sat basking at the fire in the courtyard. Then they would move indoors and he would pull a blanket over himself and retire. His wife used to put the kettle on the fire and come and sit at his feet. She would gently press his feet which were stiff with cold. It was so comforting, and his feet began to warm up; the stiffness vanished and a gentle sensation of pain remained.

She would get ready the gruel and pour it out into two earthern bowls and they would both sit drinking it and talking of their daughters and grandchildren. It was delightful to sit drinking the hot gruel in the cold weather. As it trickled down the throat, the blood warmed up in the chest. Then she would wash the utensils and arrange them properly on the wall. In the end she would retire and wrap herself up in the blanket.

How smart she was and what a lithe figure she had. Although she was the mother of three grown-up daughters, she looked quite young. Of course she was not very old, not much more than forty. Her daughters were hardly fourteen when they were married off, and so she became a grandmother at an early age. She was very fond of make-up and never appeared before him negligently dressed. Her image danced before his eyes—silver bracelets on her wrists and green glass bangles; a silver necklace round her neck; and a small nail with three studded gems in her nose. On her sharp and finely shaped nose, how beautiful

59

the jewels looked. She was always neatly dressed—a skirt of thin handloom cloth, a white printed sheet on her head, and a blouse of some soft pastel colour. She looked charming and the Begum used to call her Rim Jhim Bride.

The Begum was a woman with a very good heart. But even so when he thought of her house and of the Khan Sahib he was full of contempt. For six years he had worked in their house. Actually, he was an employee of the Office. They had no right to make him work in the home. Even so, he did what he was told, but without appreciation. The Khan Sahib called him a liar. No matter if he was poor, he had a sense of honour and protested strongly. Upon this, the Khan Sahib abused him. It was only that he was poor and helpless and the Khan Sahib was a rich man and highly placed. That was no reason why he should abuse and look down upon others. He could never bear such an insult as the Khan Sahib uttered. That very minute he left, without collecting his dues.

Begum sent for him time and again but Fakhru never went. Occasionally, he paid visits to the house of the Khan Sahib's and the Begum's daughter, Suraiya. Little Suraiya was dear to him. There was a time when he would put Suraiya on his shoulder and take her out for an airing in the park, or sight-seeing in the bazaar. The girl also loved him and called him uncle. She would come and sit in his lap and pull the hair of his sparse beard. What a tiny tot she was in those days. Now she was the mother of two children. She was extremely kind to him. Even now, she would talk to him smilingly and with courtesy. When he confided his sorrows in her, she would listen with sympathy. Therefore, now and then he used to go and spend an hour at her house. Suraiya understood his worth—at least treated him like a man.

He placed some cowdung fuel on his hearth and some dry brush wood on top, and lit a fire. As the flames rose he stretched out his hands and basked in the warmth. Suddenly the wind rose. The rain fell in torrents. The roof started dripping at one end. It was a thatched roof and he was thankful that it did not fly away in the wind. He dragged the pots and pans, the bags and mats to the dry corner. Suddenly somebody knocked at the door. "Who could be there in this heavy rain," he wondered.

"Open the door, grandpa, this is Jora." The old man opened the door. The new-comer set down the pile of straw which he carried on his head and said:

"Aunt told me yesterday, grandpa, that your roof was dripping. The day before yesterday in the storm our roof blew off. It was lucky that for the last two days there was only a light drizzle. Today after I had earned some money I went and bought some straw in the bazaar and thatched our roof. Some straw was left over. I thought I would pass it on to you."

He sat drying his clothes near the fire.

"Come and sit on this side," said the old man, moving aside from the front of the hearth. He stirred the fire and big flames leapt up.

"Why did you take the trouble to come in such heavy rain? You could have brought it tomorrow."

"No grandpa, it is beginning to rain hard. If your hut was full of water, where would you spend the night."

"Still my son, you should have been more careful. At least you should have put a sack on your head to protect yourself from the rain. Well here you are," said the old man taking out a two anna bit from his pocket.

"Why now, what is this?" said the young man.

"Nothing much, my son, just a few pice to buy sweets for your little daughter. Straw is so dear now-a-days and you have brought such a lot for me."

"No, no, grandpa. Keep the money. We also will need your help some time. If you pay me for such a small thing, how shall we have the courage to come to you for help? If neighbours cannot be of any use to each other, what good are they? Tell me grandpa, which side is the roof dripping? I shall repair it in a minute."

"No Jora, my son. You keep sitting there and watch me repair the roof. When I do the job you will see how long it will last."

Of course, this was just a way of refusing to take a favour. As far as he could, Fakhru always did his work himself and never allowed himself to become a burden on others. If he let people do small things for him, he thought, very soon he would depend on them for everything, and Fakhru did not want to become dependent.

"No, no, grandpa, I can do excellent thatching," said the young man standing up.

"Hold on, Jora. Let us sit and talk. The rain too has stopped now, so there's no hurry. Besides I have one or two things to ask you."

"What is it grandpa?"

"You said Jora that you had earned well today. But your aunt told me the other day that you had been idle for long. What work have you got hold of now."

"Don't you know, a fuel-wood depot has been opened in this quarter—and with it the doors of prosperity for us poor folk. All the young men of the street hang around it now-a-days. Many have given up regular employment to work there. There is work for everyone in the depot, grandpa."

"If they give good wages, there must be hard work to do. One would have to hack and hew tons of wood before the depot-holder shells out a few coins."

"No, grandpa, the work is light and the wages are good. At first one had to hew a cartload of wood to get a rupee. Now the rate is three annas for every rupee worth of fuel. If you hew into thin pieces, three annas; and if into thick ones, two and a half annas. There is extra money to carry the load to the buyer's home—two annas for a rupee-worth of wood. But we don't do the hewing; there are separate workers for that. Hewn wood is so much dearer that few will buy it. We do the carrying mostly."

"If that is so, I shall come with you tomorrow. For many days I have been looking for work, in vain."

"Will you, grandpa? Can you do such hard work?"

"I shall try, son. Although I am old, I am fit. I have always worked hard and so my body has not softened. Before this also I have done this work. What hard labour is there that I haven't done—hewn wood, carried loads at the railway station, walked miles in the sun for the Khan Sahib. When have I known a life of ease?"

"You are a brave man, grandpa. Even at this age you can earn your living. Aunt says you have three daughters. Have you no son?"

"Never had a son, worse luck. All three were girls. One died;

the elder one was married in village Hosli; the third lives here on Market Road."

"Then why don't you go and live with her. Is this the time for you to work?"

The old man nodded his head.

"I don't want to become a burden on any one as long as I live. Even if I had a son, I wouldn't have lived on his earnings. And to live with my daughter, on the charity of my son-in-law, is unthinkable. As long as there is strength in my arms, I shall earn my own bread. Would to God, that in my last days I do not have to lie helplessly at others' mercy."

"Yes, grandpa, may everyone die so honourably."

He sat lost in thought for a while, then he stood up.

"It is getting late. The wife must be waiting."

"Right, son. God bless you."

Basking in the fire, the old man was now warmed up, he now went looking for his axe. He was happy that he would soon go to work again.

He had had to spend out of his savings. Lately he had been eating only once a day.

Getting up early, he sharpened the axe thoroughly and set off towards Jora's house. Jora too was just now coming out of his house, after having eaten his breakfast.

"Come on grandpa, let's go."

They walked on quietly and soon reached the depot.

"Lord, what a crowd," said Fakhru. "Do even women come here?"

"Sure, and special consideration is shown to them. The wood is weighed out for them first, even if their turn comes after."

There was a long queue in front of the shop. On the right was a big balance in which the fuel wood was being weighed out. Nearby was a crowd of labourers waiting to hew wood or to carry loads. Fakhru and Jora went to join the crowd. When the men at the balance called out the number, one man from the queue stepped out and handed over his coupon. The wood was weighed out for him. If he was a poor man he would lift the load himself, because his purchase also was usually small. The rich, however, often had their servants with them. Others called in the labourers to carry loads for them. Fakhru also got

63

work quite often. Once when he got very tired, Jora hired for him a push-cart at three annas per day. On this little cart one could quite easily transport a few maunds of wood. In this way Fakhru earned as much as three rupees in one day. After remaining idle so long, to get three rupees made Fakhru immensely happy. He decided to pay a visit to his daughter and grandchildren and also to little Suraiya—Suraiya who used to feel so sorry for him at being unemployed.

Next day he got four annas worth of sweets and went to his daughter. From there he went to Suraiya's house.

"Suraiya, my child, may you live long," he said and sat down wiping the sweat from his face.

"You have come after a long time, uncle Fakhru."

"Yes my child. I have been going about looking for work."

Suraiya's child of two and a half years was playing in the courtyard. Fakhru tried to pick him up in his lap but the child snatched his handkerchief and started opening the knot. When Fakhru helped him to find the sweets inside, the child came and sat in his lap.

"There was a time when you also used to sit in my lap, Suraiya, my child, and now you are a mother yourself, by the Grace of God."

He looked lovingly towards Suraiya as if to say you are dearer to me than my own daughters, and that was a fact. He would not say such a thing, of course, lest it should be taken as flattery. Everyone flatters the rich. Suraiya watched her child eating the sweets. What a strange man is uncle Fakhru. Other poor men when they come, always beg for something. This man always brings something. He has never asked for a pie (small coin). If of herself she wanted to give him a few annas, he would say:

"No, my child, God has given me enough. I am all alone and have no liabilities. Whatever I earn is enough for me. If I have too much money, I shall only waste it. So you keep it now; when I want it, I shall not hesitate to ask for it."

But of course he would never ask even if he was in great need. He certainly told her of his trials and troubles, because she always gave him sympathy. If, however, she ever forced him to accept any money, she would make out from his face that he did not like it, and he always looked out for some work, to do in return for the favour. "Where is the baby's pram. Let me take her for an outing. Do you want any letters to be posted? The Post Office falls on my way and I can easily post them." Suraiya well knew that the Post Office was far away but he only wanted to do something in return.

"Hasn't your husband returned from the office?"

"No, uncle."

"I love to see you two together. It is a fine couple."

She blushed and changed the topic.

"Yes, uncle you were saying that you have got some work now. What work is it?"

"It is no permanent work, my child. They have opened a fuel-wood depot in our quarter. So I go there. Somebody asks me to carry his wood home for him or sometimes I hew the wood. Yesterday I made as much as three rupees." The old man's eyes gleamed with joy.

"But are these the days for you to earn, uncle? You have told me that you have relatives in the town and your own daughter. Why don't you go and live with them. Will your daughter consider you to be a burden, her own father? You have brought her up, wedded her—can she forget all these obligations and leave her old father like this?"

"No, no, my child, my daughter is not like this. She may be poor but she is a good girl. She always asks me to come and live with her."

"Then is it your son-in-law that objects? Perhaps it is he."

"No my child, he is a good boy too. But my sense of honour does not let me accept the idea of living in another person's house. As long as there is strength in these arms, I shall earn my own living."

"And when you cannot work at all?"

"For that time, child, I have put by some money. I shall hand it over to my daughter and shall go and live with her. The rest of my life, I shall pass sitting in one corner in meditation and prayer. For my burial too, I have kept aside twenty rupees. Even so, there is enough money left to last me the rest of my life. After all how long shall I live."

He stood up to go. Suraiya watched his eyes.

"God bless you, child."

He was gone. But Suraiya was still, as it were, gazing at his sparkling eyes. May he maintain his high resolve like this. The day before yesterday she felt so sad on hearing the tale of her husband's lawyer friend—how he decided never to take up a false case, but starvation soon forced him to do so. But this old man, so poor and so weak, what a brave fight he is putting up! Those days when he was out of work, he starved himself. Now he is hewing wood. For long she stood watching him.

He went every day to the depot. As he had done this work before, he knew how to wield the axe, so as to split the log easily. But still, hewing wood is not a joke. He had lost his strength. He had to pause after every little while. Even then it was terribly painful. It seemed as if his chest was becoming hollow; as if someone was tearing off the muscles of his arms. When he returned, his shoulders and arms were badly aching. But when he had rested and washed, and sat down for his meal, he felt an indescribable satisfaction. He was eating his own hard-earned bread. He used to go to only two houses, and hewed four rupees worth of wood for each.

Then summer came and the wood hardened up. So far he had been hewing only juniper wood, because this was easier to split. Now it had become harder than other woods.

Once in a hot afternoon he stood hewing wood in the torrid sun—the hard juniper wood. The logs were gnarled. To hew each log took him as long as he used to take in hewing a rupee worth of wood before. Even at the strongest strokes, the axe did not pierce the wood. He was panting—and covered with sweat. As he swung the axe with full force, it seemed as if he was at his last gasp. His throat was parched. The excrutiating pain made him groan. But the gnarl in the wood refused to be split. With a great effort, he lifted up the log and the axe fixed in it, and swung them down with full force. A terrible pain shot through his chest. Everything turned dark. He grasped his chest, and sat down.

The mistress of the house came out, and called out in a rasping tone:

"Why are you sitting dozing, you there. It is no more than four rupees worth of wood. To hew so much wood, you want rest also in between. Come on, finish off quickly. We are having guests at dinner this evening, and want a lot of fuel."

"I cannot hew any more, mother. The wood is very hard and gnarled. I have hewn half the wood. Please pay me for that much."

"When you can't do the work, why did you come?" she shouted angrily, and flung two annas at him.

"Only two annas, mother? I have hewn half the wood and now-a-days everyone pays four annas for a rupee worth of wood. No one hews such hard wood for less than four annas. At this rate, it makes eight annas."

"Oh now! Fancy that! You shouldn't be paid anything actually. You have put us to more bother. Now we have to look for another man. I shall not pay a pie more."

And she walked away. He waited for long thinking perhaps she had gone to get more money, but she never came back.

He went and lay down in his hut. There was no one to enquire after him. When in the evening Jora came, he saw the old man had developed fever.

"Oh you have high fever, grandpa! Shall I bring a carriage and take you to your daughter's? Will you go to your daughter's?"

"Let me be. I have lived so long; brought up children, grand-children; married them off. What more do I want? If I only die peacefully. . . ."

"Don't say so, grandpa. I shall just now go and get a *hakim* (doctor). Shall I send word to your daughter?"

"No son. Don't tell her. She will be upset. And after all, what is the matter with me? Only the logs were hard and I have developed a pain in the chest, and that's caused a fever. In a day or two, I shall be all right. She has her own worries. Why should she leave all her household for my sake."

For a month, he lay in bed. When he recovered completely, Jora cleared the doctor's account, and returned his wallet to Fakhru—this wallet which contained all his substance, and which he had handed over to Jora to spend during his illness. With trembling hands, he opened the wallet. There were only five rupees inside. How long he will have to work to replenish this wallet again. He will start going to the depot right from to-morrow. Of course he will no longer be able to hew wood, but he could carry loads—at least two rupees worth of wood at a time. Or he would hire the depot cart at three annas a day.

The next morning, he again went to the depot. It was all changed now. Previously only a few young men were among those hewing wood. Now there was a whole crowd waiting for work. Before this people used to look for porters to carry their wood; now the porters themselves descend on the man as soon as he has had his wood weighed out. Every man was surrounded by four or five coolies shouting, "Sahib, let me carry this for you." How could he force his way into such crowds? Always when he was watching a man buying his wood, thinking this would be a good load for him to carry, another would rush up and whisk away the load while he stood gaping. Once he also tried to push his way through, but there was a terrific crush. On every side people were shoving and heaving. He could not keep his balance. After the long illness he had grown very weak.

He stinted and spared expense, but even so, how long could five rupees last. He began going without food for most of the day. A long illness, and then this starvation—naturally he grew very weak. Even if he drew the attention of a client to himself, he would just look at him and turn away, as if saying, "What can this skeleton of a man do? Can he lift the load of wood, let alone hew it?" They always preferred healthy people. He was weak and starving so no one gave him work; so he remained weak and starving.

The thought came to him, Why not go to little Suraiya. He would do some little chores for her and get paid a few annas. Thus he would regain his strength, and he would be fit for work again. He set off slowly, with determination.

Suraiya was combing her child's hair, as if in a great hurry. The house looked desolate. The old man stood amazed. There was no furniture or anything.

"Well child, are you shifting?"

"We are going to Bangalore, grandpa. He has been transferred."

She looked happy. "It is not a transfer only but a promotion. The luggage has all been sent to the station, and he has gone along with it. The servant has gone to get a carriage for us. I was wanting to see you before going, and it is good you came. Tell me how are you now?"

The old man heaved a sigh.

"What shall I say. For one whole month I was lying in bed, seriously ill, and now that I have got up, I have no strength left in my arms to work."

"Why? What happened uncle?"

"Nothing, child. One day as I was hewing some gnarled logs of wood, I developed a pain in the chest, and had fever for a month. Any excuse is enough in old age to fall sick."

"Didn't I tell you uncle, not to do such hard work? You never listen to me. Now you have been taught a lesson. I tell you, go and live with your daughter. Wasn't it for this time that you had saved up your money?"

"That is all spent, child."

"How, uncle?"

"On medicines and so on."

"Spent so much money on your treatment? How much money did you have?"

"A little less than three twenties. The treatment cost about thirty rupees, including the doctor's fee and medicines. Before this I had bought a gold ring for my grandchild's husband. . . ."

"What did your grandson-in-law want with a gold ring? That was very silly of you. It is all your fault."

"My innocent child, you do not know the ways of the world. I had to present a gold ring to my grandson-in-law last time to humour him a little. Now I have spent my savings and cannot go to live with my daughter also. . . . No, I shall not go. I shall keep trying. I am still going to the depot. But you see my condition. Who will give work to such a weak person? It occurred to me, why not go to little Suraiya. Perhaps I will be able to do some work for her and get paid a few annas."

"Must you work, uncle?" She looked around for her purse, but the purse had been locked up in her box, and all the luggage was at the station. She could not help this proud old man even in such difficulty. She felt very sad. Her husband also had not returned yet from the station, or she could have borrowed some money from him. Suddenly an idea struck her.

"Come uncle, come along with us," she spoke out joyously. Before this also she had often thought of keeping the old man in her house, but she already had two or three servants. What will her husband say? Even after having so much help in the house, she still wants more. He never said no to her but still Suraiya did not like to take too much advantage of his good nature. In this case she felt sure that he too was a very soft-hearted and god-fearing man.

"Will you come with us uncle? I should not give you much work. You will only have to take the children out occasionally or do some errands. What do you say?"

The old man stood lost in thought for some time. Then he spoke slowly.

"No child, I cannot come. I cannot leave this place. I have spent all my life here. My father and grandfather have lived here and I too was born and bred here. My house is an ancestral house. In this house I spent twenty years with my wife. She lies buried here and so do my father and grandfather. I cannot leave this village. If I die in a strange land, I shall miss the soil of my own village for my grave. I shall try to support myself as best I can, and if not, I shall die."

She could not force him. Soon a servant came, saying the carriage had arrived. Suraiya picked up her three-month baby. The servant lifted the bag of the child's clothes and bedding, and also the elder child.

"Well I am going, uncle. May God help you."

"God bless you, child."

Fakhru had lost all hope but still he kept going to the depot. Every day he returned disappointed. Nobody paid him any attention. Hunger often made him faint, but he did not die. He went to the depot at eight in the morning and stayed there till the depot closed. All the other labourers had left either for their homes or for the house of someone to hew wood. But he still hung on, for some reason.

"Oh, are you closing the depot," said someone who had come racing on a cycle. "If you could please give me wood today, I shall be obliged, as I cannot come tomorrow, and our servant is ill."

The depot-holder opened the shop and got the wood weighed

out. After getting the wood, the man looked around for a coolie, but there was no one except the old man. Hesitatingly he asked him, "Are you a coolie?"

"Yes, sir."

"Will you carry this? Our house is nearby."

"Very well, sir."

"What will you charge?"

"The usual rate, sir. Two annas per rupee worth of wood."

"Good. Come on."

Another coolie came running. He had just come away after hewing wood at some place. At once he shouted.

"I shall carry it for you, sir."

"No I have settled with the old man."

Fakhru at once lifted the bundle.

"Hugh! What can this old man do? I shall carry them in a jiffy—and shall hew them right away."

"Yes, old man, can you hew the logs?"

"No sir, I cannot. I used to hew wood but starvation has made me very weak. Since yesterday, I have not had a morsel. How can I wield the axe?"

"Didn't I tell you? He can't do a thing."

But the man took pity on Fakhru.

"Let him carry it, and you do the hewing. This way, you will both get something."

"Why should I walk all this way for nothing," said the boy, walking away.

"Come here," called the man. Fuel was badly needed at his house. His wife had told him there was no wood to cook the dinner tonight. Now where will he look for another man to hew the wood?

"Come here."

The boy turned and said:

"I shall hew it into such thin pieces, that the mistress will be really pleased."

The old man still stood carrying the wood, but when you stand at one place, the burden becomes heavier. In his enthusiasm, he had lifted up four rupees worth of wood all at once. Now his shoulders were aching. The man stood silent for a while. He did not know what to say.

"Come, I shall carry it for six pice per rupee worth," said the boy.

The difference of two pice settled the question. Two pice per rupee adds up to two annas for four rupees. For a poor clerk this was consideration enough.

"Right, put down the wood, old man."

Quietly he threw down the load. All the despair of the world gathered into his eyes. The boy lifted up the wood and both set off on the road. Even after they disappeared from sight, he stood there—unconscious of his surroundings. The heat became unbearable. His temples were throbbing feverishly as if the arteries would burst. He sat hanging his head and brooding. Suddenly he burst out crying. Then he got up slowly and walked away. In the distance he could see the familiar walls of a house. He was walking with his eyes fixed on it. He could hardly walk but some unknown power impelled him on. At the threshold, he stopped, and stood leaning for a long time. The conflict of strong emotions was raging like a fire in his heart. His trembling hand rose and then stopped; rose and stopped again; then rose and knocked at the door of his daughter's house!

Pakistan

"Faiz"

A PRISON NIGHTFALL

STEP by step by its twisted stairway
Of constellations, night descends;
Close, as close as a voice that whispers
Words of passion, a breeze drifts by;
Trees in the prison courtyard, exiles,
Heads sunk low, are lost in broidering
Arabesques on the skirt of heaven.

Splendidly on that roof's high crest
The gracious hand of the moonlight gleaming;
Star-glitter swallowed into the dust,
White radiance blanching the purple sky;
Bluish shadows in those green corners,
Waveringly, like separation's
Bitterness eddying into the mind.

One thought keeps running in my brain—
Life is so exquisite in this moment,
Those who compound the tyrants' poisons
Never can, now or tomorrow, triumph.
What if they put the candles out
That light love's altar? if they would have us
Fear, let them put out the moon.

Ahmed Ali

HAVING BEEN ATTACKED FOR
SPEAKING THE TRUTH
MY HEART WAS FILLED WITH SORROW
AND I WROTE THIS POEM

In Autumn the War began.
Men went out, but they did not return.

In Winter I sat by the stove to keep me warm.
But the wind howled through innumerable cracks.

When Spring came and the flowers appeared
And the skies were blue and the swallows returned
I took my stick and went forth from my house,
Hoping that they will leave me alone.

I saw the sesame in yellow bloom,
The fields green, green,
The jade of the bending willows,
The grace of the poplars tall, tall,
The gold of the fish in the clear streams.

I sat under the Purple Mountain,
Contemplating the Lotus Lake and the peaceful scene.
I belonged neither to this warring lord nor that,
Only a poet in search of peace.
Yet the soldiers beat me all the same,
For having no hatred and being serene.

Geoffrey Dutton

THE WEDGE-TAILED EAGLE

THROUGH the hot, cloudless days in the back of New South Wales there is always something beside the sun watching you from the sky. Over the line of the hills, or above the long stretches of plains, a black dot swings round and round; and its circles rise slowly or fall slowly, or simply remain at the same height, swinging in endless indolent curves, while the eyes watch the miles of earth below, and the six or maybe nine-foot wingspan remains motionless in the air. You know that there is nothing you can do which will not be observed, that the circling eagle, however small the distance may make it, however aloof its flight may seem, has always fixed upon the earth an attention as fierce as its claws.

But the eagles watch the sky as well as the earth, and not only for other birds; when an Air Force station was established in their country in 1941, they were not alarmed by the noisy yellow aeroplanes. Occasionally they would even float in circles across the aerodrome itself, and then disappear again behind the hills; the pilots had little fear of colliding with one of these circling, watchful birds. The vast, brown-black shape of the eagle would appear before the little Tiger Moth biplane and then be gone. There was nothing more to it. No question of haste or flapping of wings, simply a flick over and down and then the eagle would resume its circling. Sometimes a pilot would chase the bird and would find, unexpectedly, a response; the eagle would seem not to notice the aeroplane and hold the course of its circling until the very moment when collision seemed inevitable. Then there would be the quick turn over, under, or away from the plane, with the great span of the wings unstirred. The delay and the quick manoeuvre would be done with a princely detachment and consciousness of superiority, the eagle in the silence

75

of its wings scorning the roar and fuss of the aircraft and its engine.

Two pilots from the station were drinking one day in the local town with one of the farmers over whose land they used to fly.

"Two of us, you know, could do it," one of them said. "By yourself it's hopeless. The eagle can outfly you without moving his wings. But with two of you, one could chase him round while the other climbed above and dived at him. That way you'd at last get him flustered."

The farmer was not at all hopeful.

"Maybe it'd take more than a couple of planes to fluster an eaglehawk. There's a big one around my place, just about twelve feet across. I wish you could get him. Though if you did hit him, there mightn't be much left of your little aeroplane."

"It always beats me why you call them eaglehawks," said one of the pilots. "The wedge-tailed eagle is the biggest eagle in the world. You ought to pay him more respect, the most magnificent, majestic bird there is."

The farmer was hostile to this idea of majesty.

"Have you ever seen them close-up? Or ever seen them feeding? The king of birds landing on a lolly-legged lamb and tearing him to bits. Or on an old, dead, fly-blown ewe that's been fool enough to lie down with her legs uphill. Watch him hacking his way into their guts, with the vermin dancing all over his stinking brown feathers. Then all you've got to do is to let him see you five hundred yards off and up he flaps, slow and awkward, to a myall where he sits all bunched-up looking as if he's going to overbalance the little tree. Still, go ahead with your scheme. I'd like to see you beat one at his own game."

He left, and the two others continued discussing their plans. A pilot in a small, acrobatic aircraft is like a child. He longs for something to play with. He can be happy enough rolling and looping by himself in the sky, but happiness changes to a kind of ecstasy when there is someone against whom to match his skill, or someone to applaud him when he low-flies through the unforeseeable complications of tree and rock, hill and river. The contest becomes more wonderful the nearer it approaches death, when all else is forgotten in the concentration of the minute.

The pilot who fights with bullets and shells is ecstatically involved in his actions. This fight with the wedge-tailed eagle was to be to the death, not a battle of bullets or shells, but of skill against inborn mastery. The risk of death would be there, just the same, both for the bird and for the pilot supported by the fragile wood and fabric of the aeroplane.

One cloudless morning the pilots flew off together, in close formation, towards the valley of the farmer's house. The sky was as clean as a gun-barrel and the sun hit them both in the back of the neck as they flew westward towards the scrubby range and the valley beyond. The pilot of the leading aircraft loosened his helmet and let the wind, like a cool rushing sense of elation and freedom, blow around his neck and hair. Like the eagle, he was a watcher, one from whom no secrets could hide on the earth below. The country matched the element in which he moved: both hard and unforgiving of mistakes, yet endlessly stretching, magnificent in freedom. Neither the air nor this land would bring anything for the asking; but they would offer all manner of their peculiar riches to anyone who could conquer them by work and vigilance and love. The foolish and the weak perished like the sheep stuck in the wet mud of the drying dams, in sight of the water for the lack of which they died.

As he approached the hills, the earth below him and the creeks were brown and dry as a walnut, with a strip of green along the river and a few bright squares where a farmer had sunk a bore and put in a few acres of lucerne. A mob of sheep stirred along in a cloud of dust through a few scattered myalls and gum trees. He finally bounced over the hills through air rough from the hot rocks, and turning away from the other aeroplane, moved up the broad valley, searching the sky for the black dot of an eagle wheeling and wheeling like a windmill on its side. There was no sign of anything, not even of a cloud or a high whirly of dust, which in an empty sky looks like a patch of rust in a gun-barrel. Everything seemed to him shiny and empty, yet somehow waiting to go off.

He made a long leisurely run up the valley, a few feet above the ground, lifting his wing over a fence or two, turning round a gum tree or away from a mob of sheep. The only other sign of life was the farmer standing near his truck by the gate of a paddock. He answered his wave, turned and flew over him, and then continued up the valley. Above him, in the other aeroplane his friend waited for something to happen.

He ran his wheels almost along the ground and turned across another fence. Suddenly the whole top of a tree flapped off in front of him and the eagle disappeared behind him before he could turn. Another bird rose from a dead sheep a few hundred yards away, but the pilot's whole attention was concentrated on the bird that had risen from the myall tree. It was undoubtedly the big eagle of which the farmer had told them.

By the time he had turned and come back in a climb the eagle was five hundred feet above him. He opened the throttle wide and pulled the strap of his helmet tight. He looked for the other plane and saw that his friend was moving towards them and climbing also, so that with the added height he could dive as they had planned.

The pilot was astonished to find that he was being out-climbed without the bird even moving a feather of its wings. On the hot, unseen currents it swung lazily round and round, its motionless wings always above the quivering, roaring aircraft. To make things worse, the pilot, in order to climb as quickly as possible, had to move in a straight line and then turn back, whereas the eagle sailed up in a close spiral. His hand pushed harder on the small knob of the throttle already wide open against the stop. Perhaps the battle would come to no more than this, the noisy pursuit of an enemy who could never be reached.

Yet the eagle, its mastery already established, now deliberately ceased climbing and waited for the aeroplane to struggle up to its level. The pilot, wondering if the farmer below had seen his humiliation, pressed on above the bird, where at about three thousand feet he levelled off and waved to his friend above that the battle was about to begin.

He came round in a curve at the bird, the aeroplane on the edge of stalling, juddering all over, the control-stick suddenly going limp in his hand as a pump-handle when a tank is dry, the slots on the end of the wings clattering above him; and then, just as he ducked his head to avoid the shining curved beak, the braced black and brown feathers, the sky amazingly was empty in front of him. The eagle had flicked over as lightly as

78

a swallow, with no sign of panic or haste. He looked over and saw it below him, circling as quietly as if nothing in the whole morning, in the sky or on the land, had disturbed its watchful mastery of the air.

As the pilot dived towards it and followed it around again, he saw his friend drop his wing and come down, steep and straight, to make the attack they had planned. He could see that the eagle, under its apparent negligence, was watching him and not the diving plane. This was the moment for which they had waited, when the eagle would break away as usual, but to find another aeroplane coming at it before it had time to move. The pilot's heart lunged inside him like the needle of the revolution counter on the instrument panel. Waiting until his friend had only another few hundred feet of his dive left, he jerked the controls hard over towards the shining feathers of the bird. It turned and fell below him, exactly as they had hoped it would. The pilot pulled himself up against his straps to watch its flight. The other aeroplane was on it just as it began its circling again. But the collision did not happen. The plane shot on and began to pull up out of its dive; the eagle recovered again into its slow swinging, a few hundred feet lower.

Yet it had shown a little concern. For the first time a fraction of dignity had been lost: momentarily the great wings had been disturbed a little from their full stretch. It had been startled into a quick defensive action. The pilot's excitement now blotted out everything but the battle in progress, leaving him poised between earth and sky, forgetful of both except as a blur of blue, a rush of brown. The last thing he saw on land had been the farmer's truck coming across the paddocks to a point somewhere below. Then all the vanity and pride in him had responded to the fact that there was someone to watch him. Now no response existed except to the detail of the black, polished brownness of the eagle's plumage, the glistening beak, the wedge-shaped tail. His excitement was at that intensity which is part of hope, his first sight of achievement. Previously the insolent negligence of the bird had destroyed his confidence, and had almost made the air feel the alien element it really was. In contrast with all his noisy manoeuvring, his juggling with engine and controls, the eagle had scorned him with its silence, with its refusal to flap its

79

wings, its mastery of the motionless sweep, the quick flick to safety and then the motionless circling again. The pilot had begun to wonder who was playing with whom. Perhaps the bird would suddenly turn, dive, rip him with a talon, and slide sideways down the vast slope to earth.

Yet now the eagle had been forced to move its wings, and he had seen the first sign of victory. Sweat poured round his helmet and down his neck and chest. His shirt clung wetly first to his flesh and then to the parachute harness. He looked at his altimeter and saw that they were down to seven hundred feet. Above him his friend was ready.

He turned in again towards the eagle. The aeroplane shivered and clung to height, on the last fraction of speed before the spin. Feeling the stiffness of his hands and feet on the controls, he told himself to relax like the eagle in front of him. He looked quickly upwards and saw his friend begin to dive. This was the second stage of their plan. The eagle, however little sign of it appeared, knew now that both aeroplanes were attacking. It circled, still on unmoving wings, but subtler and harder to follow, and shifted height slightly as it swung around.

The other plane was almost past him in its dive when he completed his turn in a vicious swing towards the eagle; he missed, spun, corrected, and looked up to see the other aeroplane, which had dived this time far below the eagle, coming almost vertically up below the just-levelled bird.

The eagle heard and saw, and flicked over to where, before, safety had always been emptily waiting for it. It flashed, wings still gloriously outstretched, straight into the right-hand end of the upper mainplane of the aircraft, exactly where the metal slot curves across the wood and fabric. Its right wing, at the point where the hard, long feathers give way to the soft, curved feathers of the body, snapped away and fluttered down to earth. The left wing folded into the body, stretched and folded again, as the heavy box of bone, beak and claw plunged and slewed to the ground. The pilot could not watch the last few feet of its descent. For the first time he was grateful to the roar of the motor that obscured the thud of the body striking earth.

The two pilots landed in the paddock, and, leaving the engines running, walked over to the dark mass of feathers. One of them turned off to the side and came back holding the severed wing. It was almost as big as the man himself.

The two of them stood in silence. The moment of skill and danger was past, and the dead body before them proclaimed their victory. Frowning with the glare of the sun and the misery of their achievement they both looked down at the piteous, one-winged eagle. Not a mark of blood was on it, the beak glistening and uncrushed, the ribbed feet and talons clenched together. It was not the fact of death that kept them in silence; the watcher could not always keep his station in the air. What both of them could still see was the one-winged heap of bone and feathers, slewing and jerking uncontrolled to earth.

In the distance they heard the noise of the farmer's truck approaching, and saw it stop at a gate and the farmer wave as he got out to open it. They quickly picked up the bird and its wing, and ran with them to the little hillock covered in rocks at the corner of the paddock. Between two large rocks they folded both wings across the bird and piled stones above it; and then, each lifting, carried a large flat stone and placed it above the others.

As they ran back towards the aeroplanes a black dot broke from the hills and swung out above them, circling round and round, watching the truck accelerate and then stop as the two aeroplanes turned, taxied and slid into the air before it could reach them.

David Campbell

WHEN OUT OF LOVE

WHEN out of love, and reason goes
From bird to book and finds no rest
(For songs are silent, sonnets prose,
Without a singer in the breast),
I stand and stare at a green stone,
A hill, a hawk above the hill
That hangs upon the wind alone—
And suddenly my mind is still.
It hovers with the dreaming bird;
Below, in briars, the wrens begin
Their summer song, and at a word
O all the coloured world comes in
With cocks and larks, and then I find
I have a sonnet in my mind.

Judith Wright

SANDY SWAMP

FROM the marble-dazzling beaches
or the tame hills where cattle pasture
the eye that ranges never reaches
the secret depth of that storm-cloud
the bitter and thorny moor
that sets its bar between
hill's green and sea's glitter.

No visiting traveller crosses
by the pale sandy tracks that vanish
under the banksias hung with mosses.
In yellow evenings when the sea sounds loud
night rises early here,
and when white morning sings
here clings the darkness longest.

Who walks this way, then? Only
the rebel children who fear nothing
and the silent walker who goes lonely,
silence his goal, out of the holiday crowd.
And these, if they go far,
will find the clustering moons and stars of white
that jealous night saves for her wanderers.

Maxwell Hall

THE SPIRIT OF THE BLOWPIPE

THE Murut boy ran silently and swiftly between the rubber trees to the safety of the Chinese shop. He had just seen his father killed by Molog; Molog the implacable enemy of his family, Molog a well-known Murut headhunter. The feud had been fought out for generations and the boy's father was the latest victim. He had been taken unawares, unarmed, tapping a rubber tree on the big Sapong Rubber Estate. The boy had fled from the scene where Molog hacked at the head with a cutlass. The boy—his name was Lotok—knew where his father's blowpipe leaned against a wall in the tappers' lines.

The blowpipe now belonged to him. It was made of *billean* iron wood, the best tree that had ever been felled in the Tagul Valley. All the Muruts in their villages high up on the mountain slopes knew this famous blowpipe. The blowpipe held at its end a spear-head of steel, Sheffield steel of England, reputed to have been the spear-head of an early explorer who had lost his life and his head in Lagungun River. The blowpipe's bore was smooth as glass, and the pith of its poisoned darts fitted that bore exactly.

Lotok, young as he was, hoped to live to drive that spear-head or to puff a poisoned dart into Molog's breast.

A Murut woman, wife of the kindly Chinese shopkeeper, befriended the boy. She had changed her customs and was a Muslim. She called herself Fatimah, obeying the teachings of the Prophet and following the customs of her Chinese husband so far as the varied teachings and customs were compatible.

She brought up Lotok and adopted him into her family as a son. The generous and tolerant Chinese shopkeeper stroked his beard and watched complacently, while Fatimah cut Lotok's long hair behind, trimmed his deep fringe in front and fitted

84

trousers to his bare legs. She smacked him when he threw them away because they itched him.

"My father never wore such pantaloons!" he cried, "nor shall I when I take my blowpipe to search for Molog."

"Revenge," said Fatimah, "is like a muddy river. Many lose their lives following it in flood. Forget it!"

Lotok knew that his mother still lived in Tagul Valley. In a year or two he would be old enough to visit her.

"I can reach her village on the sixth night out from Sapong," he replied to Fatimah. "People from Tagul tell me so."

"Your blowpipe recalls revenge. Burn it!"

"Not so, Mother new! The day my blowpipe is burned, that day I shall leave your home."

And Fatimah could only bide her time.

Lotok attended a small school held in a single room on Sapong Estate and there he came under the eye of Mr Frank Lease, the manager. Mr Lease was a big corpulent man who worked in the East Indies though he came from the West Indies, and he had a reputation for hospitality and for getting things done. He formed a club and encouraged tennis and football, cricket and billiards. In addition to a small rifle shooting gallery, he fixed a model deer which ran on wires and made a very good target for the blowpipes of Murut rubber tappers. Mr Lease boasted that he was a fair shot with a blowpipe and could hit the painted target on the wooden shoulder of the deer as it ran along its wires.

But the big man met his match in the little boy as soon as he was old enough to handle the blowpipe. New Year's Day was the annual holiday for sports and so famous did these sports become that in a few years *main* (sport) *januari* included *every* holiday wherever and whenever sports were held in the interior of North Borneo. Lotok never missed a *main januari* and never missed a prize.

It was at a *main januari* that Lotok heard again of Molog, for Molog's son was present, had shot his way through the heats and met Lotok in the final.

"Your blood shall stain this spear-head," said Lotok to the older boy. "Your father slew mine. The feud lives while this blowpipe is mine."

"See!" replied the other, "this is the tattoo of a man who has already taken a head. Your tongue will taste sweeter in my mouth that its words sound in my ear."

"Peace! Peace!" ordered Sergeant Duallis, who was in charge of the competition. "*Main januari* is no place for quarrel. Peace I tell you!"

One of the best results of a *main januari* in by-gone days was that enemies met each other on a common ground. Muruts met European officials, Chinese traders, Indian police and their own people. Muruts from Tagul Valley called to a *main januari*, on arrival, would find their bitterest enemies from Telecosan Valley already seated on the ground. Tribesmen who had never looked on each other without shouting a war-cry, brandishing a cutlass or pointing a blowpipe must now pass in silence with only a purposeful gleam of the eye. To utter a word of defiance meant that a Murut policeman would take his name.

"*Sengaran nu?*" ("What is your name?") the policeman would ask. And it was no good pleading to another Murut that it was against tribal custom to mention one's own name. The other had ways of finding out.

Lotok held his peace. He let his hand run fondly up and down the smooth blowpipe, tapped the bamboo case of darts to show he had a stock of them and stepped aside.

"The son of Molog can win the prize," he muttered and held the spirit of the blowpipe firmly in subjection.

A few years passed and one day Lotok's mother arrived to see her son. She had walked from Tagul with a party carrying loads of wild rubber, damar and beeswax on their backs for sale at Sapong. Her small *sikutan*, a basket of woven cane, was strapped to her skinny shoulders with strands of stringy bark; it contained rice, tapioca and salt sufficient for the journey, and a spare sarong of Javanese design with a length of cloth to cover her bosom while she slept, for nights amongst the mountains are chilly and the camp fire may burn low.

Round her neck she hung the cord of a hunting knife secure in its sheath of monkey skin. Her husband, before his death, had fashioned it from a steel bolt and she intended to give it to her son.

The shopkeeper had prospered and Fatimah in middle age

was a woman of grace. She had kept her figure. She wore few ornaments, but had one stunning gold button on her blouse. She wore yellow-flowered silk trousers, Chinese fashion, and a simple cotton blouse of turquoise blue. She looked cool and flowery, calm and intelligent. Her Murut past was long forgotten.

Lotok's old mother made a sad contrast with this handsome figure. Her black untidy hair, her ill-shaped earrings of brass wire, her blue and white beads chipped and broken and the drab skirt from waist to knee compared ill with the other woman's dress.

"I am Lotok's mother," she said, setting her basket on the floor. "Give me a little tobacco to relieve my weariness."

"You are welcome! See, here is a cigarette! Lotok will return at noon."

"Men tell me that my husband's blowpipe is here and that Lotok's height is greater than its length."

"Let there be no talk of blowpipes here!"

"See!" hissed the old woman. "This knife is sharp and heavy to hack Molog's head from off his shoulders. His brains and blood shall simmer in my jar and *daun silat*, the leaves of triumph, shall decorate his bare skull when all skin and hair have been loosened from it."

Her shill voice sank to a whisper.

"My thanks to you my son's second mother from my inmost liver," she murmured, knowing that the seat of Murut emotion is in the liver and not the heart. She unsheathed the knife.

Fatimah possessed the dominance of a woman who had been much courted by men. Her husband stood in the doorway and she moved ahead of him swiftly to the Murut woman.

"This woman has suffered much. There is nothing to fear!" With a deft movement she took the knife from the other's hand and the sheath from her neck, and coolly measuring the string of it she drew it over her own head and hair to wear as the other had done.

"This knife shall remain with me. I'll have no talk of revenge here!" So once again the spirit of the blowpipe was held in subjection.

The years passed.

"I have a woman in my mind, Mother new!" said Lotok to

Fatimah one day. She ignored the remark and went on wiping dishes.

"Monia is the woman I have in mind," he continued.

"No man can escape the heat of fire if he touches it," she twitted him. "Keep away from the burning!"

"When I was yet a boy without a father, you took me in and gave me food and happiness. In my eyes and by custom you are now my mother. It is for you to find me a wife. Monia may be the woman."

"Give me time! Courting is like cooking fish, and you must not hurry it or you will spoil it."

Monia was the daughter of a Javanese overseer on the rubber estate. Her family looked down upon Murut people as uncouth and ill-favoured. They knew something of the headhunts that took place in the mountains and even in the forests near the estate. Monia knew Lotok's history, how he had run for his life and escaped from the hands of Molog. She had met Lotok often, and she liked him, but she had no wish to be drawn into the blood-feuds of his family. She was black-haired and dark-complexioned. Her saucy brown eyes were ablaze with curiosity when she first saw Lotok handling his blowpipe.

"I'll pitch this spear-head into Molog's son one day and cut his father's head off into the bargain," he gloated. "Afterwards I'll marry you!" he added cheekily.

"Would you rather live with me or with Molog's head?" she asked. "You can't have both!"

"Would you have me shamed? Years ago I swore to take his head. I am a Murut. My liver hankers for Molog's blood. My hatred is not like a thorn that I can pull out from my flesh."

"Will you try one thing?" asked Monia gently. "Meet Molog's son again as you did before. Go and make peace with him and purge your liver of this hate."

And for the love of Monia he went.

At ten o'clock in the blazing sunshine a crowd watched the competition. The wooden deer ran smoothly on its wires and three darts puffed by the lips of the son of Molog transfixed its shoulder. Good shooting! Up the hunters of Telecosan! Up! Up!

"Lotok! Lotok!" someone cried. "Where is Lotok the champion of the hunters of Tagul?"

He stepped forward clothed in a loin-cloth of cardinal red whose ends swung level with his ankles as befitted a Murut of the blood. His throat and shoulders were unmarred by tattoo. His hair was cut in the latest fashion and he trod on bare feet. In his hand was the famous blowpipe.

"I too can shoot," he said modestly and he puffed two darts so near to the others than you could not see a space between them. Taking the third dart, he snapped it in two.

"So ends our feud," he said. "My friend has three darts in the shoulder and I have but two. He wins the prize, but I go to get a greater prize."

So he married Monia.

They prospered.

"I am now a man of peace," said Lotok looking at the knife and the blowpipe festooned with cobwebs upon the wall.

When their son grew of age, he took down that blowpipe from the wall and played with it.

"Look," said Lotok to his wife. "That son of our does not hold the blowpipe the proper way. He is old enough now to learn. He must put the palms and knuckles of both hands underneath the shaft of the blowpipe, he must put his fingers on top, his thumbs towards the blade. He should press his elbows firmly to his chest. Shall I show him how?"

"No! No!" cried Monia. "The spirit of the blowpipe may live again in him! Don't show him! In the name of Allah, No!"

Pham Duy Khiem

❧❦❧❦❧❦❧❦❧❦❧❦❧❦❧❦

THE MANDARIN AND THE FLOWER FESTIVAL

M ORE than five hundred years ago, during the reign of King Tran Thuan Ton, lived a mandarin by the name of Tu Thuc. Born in the province of Thanh Hoa, he was sent to govern the district of Tien Du. Near his residence was an old pagoda, famous for a magnificent peony shrub which grew in its grounds. Whenever the shrub flowered it drew a crowd of pilgrims, so each spring there was a festival.

In the second month of the year Binh Ti (A.D. 1396), in the middle of the festival, along came a girl of fifteen or sixteen, serenely beautiful. Bending down a young branch to admire a flower, she broke it off. The crowd would not let her go. Already night was falling and no relative had appeared to pay damages to the pagoda and take the young girl home, when Tu Thuc happened to pass by. As soon as he learned what had happened, he took off his brocade robe and offered it in exchange for the girl's freedom.

From that day on everybody praised the mandarin's kindness.

Unfortunately, Tu Thuc liked only music, wine, poetry and Nature. He neglected his official duties and was often reprimanded by his superiors.

At last he thought sadly: "I simply can't, for a few bushels of rice as my only salary, remain for ever chained on the Wheel of honours and intrigues. Why not trust my life to one thin oar which will take me off to limpid waters and blue mountains. In that way I won't betray the secret desires of my own heart."

So one fine day Tu Thuc untied the cords of his mandarin's seal and returned it to his superiors. He withdrew to the district of Tong Son where his favourite springs and grottoes were.

In all the excursions that his ample leisure permitted him to make, a child followed him, carrying a gourd of wine, a guitar and a book of poems. When he arrived at a spot he liked, he would sit down to drink and play the guitar. He sought out strange and picturesque spots. Chopstick Mountain, Green Cloud Grotto, the Lai River, the Nga Estuary—he visited them all and sang their praises in his poems.

One morning, having got up before dawn, Tu Thuc saw, a few miles away, coming from the sea, five clouds of different colours which spread quickly and took the form of a lotus flower. He had himself rowed towards them in a boat. Then he saw a superb mountain. He stopped the boat and climbed up the mountain. Bluish mists covered it to a dizzy height.

Inspired by the beauty of the spot, Tu Thuc wrote these lines:

> In the high branches tremble a thousand reflections;
> The grotto's flowers welcome the entering guest.
> Near the spring, where then is the herb-gatherer?
> Around the fountain, only the boatman with his oar.
> The seat is wide and cool, the guitar sings two notes,
> The boat glides carefree along, the gourd is full of wine.
> Why not ask the fishermen from Vo Lang—
> Where are the peach trees of the Village of the Immortals?

After writing this poem, Tu Thuc admired the view for a long time, then regretfully turned back his boat and slowly tore himself away.

Suddenly he saw the mountainside open up as if inviting him to enter. He went into the opening. Soon it became completely dark: the mountain had shut behind him. Nevertheless he continued to feel his way along, his hand never leaving the mossy side of the grotto. The path was winding and narrow; at last he saw a gleam of light. He looked up and saw above him some very high peaks. Clinging to the rough rocks he climbed up without difficulty, and gradually the path grew wider.

When he reached the top, the air was clear and a gentle radiant sun was shining. On all sides were richly decorated palaces, pleasant green trees, like a place of pilgrimage.

He was enjoying this enchantment when his attention was drawn by two young servant girls dressed in blue. One was saying to the other: "Here is our young bridegroom already."

91

They disappeared into the palace to announce his arrival, then came back and bowed before him. "Please enter, my lord."

Tu Thuc followed the two girls. He saw brocade-covered walls, red lacquered doors, forbidden apartments resplendent in silver and gold, on which he read "Jade Heaven" and "Light of Jewels".

Upstairs was a fairy dressed in white silk, who invited him to sit down in an armchair of white sandalwood. Then she said to him, "You like picturesque spots so much; do you know where you are now? And do you remember a certain predestined meeting?"

Tu Thuc replied: "It is true that as a faithful lover of lakes and rivers, I have wandered far and near, but I didn't know that there existed here a country fit for the Immortals. A simple leisure-loving mortal, I go where my feet carry me, knowing nothing of my destiny. Might I dare ask you to enlighten me?"

The fairy smiled. "How could you have known this place before?" she said. "You are in the sixth of the thirty-six grottoes of Phi Lai Mountain. This mountain sails all the seas, without touching land anywhere. Born of clouds and rain, it appears and vanishes according to the winds. I am the fairy of Nam Nhac Mountain and my name is Nguy. I know the nobility of your nature and the worth of your soul; that is why I have welcomed you here."

She turned towards her servants, who understood her wordless order and withdrew: shortly afterwards a young girl came in. Tu Thuc, discreetly raising his eyes, recognized the girl who one day had broken the flowering branch.

The fairy went on: "My daughter is called Giang Huong—Rosy Incense. When she went down to the flower festival a misfortune befell her. It was you who saved her. I have never forgotten that priceless act of kindness and I now allow her to link her life with yours to repay her debt of gratitude."

The fairies from all the grottoes were invited to the wedding, which was celebrated with music and singing.

The days sped by like a flying shuttle and Tu Thuc soon realized that he had spent a year in the fairies' kingdom. He was overcome by nostalgia.

Often in the evening he would stand motionless until the

night grew fresh with the falling dew. The breeze went by, waves spent themselves at his feet and he could not sleep. The gentle night fanned his calm sadness. The moonlight bathing the lofty mountains left him unmoved. At times the distant sound of a flute suddenly melted his heart and kept him awake till dawn. Then he would strive to hear, as of old, the cocks crowing in his village.

One day, looking towards the south, he saw a boat on the sea. Pointing to it, he said: "It's going towards my own country. It's a long way away and I don't know exactly where it is, but it's over there."

Finally he confided in Giang Huong, "You know I only went off for a morning's stroll and I have already been away a very long time. It is difficult to forget completely the human feelings in one's heart and you can see that I am still thinking too much of my old village. Do you think I might go home for a little while?"

Giang Huong seemed to hesitate at the thought of parting. Tu Thuc insisted. "It will only be a matter of days, or months at most. Let me see my family and my friends. It will all be over quickly and I will come back up here without delay." Giang Huong replied weeping, "I don't dare put forward our love to oppose my husband's wishes, only the limits of the world below are narrow. Its days and its months are very short. I am afraid it will not look as familiar as of old."

She went to tell everything to the Queen Fairy, who expressed her regrets. "I didn't think, though, that he would still be tied to the World of Pink Dust. Let him go. . . . Why all this grief?"

At the moment of parting, Giang Huong dried her tears and gave Tu Thuc a letter written on a piece of silk. She asked him not to open it until he arrived home.

He got into the chariot and in a moment found himself home again.

Everything seemed different from what he had known before, the countryside, the houses and the people. All that had remained the same were the banks of the mountain spring. He spoke to the old men of the village and told them who he was. Finally one of them remembered: "When I was a small child," he said, "I heard tell that my grandfather bore that name. One day

93

more than eighty years ago, he went into the mountains and never came back. I think he must have fallen into some gorge. That was at the end of the Tran dynasty and now we are under the fourth Le king."

Feeling lonely and sad, Tu Thuc wanted to go back to where he had come from, but the chariot had changed into a phoenix, and the fabulous bird, flying away, disappeared into the sky. Tu Thuc opened the letter and read these words:

> Among the clouds a phoenix love began,
> That past union is already over.
> Who, over the seas, searches for the Immortals?
> Little hope is there of a future meeting.

Then he realized that the parting was for ever. Later on, wearing a light cloak and a conical hat, Tu Thuc went up the Yellow Mountain in the Nong Cong district in Thanh Hoa province. He never came back. No one knows whether he went back to the kingdom of the Fairies or whether he was lost in the mountain.

This story, in its original form the work of Nguyen Du, a Doctor of Literature, in 1496, appears in *Legendes des Terres Sereines,* by Pham Duy Khiem, High Commissioner for Vietnam in Paris at the time it was received. In an explanatory note, Professor Truong Cong Cuu, Directeur de l'Ecole Superieure de Pedagogie, Saigon, says that it belongs to the stories concerning "Tiens" (Immortals) familiar in Chinese and Vietnamese literature, but contains a mixture of Taoist and Buddhist mystic elements. He adds that Tu Thuc's gesture in offering his robe of brocade in exchange for the freedom of the young girl reveals the chivalrous generosity of his character and his perfect aloofness from the goods of the world of "red dust"; an elegant gesture followed by the more serious renouncement of administrative duties and refuge in the "country of white clouds and blue mountains". This gesture, strange to the eyes of mortals whose hearts are dulled by passions, is commonplace for a Tien—or for one who has been promised the life of the Tiens. Tu Thuc made it with complete disinterest and not out of courtesy or gallantry as the courteous Knights of the European Middle Ages would have understood it.

"Han Suyin"

❧❧❧❧❧❧❧❧❧❧❧❧❧❧❧❧

BIG DOG TSOU

*N*EO turned with care and lifted his body on an outstretched right hand. His daughter and son slept between him and his wife on the mat-covered wood planking, the family bed. Through cracks in the plywood walls of the hut a lighter darkness seeped.

In the cloth hammock suspended from the roof beam the larger baby gurgled and scuffled hands and feet. Neo Saw slept, mouth half open, the smaller baby at her breast.

Neo bent across his children and shook his wife's arm. She groaned and sat up, eyes still closed. The smaller baby rolled off her breast and wailed. She crooned "Oh sayang sayang" (darling) sleepily; mechanically put him back, holding him perched upon her right hip with one crooked arm. The smaller baby curled its legs round her waist, grasped her pendulous wrinkled right breast with both hands, and sucked at the large dark nipple, pulling strongly.

Neo Saw shuffled outside the hut through the small kitchen to the privy, narrow as a sentry box, five feet from the hut. It was so dark she could not see, but she smelt the smoke from the stoves of Fong Kiap and Big Dog Tsou, her neighbours to left and to right, a sharp tang within her nostrils which woke her up. She returned, seized the face towel inscribed "Good morning" hanging on a nail in the wall, dipped it into a basin of water, and wiped the smaller baby's face around his busily sucking mouth. Then she washed her own. She swilled water in her mouth, rinsing and gargling, and expectorating in the tangle of tapioca, which grew its sprays of leaves on man-tall thin stems between the privy and the hut.

Neo lit the small kerosene lamp, and the black and gold shadows of flame danced upon walls and faces. Daughter, padding barefooted, lifted the larger baby from its hammock and took it to the privy with her, whistling enticingly. When she

95

H

returned she took the tin of condensed milk out of the food cup-
board, with its wire net doors and its legs dipping in cigarette
tins full of water, and measured two teaspoonfuls of gluey yellow
liquid into a glass. The rubber twigs in the earth stove were
burning and the water was hot in the aluminium kettle. Neo
Saw poured some water into the glass, and Daughter stirred the
mixture, dribbled it into a feeding bottle, capped it with a rubber
teat, and pushed the teat into the larger baby's mouth. He drank
eagerly, choking over the air sucked in with the warm milk.

The family swallowed their morning rice, shovelling it with
chopsticks into their mouths. Neo Saw fed the babies spoonfuls
of rice, and later spoonfuls of muddy black coffee streaked with
condensed milk. Neo put on his black tapper clothes, stiff with spilt
latex. Neo Saw, baby hanging fast to her, knotted her sweat cloth
round her head. They took their tapping knives, wheeled their
bicycles out of the hut, walked them down the dirt road of the
wired-in labour village to the police post guarding the gate. The
smaller baby, ten months old, sat astride Neo Saw's left hip,
supported by a piece of cloth which went round his buttocks
and over his mother's shoulder. Daughter, aged eight years,
carried the larger baby, aged two years. Son, aged thirteen, came
behind, stumbling sleepily, his thin arms wrapped round a bottle
of water, the only food or drink allowed out of the perimeter
wire fence which surrounded the village.

In the cool, iron-grey softening of dawn, the stars were small,
remote and high. Shafts of pallor surged and ebbed in irregular
waves above the trees to the east, and Son remembered a grey-
blue balloon he had burst. Wrinkled and small, dark and
crumpled as night in a hut, it had lain in his hand. He had
blown into it, and it had grown, had swollen and thinned into
a translucent sphere, shimmering with silver streaks, as now
shimmered, with pale light spurting above the trees in gusts,
the orb of a rapidly thinning sky.

In front of Neo walked other tappers, among them Fong
Kiap in her dark clothes, wheeling her bicycle. Its chain
whirred, a soft, hasty tick and prick of the stillness. Fong Kiap
had a large, calm face; she was sturdy and big with child, and
from her waddle every tapper knew that she had food hidden
between her thighs.

Neo slowed his steps, not wishing to be near Fong Kiap, should the Malay mata-mata at the police post find her out. His thought, of a few words, dull and slow, duller now because of the constant fear that was upon him, as upon them all, informed him that it had been thus during the years of the Japanese devils, and that it was natural and wrong that it should be thus again.

Neo and Fong Kiap's husband had run away together to the jungle to escape being massacred by the Japanese. That was ten years ago. Neo Saw had smuggled food to Neo her husband then. Fong Kiap was now smuggling food to her husband, who had gone back Inside. He had become one of the People Inside, and Neo was now afraid of him, nearly as frightened of his old friend as he was of the police.

As Neo slowed down, Big Dog Tsou glided past on noiseless feline feet, walking softly, treading a jungle path always, a quiet and dangerous smiling man who collected money and food for the People Inside.

At the police post the tappers handed in their identity cards; the Malay mata-matas kept them till their return from tapping on the estate. The mata-matas searched the tappers, ran their hands over them, undid their belts, looking for rice, meat, bean-curd, cake, tinned food, ammunition, matches, cigarettes, tobacco, a watch, a pen, a pencil, paper of any kind, money, jewellery, an extra garment or towel, a small rubber sheet, string, a fishing hook, a penknife, a piece of soap, medicine pills. They tasted the water in the bottles to make sure it was not sweetened. They shone their torches on the tappers' shoes to see if they were new. They poked the bicycle saddles, squeezed the tires. Sometimes they ran their hands through the women's hair. Neo's mind, geared to evasion, refused to remember how his wife in Japanese times had smuggled tobacco under a piece of sticking plaster on her belly, and money in her private parts.

A young mata-mata put his hand on Fong Kiap's belly and she tittered, a chuckling coy sound. The boy grinned, withdrew his hand and waved her on. Rubber estate mata-matas were usually slow, indolent boys, hastily recruited from the Malay kampongs, cruel only by fits and starts, when their religious or racial feelings were inflamed. Most days they found it too

97

strenuous to search, and waved the tappers on but they some-times searched the women, for their pleasure.

It was Neo Saw's turn, and Neo, pretending indifference, looked blankly away, feeling the tightening in his heart, the coiled rankling fury which dwelt within him at the sight of another man's hands upon his woman; rage unbetrayed by tremor or word, endured, as so many things were endured in these days between two terrors, that of the police, and that of the People Inside.

They passed the police post and the wire gates, and were outside the village and on the road to the estate. A man grinned, a woman jeered. That dawn Fong Kiap had carried out a kati (1¾ lb.) of pork between her thighs, Big Dog Tsou three messages on thin cigarette paper in his mouth, Old Heng's son an extra pair of drawers, and his mother, who had two other sons with the People Inside, six bullets from a revolver bought from a rapacious mata-mata on estate patrol fifteen days ago.

Neo and his wife, each with a baby tied to the body, with Son and Daughter astraddle the saddle carriers, rode the mile and a half to Division 1 of the Langtry rubber estate where they tapped, bumping and dipping on the uneven road, and came to their portion of trees to tap.

There was always a feeling of dissolution, a languid and inescapable stupor, a pause which fell upon the tapper when he walked under the trees arched so regularly overhead, in end-lessly repeated criss-crossing alleyways. Perhaps it was the over-whelming uniformity of hundreds, thousands, tens of thousands of trees, equidistant from each other, all the same height and size, thousands of acres of rubber, millions of rubber trees. Not a breath of air moved under their identical foliage. At seven in the morning already the coolness was going. An insidious, moist heat oozed between the rows, clinging to the tappers' clothes, to their sweat-covered faces, their damp hands, and the knife handles. It was light enough to see the straight boles dappled with patches of silver and rust, girded with sloping broad belts of shorn bark. Along their lower rim the grey-white congealed latex of the night ended in a glazed runnel into the collecting cup, fastened with wire round each tree. Tree after tree after tree, through which the earth's damp rose, sucked upwards in the trunks, lifted drop by drop, to vanish, insubstantial vapour in the pale empty sky. Tree after tree after tree, quietly bleeding its white, smooth seeping blood, latex, into cups.

Daughter and Son ran ahead, stripping the greyish hardened latex along the cut, scrap rubber, to be handed in to the estate. Husband and wife followed quickly, sprinting from trunk to trunk, bending over the cuts like black parasites gorging, their tapping knives gouging thin, precise strips of bark. Too deep a nick, a careless slash, and the tree, wounded, would bleed to death. And now so many trees in rows were slashed at night, by the People Inside.

The sky, now blue, was peopling itself with the white, full-bellied muster of rotund morning clouds. Leaden-footed, the heat trod in the orderly man-made jungle of rubber. Mosquitoes sing-songed round the tappers' heads, then dropped to the damp hollows in the clefts of boughs. A stray bulbul began its beauty-haunted tune, but lost the thread, faltered and stopped. A muted lowing echoed distantly from the cattle of the Tamil rubber tappers who tapped Divisions 2 and 3 of the estate.

At this time of the morning, all over Malaya's gigantic mono-tony of rubber trees, tappers were tapping, as Neo and his wife, gouging the bark, stripping, and sprinting to another tree; a per-formance repeated hour by hour, tree after tree after tree. Cut, strip, sprint; cut, strip, sprint. All over Malaya, rich and creamy, languorously drop by drop, the white latex dripped into the cups.

Ten o'clock. Neo had finished five hundred trees and his wife three hundred. They stopped, trembling with weariness, unable to wipe the sweat off their faces, licking their dry lips with dry tongues, tasting the salt on their skin. Son and Daughter lay on the ground. Silently, they all shared the water from the bottle. Aching cramps in their muscles, aching bellies. Sweat and hunger. But they would have no food, and nothing else till two in the afternoon when they returned. For such now was the harsh law: No food out of the fence; to starve the People Inside. Now they would collect the latex from the cups, pour it in pails, carry the pails to the collecting shed for weighing, watch it immersed in the coagulating tank, hand in the scrap rubber. They would chalk up with the head of the labour lines their daily wage, paid to them once a month, within the fence, by the estate manager.

It was this afternoon, Neo remembered, that he was getting paid. The babies cried, and Neo Saw gave each a breast to ease them. Two o'clock in the afternoon before they would be back inside the fence, and hastily finish the remnants of the morning meal. Then Son would go to the schoolmaster whom the tappers paid to teach their children, Daughter would clean the house, Neo Saw would wash the clothes, go to the shop to buy food, and cook the evening meal. Two meals a day. Neo Saw found it hard taking the small ones with her to tap. But there was no one to look after them without money. And if she did not tap, there would not be enough money for food.

It was then they heard the screams. The first was the worst of all, a long, terrifying ululation, rising and rising and suddenly bent off in the middle, then two short screams, then moans, and silence.

Daughter and Son, still unguarded, looked up, grey-faced with fear and exhaustion, and Son said: "What is it?"

"Hush," said Neo Saw roughly. "We have not heard. We never listen. We do not know."

Neo turned to curse his daughter, meaning the words for his son. "Busying yourself with what is not your concern. Come and help me collect the latex, quick."

They rose and started emptying the cups into the pails, keeping their eyes fixed on the latex which ran, smooth as milk, into the pails. Soon the pails were full with the first load, and, staggering a little, panting as they carried, their hearts beating against their chest walls with fear and weariness, they clenched their jaws, and set off at a quick, swinging trot towards the weighing shed.

On his second collecting trip Big Dog Tsou was waiting for Neo, squatting at ease beneath a rubber tree, and with him was a girl whom Neo had seen once before collecting subscriptions for the People Inside. And then Neo remembered, pay day this afternoon, subscriptions tonight and tomorrow. Neo remembered the girl. She was dressed as a rubber tapper and had a black handkerchief round her head and tied under her chin, as his wife had, framing her smile.

"Meeting, comrades," said Big Dog Tsou, smiling.

And now out of the vaporous heat between the rubber trees they came, the tappers from the four corners of the estate, greeting Big Dog Tsou carefully.

"Tell your mother to carry the pails without me," Neo told his son and, speaking of himself as of another person, "Tell her he will be back in half an hour." And he followed Fong Kiap, waddling in front of him, again, as in a repetitious dream.

As he walked he found himself noticing, through the floating membranes of exhaustion, everything else alive, small things, like small silver fish going through an ever-spread net . . . the bark of trees, scurfed with ridges, and the millimetre amplitudes of their cuts through which the pitiless white drip fell into the cups. In this part of the estate the lalang grass grew thick up to a man's thigh. This was part of Division 1 abandoned to the People Inside by the mata-matas and the weeders, and the Estate Manager had not come round since the last shooting. The mark of the People Inside was over all, with slashed and dying trees.

"Truly," thought Neo, words going through his mind as if spoken in his ear, "truly the People Inside are strong and it is dangerous to go against them." He passed a tree with a great dark gash, pith congealed. "Fire and water," he thought, "we stand between fire and water, between the Police and the People Inside." And then they were at the old smoke house, with the derelict rubber press like a misshapen instrument of torture gone dead in the middle, for the wooden parts had been burnt down and the rusty iron alone was left. About thirty tappers were there. Among them, dressed as tappers, the People of the Movement, eager and talking, going from one to the other, happy and excited.

Neo joined them, and saw the covering tarpaulin in the centre of the standing circle, a circumference of feet. And then the girl approached, smiling, with Big Dog Tsou, and removed the sheet, and Neo looked, and knew: "This is Meng, who weighed the latex. That is why he was not weighing today."

"Comrades," said Big Dog Tsou, "this was a traitor and we have punished him."

Big Dog Tsou had made an excellent impression upon the Rehabilitation Committee. Not only was he a good basketball player and a magazine reader, but he gave the most convincing reasons why democracy was better than Communism. Armed with a glowing report, he was helped to acquire a small shop and to set up in his tailoring business.

101

"You see," asserted Hinchcliffe, "that's all people really want: decent treatment, a living wage. Give it to them, and there won't be any Communism." And went on to say a lot of things about the past, and how badly the Chinese had been treated, until Clerkwell, who listened unmoved, decided that Hinchcliffe was beginning to talk like a socialist.

"The Resurrection Smart Tailor" Big Dog Tsou named his shop, in foot long Chinese characters and smaller English ones, and hoped the red-hairs would understand the delicate allusion, without his pointing it out, which would spoil the effect.

He was an immediate success. His old clients, the mems, soon came round, glad to know he had been brain-washed satisfactorily, and genuinely wanting to help him. He put up his prices to normal, and they paid without demur. Within a few weeks he had employed two apprentices and one errand girl; the latter was small, round and had the prettiest wrists and feet and eyes, and within a month he had married her. In three she was pregnant.

And now Big Dog Tsou truly became a new man.

Thin he had been, and now waxed fat. Silent and smiling, he grew boisterous with a loud laugh and on his face a permanent bemused happiness. He had walked softly and now stepped with a swagger, as if he owned the street. He worked sixteen hours a day, and still found time to stare often at his pert and pretty wife, with the full bosom and round hips under the flowery coat and trousers, demure and childishly meretricious, stealing side glances quickly at him which made his heart beat and his hands tremble, while the thin clink of her brass bangles as she cut the cloths was like a loud bell ringing his joy to the world.

Happiness made him forgetful. He cut a dress for Mem Clerkwell out of material brought by Mem Hinchcliffe. "That's not my dress, tailor," shrieked Mem Clerkwell, as she saw the bright scarlet chiffon instead of the white piqué she had left. Big Dog Tsou tried to look concerned, began to laugh foolishly, and that made Mem Clerkwell very angry. "Sorry, mem," said Big Dog Tsou, "I very busy, nobody help, my wife . . ." He wanted to say his wife could not help him with sorting the orders, but Mem Clerkwell misunderstood. "Ah yes," she said, "I heard you'd got married very recently. I suppose you don't know whether you're coming or going these days . . . well, I hope you'll be very happy . . ." and she smiled. Absurdly Big Dog Tsou felt an intense desire to cry. Until then Mem Clerkwell, her peremptoriness and her gaunt harsh way of talking, had been one of his pet cold hatreds, but now she was suddenly human, as human as his own woman, and not a pig-face whiteskin, a red-haired she-devil, a woman-with-a-tail, an imperialist whore . . . just a nice woman. He wanted to say, "I hope you are happy too," but did not know how. It might be the wrong words, supposing she was unhappy . . . in sudden acute perception, the telepathic instinct which comes with the recognition of another's humanity, he knew she was not very happy . . . at least not as much as he, Big Dog Tsou, and something like compassion came over him. "I buy you new material, make you fine new dress, mem," he promised.

Only one thing bothered Big Dog Tsou in these days of happiness, and that was the Organization.

Until he came out of rehabilitation camp he had been faithful to the Movement, eager to be useful again.

Then had come the Resurrection Smart Tailor shop, and his wife, and the child-to-be, and now he was strangely unwilling to meet his former comrades.

So far nothing much had happened, yet . . . a member of the Movement had dropped in casually one day, with his fiancée, to have a dress made. Tailor shops, like coffee shops, are very useful meeting-places, for exchange of messages, for collecting money and subscriptions (who can tell, when one pays for a dress, whether there is not an extra dollar for the People Inside?). Tailors, like waiters, hear everything because no one sees them. Big Dog Tsou was to contact another tailor's shop, for the purpose of obtaining cloth, in Singapore, and thus establish a courier line. . . .

The other shop was one of many near the Naval Base. The apprentice in that shop was a comrade in the Movement; he had a brother who was the "Cookie" of a white officer at the Naval Base . . . so it went on. . . . .

Big Dog Tsou showed eagerness to help. But at the moment, he said, he was still being watched . . . two informers constantly dropped in, as well as policemen, to see what he was doing . . . wait a few months, and he would be able to render service.

Thus he bought time, and now fought against the knowledge,

dragging him down, slowing his step, lacquering his face into a fixed but joyless grin, that he had betrayed himself into another way of living and into a happiness which he did not want to give up.

So beguiled himself into believing that he was still loyal, of unsmirched devotion, but merely cautious, for the sake of his friends.

Chinese New Year was coming, his first New Year, in a hot February devoid of crackers because the Emergency forbade their firing, and Mem Hinchcliffe appeared at the shop, her usual energetic self, ear-rings dangling, bangles dangling, and all her curls tremulous upon her head:

"My dear boy," she beamed at Big Dog Tsou, "my dear, dear boy, how are we? And how's your wife? That little girl, why she's still a child, a child, you naughty cradle-snatcher, ha ha ha. . . ."

Big Dog Tsou was happy and miserable at once. Happy because he could no longer face Mem Hinchcliffe with that polished amiability undented by emotion, and so he showed his shop, the Singer sewing machines, the apprentices.

"Baby?" asked Mem Hinchcliffe, pushing an inquisitive finger in the direction of the wife's navel. "Yes, thought so, well don't be in too much hurry with the next one, dear boy . . . here." She dug into the huge carry-all she trundled and extracted some Family Planning leaflet. "I've only got them in Tamil and Malay, I've given all the English ones away and the Chinese ones aren't printed yet." Amiably she gave some to the two girl apprentices, who examined them with astonishment mingled with fear. "And now," said Mrs Hinchcliffe, "I want all of you to come to the tea party at my bungalow. I'm giving a tea party for those from our detention camp who've made good. You must come, tailor, you're a winner."

With panic in his heart Big Dog Tsou said he would come of course, but on that day sent word that he was dangerously ill with a high fever, and kept a handkerchief knotted round his head for a day or two after, lest Mem Hinchcliffe should suddenly descend upon him and doubt his word.

Came the devil month, crawling torrid day by day to the Devil's Jubilee when all hungry and sad spirits are solemnly sent back to Hell. His little wife was heavy upon her feet, but went on cutting cloth; Big Dog Tsou had booked a bed for her at the hospital, wishing all to be done in a modern manner. He bought tins of Brand's chicken essence, and followed the doctor's advice religiously, but also let his wife paste charms and invocations in yellow paper above doors and windows, and mirrors at the entrance. He went into Singapore and bought soft gamgee cloth for nappies as he had seen upon the white babies of his clients. But he bought nothing else, lest the devils be aware of the new life sleeping, and he put the cloth away, saying loudly it was for shirts.

And so he revolved his little world of happiness and absorption with the woman carrying the child that was coming, absurdly reassured against the fear of that other world, the world of the Movement, once so full of power and triumph and now empty of meaning. And made all preparations within his power to the limit of tempting fate; but was never prepared for what he had prepared to happen.

Not expecting the smiling face of Pang, the detective, so friendly but for the too-white flash of too many teeth in too bared a grin; not expecting Pang, and the three other men, two detectives and the informer, a thin sallow-faced youth walking negligently whose hair thick with oil was held in place with a large aluminium clip.

Big Dog Tsou was standing behind his table, heaped with cottons and silks and nylons. The young coffee-shop waiter looked at him indifferently and looked away again, a little over his shoulder, at the wall. This look, like the kiss of Judas, betrayed Big Dog Tsou, but might buy his own freedom. "Okay," said Pang, grinning.

So the time had come, the end that was waiting since the beginning in the rubber trees when Meng, the latex weigher, had put up his hands begging mercy and obtained none. Only it was another Big Dog Tsou who had lifted the changkol till the screaming had stopped, indissoluble in body from the man now smiling for the last time, horribly, smiling with his world ebbing and dissolving as the detectives closed upon him, and who could not, did not believe that he was the same man until he heard his little child-wife scream and scream.

"Dok Mai Sod"

THE GOOD CITIZEN

The train, full of passengers in every compartment and even overflowing into the corridor, started off from Hualumpong Station, in Bangkok, at four o'clock in the afternoon. At five minutes to seven it dragged its heavy load into a small station by a river.

The train stopped here for only two minutes. The passengers to this little place rushed out in a hurry, carrying their belongings in both hands. The lucky ones had their families and friends waiting, ready to help and to exchange news of their experiences. Those who lived on the same side of the river went home on foot; others crossed it by boats.

It was in July, 1945, after the Germans had surrendered in Europe. In the Far East, the Japanese Empire was being shaken to its foundations by increasing Allied attacks. Siam (Thailand) was then under Japanese occupation and, therefore, received its share of air raids. Many people in the capital who could afford to run away fled in every direction. Those not so fortunate had to work in Bangkok during the day and rush back before nightfall to wherever they had evacuated themselves. That explains why the evening train was so crowded.

Nai Mai, a Bangkok man, had to move his family to this little village in order to get out of danger. Every day he went up to work in the capital before daybreak and came back in the evening. It was an extremely tedious journey. But what could he do? He spent at least four hours each day in travelling, sometimes even much more than that; especially when an air-raid was on and the train had to stop for hours.

But on that day the train arrived on time. The sky was clear blue, with no signs of rain anywhere. How unlike the past two weeks, when it had teemed practically every day! Nang Somchit, Nai Mai's wife who was with child at the time, was excited; she had much to tell her husband, because during all the day a so-called "four-engined monster" had been hovering over Bangkok and all parts of the neighbouring provinces.

"I saw something very big and very long come down and hit the ground with a thud," she told her husband while they were crossing the river in a boat. "Everybody ran away into the fields. I started to run too, Mai; but I came back, otherwise there'd be nothing left in the house."

"The soldiers stationed at Rangsit told me that the planes dropped only leaflets," Nai Mai said. "Bangkok was alerted; but there was no siren. There was only one aircraft, flying very high and dropping only leaflets."

"Do you know whether anyone has picked them up?" Somchit asked.

"You have to wait until tomorrow."

Then Nai Im, the boatman, put in: "They say that a few bombs were also dropped at Bangsai."

"What?" Nai Mai exclaimed incredulously. "Why should they do that? There's nothing important there."

"It might have been the big long thing that I told you about," Nang Somchit interrupted. "Perhaps it's a leaflet container."

The residence of Nai Mai and Nang Somchit was a little thatched-roofed, four-room house, with a long veranda. The floor rested upon poles seven or eight feet above the ground, with a wooden ladder leaning against the veranda; it was the only means of going up to or down from the house. The four rooms were all in the same line, parallel with the veranda. No room, except the third, was walled; in each there was a window. To-wards one end of the veranda was the kitchen, with a single door just enough to keep stray dogs away but quite useless against either human beings or vermin.

As soon as the boat arrived at the boat-landing in front of the house, a little boy of no more than four years old ran out on to the veranda and waved his hands in excitement. Both Nai Mai and Nang Somchit, seeing their son coming near to falling into the river, were frightened. Nai Mai ran up the six or seven steps of the ladder and caught hold of his son.

"The boatman wants to know whether you'd like him to come for you tomorrow, dear." Nang Somchit shouted from the boat.

"What for?" Nai Mai shouted back.

"You were thinking of going to Nang Yam's party, weren't you? She's celebrating her son's entering the Buddhist monkhood."

"Oh that! What do you think? Should we go?"

"Well, I don't know. Anything you like."

"I want to go with the party to the monastery; but, if you'd like to come too, it would be awkward; their boat might be full and the sun would be too strong for you."

"But what would you decide, any way?" Nan Somchit shouted in an irritated voice. Nai Mai realized that since their evacuation from Bangkok his wife had begun to show signs of impatience and moodiness.

"Anything you like," Nai Mai said and sat down. For a long while past he had been wanting to have a railing made round the veranda to prevent his son from accidentally falling into the river below. He had discussed it with his wife several times; but in the end, when the problem of finance came up, the matter was dropped. His salary was hardly enough to cover current expenses; and there were times when he had to sell some of his belongings, such as personal ornaments and household furniture, just to make ends meet. Both husband and wife hoped that the war would soon be over and they would be able to return to Bangkok. In that event, it would not be worth while to have the railing made anyway. But every time Nai Mai saw his son playing on the veranda and perilously near to falling into the river, he thought of the subject.

Then there was the lavatory problem. In this little village where poor folk lived, no house had a lavatory, for it was by a big river, surrounded by a great expanse of open fields, where its inhabitants could ease themselves privately almost anywhere; hence the need for a lavatory had never arisen. Both husband and wife agreed between themselves that they should have one; but then it cost money.

Nai Mai slipped into a pakama, hung a towel over his shoulder, put on his wooden clogs, lit a cigarette and carried his son down to the river to bathe. Meanwhile, Nang Somchit went into the kitchen and did her cooking. At this time Nai Kloi, the owner of the house, who let it to Nai Mai, walked up the steps into the house smiling.

"What, haven't you had your dinner yet? I've had mine," he said, puffing his home-made cigarette.

"Didn't you go to the party?" Somchit asked. "There seems to be quite a do over there. I've heard them pounding mortars in preparing food since early in the afternoon."

"You mean at Nang Yam's house?" said Nai Kloi. "No, I didn't go there. Perhaps I'll go tomorrow. Today I haven't time; just back from attending to my rice fields."

"Oh, you mean to go just when the ceremony begins, is that it?" Nang Somchit asked, "I don't know yet whether I can go then. If Mae Perm goes, I shan't be able to go. Aunt Un is afraid of being left alone in the house."

Mae Perm was Nai Kloi's sister-in-law who came to work as a maid and charwoman combined at Nai Mai's residence. Aunt Un was a distant relative of Nang Somchit's mother. She was quite well-to-do, with a fine house in Bangkok, which she had left because of the air raids.

"What is she afraid of any way?" Nai Kloi asked. "Nobody would dare to do her any harm in broad daylight."

"I don't know; but I think it's you and your friends that scare her with your news of dacoity, hold-up and what not. Not only Aunt Un, but even I am afraid. It doesn't matter whether it's day or night, when an air-raid warning's on and everybody's running for dear life into the fields, I often feel quite afraid when I'm alone in the house."

"Was there an air-raid warning this afternoon? I was in my rice fields and didn't hear anything, only saw a plane, that was all."

"Nobody could hear anything for the noise they made at Nang Yam's house. Anyhow, I believe there were quite a number running into the fields; but I didn't, mind you. I was afraid that someone might come in and steal our things."

"Oh, nobody would dare steal anything." Nai Kloi said, laughing. "Your husband also has his firearms and the thieves here are scared of modern weapons."

Nang Un emerged from the kitchen, wiping her hands with a piece of cloth.

"When Mai's at home, I'm not afraid of anything," she said.

109

"There's no need to be afraid even if he's not in; I've just told you that there's no thief here."

"It's you all over." Nang Un remarked. "No thief, no thief. Then why did you tell us to close all our doors and windows right after sunset? We could hardly sleep it was so hot and stuffy with no ventilation. And now you say there's no thief!"

Nai Kloi could only laugh drily. He was the sort of man who could not offer any reason for anything he said. To help him out, Nang Somchit put in:

"He means, of course, that there is cat-burglary in this district, small pilferage, things like that, you know. But large-scale robbery is unlikely because we have our guns. Our house is in a central position; everybody knows us very well. At night the men in this village often get up and have a look at their bulls and cows to see whether they are stolen or not. So it's just like having nightwatchmen about every night."

"I myself sleep with my own bulls and cows," Nai Kloi affirmed, feeling quite satisfied with Nang Somchit's explanation of what he himself could not make clear. "Nai Pew also sleeps with his cattle; while Nang Yam doesn't seem to sleep at all; the noise she makes pounding her betel-nut seems to be going on all night. Perhaps she's chewing all the time."

At daybreak ten days later, Nai Mai, his wife, and Aunt Un were awakened by loud noises. They came out of the house and found that the villagers were gathering and talking about an incident which just occurred during the night. It was said that one cleric preceptor of Nang Yam's son, who was recently ordained, fell ill with stomach trouble. Nai Khem went to stay with him at the monastery, leaving Nang Yam with a daughter, only twelve years old, in the house. It had been raining almost all night. At three o'clock in the morning, Nang Yam woke up because she heard her cattle making strange rustling noises and lowing loudly. This, however, lasted only a few minutes and so did not rouse her suspicions. At four o'clock she got up and went into the kitchen to make a breakfast packet for her husband. She then came downstairs with a lighted coconut-oil lamp in her hand. To her dismay she found that, out of the six bulls that she had, four had disappeared.

Nang Yam ran to the nearest house, Nang Perm's, and poured out her tale of woe. Nai Pik, Nang Perm's husband, and Nai Kloi, instantly started off to the monastery to break the bad news to Nai Khem. Then the three of them went off in pursuit of the bulls, following the trails left by their footsteps on the soft mud of the rice fields. They walked for about five miles and the sun rose high in the sky. So they gave up and came back exhausted. They stopped near Nai Mai's house and discussed the matter vociferously and frantically. This noise woke up Nai Mai's household.

Nai Mai had not much time left to find out the details of the matter; for he had to take a boat to catch a train for Bangkok. When he reached the capital, everybody seemed to be in high spirits and said that the war would soon come to an early end; for the Americans had just dropped an atomic bomb on Japan. Nevertheless, some were not so hopeful, because they thought that the Japanese would not give in so easily, especially when an unconditional surrender was demanded of them. Nai Mai's mind was occupied with world affairs until he got back home in the evening.

There, almost in front of his own house was a crowd of people discussing the theft of Nang Yam's oxen, and Nang Yam herself, sobbing. The thieves had demanded a sum of four hundred bahts (£A8.16.0) for the return of the four head of cattle. Nang Yam had not enough money, for the proceeds from the sale of the previous year's crop had already been spent on the ordination ceremony of her son.

"What does it matter if she has not enough money?" Nai Mai asked, rather bewildered. "Since now she knows for certain the whereabouts of her beasts."

"If she has no money, she'll not have the cattle back," a fellow in the crowd explained.

"Don't we know where the bulls are?"

"Do we, really?"

"Haven't we been told where they are? We can tell the police and let them get the bulls back."

"Oh no! That won't do at all. That'll be the end of everything." Nai Pik interrupted.

"What do you mean?" Now Nai Mai was really annoyed.

I

"If we call in the police, there would not be any bull left alive."

There seemed to be neither rhyme nor reason for this argument, which had the effect of infuriating Nai Mai.

"Why should they be killed?" he asked.

"Well, because the thieves will kill them," Nang Perm explained bluntly, "if they don't get the money by tomorrow."

"What! D'you mean to say that there's no law and order in this country?" Nai Mai was now at the height of his indignation. "What does it matter if some of the wretched beasts got killed if we can catch thieves and bring them to justice . . ."

"No, no, that's not the way," said a woman.

Nai Mai was so angry that he did not think it worth while discussing the matter any longer. So he went to have his bath and then straight on to Nang Yam's house where he thought he might find out the truth.

Nang Yam's husband was not at home, having gone to the district officer. Thus it seemed to Nai Mai that the matter had been put in proper hands. So he took his leave.

That night Nai Mai could not sleep until very late. To a Bangkok man like him who had never seen or experienced any theft or robbery of any kind, the whole thing offended his sense of justice. He was lying thinking of getting up and going to the district officer at once but rain was threatening and the night was pitch dark so he gave up the idea.

The next day was a Saturday. He was catching the train to Bangkok as usual and it so happened that, on the very same train, the district officer was also travelling to Bangkok. Nai Mai had known this official slightly, having met him three or four times in the past. On being asked whether he had been informed about the theft, the district officer was surprised and in fact as much annoyed as he himself was.

Nai Mai did not get back till nightfall, the train having been delayed by an air-raid in Bangkok. In front of his house, Nai Mai saw Nang Yam and a few others.

"We have our bulls back," Nang Yam reported, her voice trembling with emotion. "Oh, without them, we would not be able to grow any rice next season."

Before Nai Mai could say anything, a woman in the crowd

said: "A hundred baht each isn't too bad; to buy new ones would be far more expensive."

It soon transpired to Nai Mai that when the owner of the lost cattle, together with a party of three, kept on pursuing the spoors for almost seven miles they came upon two villagers who had come out to meet them and who escorted them to one of the houses. There the visitors were entertained with victuals and drink in accordance with the local rule of hospitality. During the meal, however, the self-appointed hosts kept on dropping hints that by this time those missing oxen must have wandered very far and as the sun was now too hot to be comfortable, the party should retire for the time being and come back again in the evening of the next day. They would then be certain to get their animals back again, especially if they would bring with them a sum of 560 bahts to provide for appropriate rejoicing for the occasion.

As the pursuing party realized that they were not sufficiently armed, whilst the other side's strength could not be determined accurately, they deemed it more expedient to resort to diplomacy rather than force. They pleaded, on the ground of poverty, to have the ransom money reduced to 400 bahts. To this, after due bargaining, the other party agreed.

On the morrow Nai Khem succeeded in securing loan from a wealthy Chinese who ran the largest grocery store in the district and who owned a fleet of rice boats used in transporting paddy from local farmers to rice mills in Bangkok. Thus provided, Nai Khem, with his three friends, made off in the afternoon for the home of the intermediaries who, once more, prepared for them a sumptuous feast. Nai Khem deposited the requisite ransom. Just before sundown, the hosts hinted to the guests to take leave by conducting them in a westerly direction for a while until there came to view four oxen serenely grazing in the neighbouring meadow. Thereafter Nai Khem and his party drove the bulls back home.

The following Monday evening Nai Mai came across the district officer at the railway station. As soon as the officer set his eyes upon Nai Mai, he left all his companions and made a bee-line for him. After a few words of greeting, he went at once

113

to the subject of their former conversation by saying: "By the way, I looked into the case of the cattle theft of Nai Khem and I was told that it was all nonsense. There'd never been any theft at all!"

"What!"

"That's what he actually said. The oxen happened to go astray for a day or two and later he found them grazing somewhere. That's all there was to it."

"That's strange," said Nai Mai, scratching his head.

The district officer laughed gently: "But, of course, I let him know that what he had done would simply make cattle theft more widespread later on. Now you must excuse me, I am afraid, I have friends waiting."

On his way home in a boat Nai Mai was still confused over what the district officer had just told him. As his boat approached his house, he saw Nang Yam bathing and scrubbing herself on the land of Nang Perm's house. He could not make up his mind whether he should approach her and greet her as usual. But it was she who gave him the cold shoulder by turning her face away. Beside her there were two other women, one engaged in plucking and preparing water convolvolus for making curry, while the other was busily cleaning her pots and pans. All three of them seemed to have been previously engrossed in a sort of animated conversation but as soon as they set eyes on Nai Mai in his boat, their conversation stopped abruptly.

"What are you doing there?" asked Nai Mai by way of greeting.

"Just nothing," answered one of them and they appeared to look uneasily at one another.

Whatever doubt Nai Mai might have on his mind came to an end the moment he stepped up to his house. His wife, Somchit, at once shouted at him heatedly: "Here comes Mr Nosy Parker. What made you carry your tale to the district officer? You are making all these people quite furious now."

Without waiting for her husband to make any rejoinder Somchit raised her voice, "Come out here, Uncle Kloi and all of you. Come out here and speak your mind." Then turning towards her husband she added: "These people kept on harping on the matter although I know absolutely nothing about it. So there you are, Uncle Kloi and Mae Perm, here comes the villain."

Nai Mai threw his hat and a packet of cigarettes on the veranda and then walked nonchalantly to the kitchen. He certainly had the happy knack of remaining cool whenever there was a storm brewing. As he perceived, Nai Klo, Nang Perm, and her sister who was Kloi's wife, kept on looking at one another somewhat diffidently. He said: "How now! Come out with what you have on your mind. You all look as if the whole world is afire. Kloi, come and have a smoke out here, please."

Nai Mai sat down on his haunch on the veranda with his feet dangling freely. He kept on coaxing the trio to join him outside. Reluctantly, Kloi sat down leaning against a red earthen water-jar. Nang Perm and her sister followed suit.

"Well, hasn't the district officer come to investigate the cattle theft?" Nai Mai asked.

"Yes, in a way," cautiously replied Kloi.

"What happened then?"

"Nothing. Since the cattle have all come back. . . ."

Nai Mai listened patiently, but Kloi kept on faltering. His wife, who was rather impatient, broke in: "He, the district officer, came here and upbraided us. He kept on reminding us that we are conniving at robbery. This upset Auntie Yam very much. She kept on weeping all the while. She said she already suffered serious loss of money, leave alone her anxiety. She can hardly swallow a morsel. And now she is accused of aiding and abetting cattle robbery again."

"So you are all angry with me because I told the D.O.?" said Nai Mai.

"Not exactly," said Nai Kloi. "But . . . but we are all sorry because it gave the D.O. the opportunity to come and say nasty things to us. He ran down all of us villagers as accomplices."

"We have never stolen anything in our lives and yet we are accused of being partners in crime with thieves and robbers!" Then Nang Perm, her sister and Nai Kloi each tried to get a few words in here and there to let off steam. Nai Mai silently listened, philosophising simultaneously on human folly; not forgetting his own share.

That night, after a square meal, Nai Mai, noting that his wife Somchit was in good humour, asked from her a black sarong and a blouse. After much heart-searching argument, Somchit gave in. He lit a candle and then took both pieces of feminine clothing with him to Nang Yam's house.

He handed his peace offerings to her saying: "Please do not take it amiss, Mae Yam. After all, I am, in a way of speaking, your kith and kin."

Nang Yam sobbingly took the proferred gifts and placed them by her side with joined palms in token of her gratitude. Turning to Nai Khem, Nai Mai began to unfold to him the news about the devastation in Japan following the announcements of the Allies in the form of leaflets dropped from the air last Saturday.

Once back home, Nai Mai went straight to bed. Just when he was about to close his eyes, he heard Somchit murmuring audibly to Aunt Un: "Fancy! Poking his nose into what did not concern him at all, and forced us to part with what we could least afford. A black sarong nowadays costs pots of money; and quite an expensive blouse too! What's the use of toiling and moiling if he keeps on doing stupid things like this all the time?"

Nai Mai turned on his side, smothered his ear with a pillow, and closed his eyes.

Thailand

Prem Chaya

ON MY SHORT-SIGHTEDNESS

To my short-sighted eyes,
The world seems better far
Than artificial aid
To sight would warrant it:
The earth is just as green,
The sky a paler blue;
Many a blurred outline
Of overlapping hue;

Shapes, forms are indistinct;
Distance a mystery;
Often a common scene
Conceals a new beauty;
Ugliness is hidden
In a curtain of mist;
And hard, cruel faces
Lose their malignity.
So do not pity me
For my short-sighted eyes;
They see an unknown world
Of wonder and surprise.

Pramoedya Ananta Toer

BORN BEFORE THE DAWN

*B*EFORE I was born my father had started a small school in Blora. Our house was always full when I was little because some of the older pupils used to board with us. The one I will never forget was Hurip, who came there when I was seven or eight. That was years before the war.

The others in the house looked up to Hurip because he had already passed his junior high-school exam. He seemed to know more than the others, and everyone listened when he spoke. Even now I still know by heart a lot of the things he said, although I didn't understand much at the time.

I remember especially the night he stood up and said: "We've been asleep too long. We need something to wake us up, and first we must get rid of the silly idea of wanting to be government clerks. The Dutch didn't come here to make us all high officials with big houses. They have taken everything they could, and now they take more with taxes. We have to pay or go to prison and work for nothing."

The next day I asked my mother what Hurip meant. She said I would know when I was older. None of my playmates understood either. Even the *djongos*, our manservant, couldn't explain.

Later my mother told me that Hurip was in a political party. This surprised me because I thought political meant p⌐lice, and, young as I was, I knew that everyone in the house hated the police. I asked if Father wasn't annoyed that Hurip was in the police. Then my mother explained that anyone in a political party was an enemy of the police.

Pleased to hear this I ran off to tell my friends. But they just laughed when I tried to talk about police and politics. The

118

djongos didn't believe me either. I was confused, but felt my mother was right.

There was another evening when Hurip talked again about government clerks. Little officials, he called them, leading useless lives, thinking they were better than everyone else. "A government clerk," Hurip said, "leaves home every morning at the same time. He sits at a desk for so many hours and then goes home. Year after year he does this. If he plays with his wife in the evening, there's another baby and not enough money. He has to live like a cart horse that can't want any more than a bit of chaff and a bucket of water and a place to rest. If the director smiles he jumps for joy, but if the director is in a bad mood he is like a beaten dog. His salary only lasts half the month. All his life it is the same. There are always more babies and not enough money. They'll have to fight back like the rest of us."

The others nodded and I wished I knew what it was all about. The bit about a clerk playing with his wife kept running through my head, and as soon as we had eaten I asked my mother whether it was true that every time a clerk played with his wife there was a baby. This was the first time I ever saw my mother angry. She just told me to go and look at my books, and when I started to ask again, she pushed me outside the room.

Even for us children our town was very quiet. Nothing out of the ordinary ever happened . . . until one year things began to change. I felt some sort of excitement in the air. Everyone seemed to speak differently—the clerks, the shopkeepers, the peasants who came to the market. The students in our house talked more seriously, often about Japan and India, using words that were strange to me, like "*Swadeshi* boycott", "tradition", and "unity".

Soon there were changes that I could see. First there were football clubs in the villages. There were other sports groups, too, even for the children. After that cultural clubs sprang up—*gamelan* orchestras, *wayang* groups, who put on puppet shadow plays. Most of the members were from among the government clerks. My father helped to organize almost all these clubs, and my mother got the women to form groups, too. We children joined the scouts, and at a camp fire one night many grown-ups were sworn in as honorary scouts.

119

More and more things were said about the Dutch that I had never heard before . . . "bandits", "thieves", "liars". I remember my father saying to my mother: "They won't be here forever, these Europeans." My mother nodded, and her eyes were dreamy. Then, when I looked at her closely as she stood there smiling at my father I saw that she was going to have a baby.

One day my mother asked me what I wanted to be when I grew up. I said: "A farmer." My father repeated my answer as if he were surprised. But I insisted. He laughed and said I mustn't be lazy any more if that was what I wanted to be.

I was given a little plot of land behind the house where I used to dig and imagine myself a farmer. My mother always encouraged me, telling me that it was good to work, to use my hands and my brains. When I was grown up, she used to say, the Dutch wouldn't rule our country any more, so I must work and learn because there would be a lot to do.

She told me that my father was planting seeds too and these seeds would grow into big plants with fruit we would eat forever. I just couldn't imagine a plant with fruit that could be eaten forever. I asked if the fruit would be melons. It seemed this fruit wouldn't be melons, or any kind I had ever seen, but I would know when I was older.

There was another change I noticed too. Suddenly *lurik*, the coarse, handmade cloth from the villages, became popular. My mother began wearing a *lurik* sarong. I didn't like it—it was rough and faded quickly—and when Hurip explained that in India the people were wearing *lurik* too and burning cloth from other countries, I said: "What a pity, I wish I could get some foreign cloth." As soon as I heard the others laugh I knew I had said something silly. I hung my head, half ashamed, half annoyed. Hurip lifted me on to his knee and told me that we should wear *lurik* and not foreign cloth so that our own people, who made the *lurik*, could live. He said this was what *Swadeshi* meant.

Every time the old woman weaver came from the village my mother ordered *lurik*. She said the weavers were working day and night, just like it had been when she was a young girl. It was because there was *Swadeshi* now, my mother laughed. The old woman laughed too and said they were always talking about

that in the village. It was good for them all . . . some of the
weavers were beginning to plant their own cotton . . . her neighbour who made sandals from old motor tyres had fifteen workers
and sold dozens every week to the co-operative. My mother
looked just as happy as the old woman.

As the weeks went by my mother became heavier and didn't
move about so much. The loom she had bought was put away.
Instead of weaving she sat in a chair on the *pendopo* porch
facing the garden, mostly reading. My father was hardly ever at
home. If I asked about him she would just smile and say he was
planting seeds for the future.

Gradually our house had become almost like an office. All day
and sometimes at night typewriters were tapping and the duplicators were turning all the time. Everywhere there were piles
of paper. By then my father's school had about four hundred
pupils of all ages, counting those in the evening classes for
reading and writing. There were only ten or so for the Dutch
course, and all of these, I think, were teachers at government
schools.

I found it all exciting, particularly because I knew my father
was an important man in the town. People often pointed me out
as his son and sometimes they would stop and talk to me.

So it was all the more puzzling for me when I began to notice
that almost every day two or three policemen would ride on
bicycles slowly past our house, looking at the doors and windows,
trying to see inside. When I asked my mother about the policemen she told me: "They don't like what your father is doing."
"But he's a teacher," I said.

That was why they kept looking at our house, she explained.
They didn't like to see our people learning to read and write.
As nothing happened in the next few weeks I forgot about the
police.

Then one day my father came home earlier than usual. His
face was pale and tired. He looked ill, but when my mother
asked him if he wasn't well he only answered "No" dully, without looking up. He shook his head when Mother said he should
rest, and sighed. It wasn't the work, there was a letter.

"What sort?" my mother asked. "From the government . . . a

121

reminder . . . or a threat. I've got to stop . . . it's all finished, the school . . . everything."

I ran to Hurip's room and announced that my father couldn't work any more. But Hurip looked tired, just like my father. He listened to me but he wasn't surprised as I had expected at this news. So I went to the *babu* in the kitchen. Before she could say anything I burst out: "Papa can't work any more, he's not allowed." She didn't believe me. "No one would dare," she said, "even the district officer is frightened of your father." This made me feel better, but only for a little while.

On the veranda I found one of the older students. I told him too, but he knew more than I did. From him I heard that the police had come to the school and had taken away cases of books. They had also cut the electric light wires so that there could be no more classes in the evening. A police officer had gone to my father, and all the other teachers were called to my father's office.

When I went back to the dining room my father was still sitting at the table, his head in his hands, not even listening to my mother's sympathy. The expression on his face frightened me.

From that day on there were no more visitors to our house. Even the other children who usually came to play with me stayed away. The school hadn't been closed down, but within a couple of weeks there were less than forty pupils. Most of the boarders staying with us left. Hurip was restless, sitting around, saying little, sometimes with a book in his hand that he didn't read. Finally he left too, and we never heard from him again.

My father rarely talked with us any more, and never smiled. Day after day he just lay on the sofa, not bothering with the kitchen or the garden. Soon I noticed that my father was going out in the evenings, as he had a few months before.

It was one evening he was away that my mother held me close, and then, taking both my hands in hers, she said: "We've had to give the foreigners in our country too much. All we've got back is misery and oppression." Her voice was low and hard, almost like a growl. She was silent a moment. Then her tone became gentle as she whispered: "I hope it will be better for you . . . Hurip is clever, but he isn't strong enough. Your father is like Hurip. So you must study and work and be stronger than they are." As she hugged me again I felt the tears on her face.

Since the police had come to the school I had often seen my father sitting in other houses playing cards or dice. Each time I saw him I felt somehow ashamed, but I never said anything at home. I realized that my mother knew where he went, although she never mentioned it.

We hadn't seen him for five whole days when my mother called me one morning and gave me a folded sheet of paper. I asked: "Is it for Papa?" She didn't answer, just turned away, her hands over her face, sobbing.

For hours I looked for my father, but he wasn't in any of the houses where he usually went to gamble. Tired and discouraged I sat on the side of the road to rest. I thought of all the changes of the last few months—the clubs that had started and then stopped, all the pupils who left the school, Hurip, the talks about the Dutch, the police, and my father's face grown lined and never smiling. Then I thought of the letter my mother had given me, and wondering whether I should read it, I took it from my pocket and opened it. Slowly I spelled the words: "Have you any thought for your child that is not yet born? Come home. If you don't want to come back after you have read this then pray that I will die and carry your child with me to the grave."

I forgot I was tired and hungry. I knew I had to find my father. Some hours after—I don't know how long it was—I did find him at last. He frowned as I came over to him. But after a glance at the letter he said: "I'll come in a minute."

He was home before I was, sitting with my brothers and sisters, talking a little too loudly as if he wanted my mother to know he was there.

For a few weeks he stayed at home in the evenings, playing with us, telling us stories, until one night three of his friends came by. I heard my mother refusing to allow gambling in the house. My father hardly protested, and after hesitating, went off with his guests. None of his friends ever came again, but he was always out, sometimes for days on end. He was out too the day the typewriters and the duplicators, and some of the furniture, were taken away in a truck.

My mother couldn't laugh and joke with the hawkers from the villages any more. She would just shake her head, barely saying a few words. The old woman weaver came once, no longer smiling, begging my mother to buy some more *lurik*. She talked about the hard times in the village . . . nobody bought any more *lurik* . . . the sandalmaker had gone to the city to work as a coolie. She sighed and turned down the road.

My sister was sent to look for my father the night my youngest brother was born. I had to go for the midwife. My father couldn't be found. The *babu* sent us to bed telling us not to make a noise.

In the morning I went to my mother's room to see my new brother. My mother lay peacefully, the little baby at her side. Her face for the first time in months was glowing and bright. She smiled at me, tired, but happy. Just then my father appeared in the doorway. "A boy!" he shouted. "He will be bigger than his mother and his father."

My mother seemed to stiffen and there was a sharpness in her voice as she answered him before he could come to her bedside: "He'll get nothing from you. He'll be able to grow up himself, and it won't matter if he has been born here and in these times." My father said nothing. I edged out of the room.

So my youngest brother was born when the wave of excitement had rolled back, when all the talk about *Swadeshi* had died down, and the clubs and reading and writing classes had folded up. The children of the government officials went to government schools. There was a lot of gambling and a few more police than before. Everything had gone back to normal in our little town. It was as if the night had fallen before the day was finished. The dawn seemed a long way off.

Rivai Apin

THE WANDERER

No more can you and I be one.
This world is secretive, endlessly varied,
Sometimes we have lain at night upon the beach
Arms inter-twined
It was no more than the reflection
Of the twinkling stars upon the racing waves.

Good-bye! I must to the helm again.
My blood throbs with the rhythm of the sails—
See, they have already begun to catch the wind.

Any star, every star, anywhere.
With longing and desire
I come, I come.
But remember, only for a moment, not for long!
This world has many forms, not one.

Mena Abdullah and Ray Mathew

❧❧❧❧❧❧❧❧❧❧❧❧❧❧❧❧

THE TIME OF THE PEACOCK

*W*HEN I was little everything was wonderful; the world was our farm and we were all loved. Rashida and Lal and I, Father and our mother, Ama: we loved one another and everything turned to good.

I remember in autumn, how we burned the great baskets of leaves by the Gwydir and watched the fires burning in the river while Ama told us stories of Krishna the flute-player and his moving mountains. And when the fires had gone down and the stories were alive in our heads we threw cobs of corn into the fires and cooked them. One for each of us—Rashida and Lal and me, Father and our mother.

Winter I remember, when the frost bit and stung and the wind pulled our hair. At night by the fire, in the warm of the house, we could hear the dingoes howling.

Then, it was spring and the good year was born again. The sticks of the jasmine-vine covered themselves with flowers.

One spring I remember was the time of the peacock when I learnt the word *secret* and began to grow up. After that spring everything somehow was different, was older. I was not little any more, and the baby had come.

I had just learnt to count. I thought I could count anything. I counted fingers and toes, the steps and the windows, even the hills. But this day in spring the hills were wrong.

There should have been five. I knew that there should have been five. I counted them over and over. "*Ek, do, tin, panch.*" But it was no good. There was one too many, a strange hill, a leftover. It looked familiar, and I knew it, but it made more than five and worried me. I thought of Krishna and the mountains that moved to protect the cowherds, the travellers lost because of them, and I was frightened because it seemed to me that our hills had moved, too.

I ran through the house and out into the garden to tell Ama the thing that Krishna had done and to ask how we could please him. But when I saw her I forgot all about it; I was *that* young. I just stopped and jumped, up and down.

She was standing there, in her own garden, the one with the Indian flowers, her own little walled-in country. Her hands were joined together in front of her face, and her lips were moving.

On the ground, in front of the Kashmiri rose-bush, in front of the tuberoses, in front of the pomegranate-tree, she had placed little bowls of shining milk. I jumped to see them. Now I knew why I was running all the time and skipping, why I wanted to sing out, and to count everything in the world.

"It is spring," I shouted to Ama. "Not nearly-spring! Not almost-spring! But really-spring!

"Will the baby come soon?" I asked her. "Soon?"

"Soon, Impatience, soon."

I laughed at her and jumped up and clapped my hands together over the top of my head. "I am as big as that," I said. "I can do anything." And I hopped on one leg to the end of the garden where the peacock lived.

"Shah-Jehan!" I said to him: that was his name. "It is spring and the baby is coming, pretty Shah-Jehan." But he didn't seem interested. "Silly old Shah-Jehan," I said. "Don't you know anything? I can count ten."

He went on staring his goldy eye at me. He *was* a silly bird. Why, he had to stay in the garden all day, away from the rooster. He couldn't run everywhere the way that I could. He couldn't do anything.

"Open your tail," I told him. "Go on, open your tail."

And we went on staring at one another till I felt sad.

"Rashida is right," I said to him. "You will never open your tail like the bird on the fan. But why don't you try? Please, pretty Shah-Jehan."

But he just went on staring as though he would never open his tail, and while I looked at him sadly I remembered how he had come to us.

127

He could lord it now and strut in the safety of the garden, but I could remember how the Lascar brought him to the farm, in a bag, like a cabbage, with his feathers drooping and his white tail dirty.

The Lascar came to the farm, a seaman on the land, a dark face in a white country. How he smiled when he saw us—Rashida and me swinging on the gate. How he chattered to Ama and made her laugh and cry. How he had shouted about the curries that she gave him.

And when it was time to go, with two basins of curry tied up in cloth and packed in his bag, he gave the bird to Ama, gave it to her while she said nothing, not even thank you. She only looked at him.

"What is it?" we said as soon as he was far enough away. "What sort of bird?"

"It is a peacock," said Ama, very softly. "He has come to us from India."

"It is not like the peacock on your Kashmiri fan," I said. "It is only a sort of white."

"The peacock on the fan is green and blue and gold and has a tail like a fan," said Rashida. "This is not a peacock at all. Anyone can see that."

"Rashida," said Ama, "Rashida! The eldest must not be too clever. He is a *white* peacock. He is too young to open his tail. He is a peacock from India."

"Ama," I said, "make him, make him open his tail."

"I do not think," she said, "I do not think he will ever open his tail in this country."

"No," said Father that night, "he will never open his tail in Australia."

"No," said Uncle Seyed next morning, "he will never open his tail without a hen-bird near."

But we had watched him, Rashida and Lal and I; had watched him for days and days until we had grown tired of watching and he had grown sleek and shiny and had found his place in the garden.

"Won't you ever open your tail?" I asked him again. "Not now that it's spring?"

128

But he wouldn't even try, not even try to look interested, so I went away from him and looked for someone to talk to.

The nurse-lady, who was there to help Ama and who was pink like an apple and almost as round, was working in the kitchen.

"The baby is coming soon," I told her. "Now that it's spring."

"Go on with you," she laughed. "Go on."

So I did, until I found Rashida sitting in a window-sill with a book in front of her. It was the nurse-lady's baby-book.

"What are you doing?"

"I am reading," she said. "This is the baby-book. I am reading how to look after the baby."

"You can't read," I said. "You *know* you can't read."

Rashida refused to answer. She just went on staring at the book, turning pages.

"But you can't read!" I shouted at her. "You can't."

She finished running her eye down the page.

"I am not reading words," she said. "I know what the book tells. I am reading things."

"But you know, you know you can't read."

I stamped away from her, cranky as anything, out of the house, past the window where Rashida was sitting so cleverly, down to the vegetable-patch where I could see Lal. He was digging with a trowel.

"What are you doing?" I said, not very pleasantly.

"I am digging," said Lal. "I am making a garden for my new baby brother."

"How did you know? How did you all know? I was going to tell you." I was almost crying. "Anyway," I said, "it might not be a brother."

"Oh, yes, it will," said Lal. "We *have* girls."

"I'll dig, too," I said, laughing, suddenly happy again. "I'll help you. We'll make a big one."

"Digging is man's work," said Lal. "I'm a man. You're a girl."

"You're a baby," I said. "You're only four."

And I threw some dirt at him, and went away.

Father was making a basket of sticks from the plum-tree. He used to put two crossed sticks on the ground, squat in the middle of them and weave other sticks in and out of them until a basket had grown up around him. All I could see were his shoulders and the back of his turban as I crept up behind him, to surprise him.

But he was not surprised. "I knew it would be you," he said. I scowled at him then, but he only laughed the way that he always did.

"Father," I began in a questioning voice that made him groan. Already I was called the Australian-one, the questioner. "Father," I said, "why do peacocks have beautiful tails?"

He tugged at his beard. "Their feet are ugly," he said. "Allah has given them tails so that no one will look at their feet."

"But Shah-Jehan," I said, and Father bent his head down over his weaving, "everyone looks at his feet. His tail never opens."

"Yes," said Father definitely, as though that explained everything, and I began to cry: it was that sort of day, laughter and tears. I supposed it was the first day of spring.

"What is it, what is it?" said Father.

"Everything," I told him. "Shah-Jehan won't open his tail, Rashida pretends she can read, Lal won't let me dig. I'm nothing. And it's spring; Ama is putting out the milk for the snakes, and I counted . . ." But Father was looking so serious that I never told him what I had counted.

"Listen," he said. "You are big now, Nimmi. I will tell you a secret."

"What is secret?"

He sighed. "It is what is ours," he said. "Something we know but do not tell, or share with one person only in the world."

"With me!" I begged. "With me!"

"Yes," he said, "with you. But no crying or being nothing. This is to make you a grown-up person."

"Please," I said to him, "please." And I loved him then so much that I wanted to break the cage of twigs and hold him.

"We are Muslims," he said. "But your mother has a mark on her forehead that shows that once she was not. She was a Brahman and she believed all the stories of Krishna and Siva."

"I know that," I said. "And the hills"——

"Monkey, quiet," he commanded. "But now Ama is a Muslim

too. Only, she remembers her old ways. And she puts out the milk in the spring."

"For the snakes," I said. "So they will love us, and leave us from harm."

"But there are no snakes in the garden," said Father.

"But they drink the milk," I told him. "Ama says"——

"If the milk were left, the snakes would come," said Father. "And they must not come, because there is no honour in snakes. They would strike you or Rashida or little Lal or even Ama. So—and this is the secret that no one must know but you and me—I go to the garden in the night and empty the dishes of milk. And this way I have no worry and you have no harm and Ama's faith is not hurt. But you must never tell."

"Never, never tell," I assured him.

All that day I was kind to Lal, who was only a baby and not grown-up, and I held my head up high in front of Rashida, who was clever but had no secret. All of that day I walked in a glory, full of my secret. I even felt cleverer than Ama, who knew everything but must never, never know this.

She was working that afternoon on her quilt. I looked at the crochet-pictures in the little squares of it.

"Here is a poinsettia," I said.

"Yes," said Ama. "And here is"——

"It's Shah-Jehan! With his tail open."

"Yes," said Ama. "So it is. And here is a rose for the baby."

"When will the baby come?" I asked her. "Not soon, but when?"

"Tonight, tomorrow night," said Ama, "the next."

"Do babies always come at night?"

"Mine, always," said Ama. "There is the dark and the waiting, and then the sun on our faces. And the scent of jasmine, even here." And she looked at her garden.

"But, Ama"——

"No questions, Nimmi. My head is buzzing. No questions today."

That night I heard a strange noise, a harsh cry.

"Shah-Jehan!" I said. I jumped out of bed and ran to the window. I stood on a chair and looked out to the garden.

131

It was moonlight, the moon so big and low that I thought I could lean out and touch it, and there, looking sad, and white as frost in the moonlight, stood Shah-Jehan.

"Shah-Jehan, little brother," I said to him, "you must not feel about your feet. Think of your tail, pretty one, your beautiful tail."

And then, as I was speaking, he lifted his head and slowly, slowly opened his tail, like a fan, like a fan of lace that was as white as the moon. Oh, Shah-Jehan! it was as if you had come from the moon.

My throat hurt, choked, so that my breath caught and I shut my eyes. When I opened them it was all gone: the moon was the moon and Shah-Jehan was a milky-white bird with his tail drooping and his head bent.

In the morning the nurse-lady woke us. "Get up," she said. "Guess what? In the night, a sister! The dearest, sweetest, baby sister . . . Now, up with you!"

"No brother," said Lal. "No baby brother."

We laughed at him, Rashida and I, and ran to see the baby. Ama was lying, very still and small, in the big bed. Her long plait of black hair stretched across the big white pillow. The baby was in the old cradle, and we peered down at her. Her tiny fists groped on the air towards us.

But Lal would not look at her. He climbed on to the bed and crawled over to Ama. "No boy," he said sadly. "No boy to play with."

Ama stroked his hair. "My son," she said. "I am sorry, little son."

"Can we change her?" he said. "For a boy?"

"She is a gift from Allah," said Ama. "You can never change gifts."

Father came in from the dairy. His face a huge grin, he made a chuckling noise over the cradle and then sat on the bed.

"Missus," he said in the queer English that always made the nurse-lady laugh, "this one little fellow, eh?"

"Big," said Ama. "Nine pounds." And the nurse-lady nodded proudly.

"What wrong with this fellow?" said Father, scooping Lal up in his arm. "What wrong with you, eh?"

"No boy," said Lal. "No boy to talk to."

"Ai! Ai!" lamented Father, trying to change his expression. "Too many girls here," he said. "Better we drown one. Which one we drown, Lal? Which one, eh?"

Rashida and I hurled ourselves at him, squealing with delight. "Not me! Not me!" we shouted while the nurse-lady tried to shush us.

"You are worse than the children," she said to Father. "Far worse."

But then she laughed, and we all did. Even the baby made a noise.

But what was the baby to be called? We all talked about it. Even Uncle Seyed came in and leant on the door-post while names were talked over and over.

At last Father lifted the baby up and looked into her big dark eyes.

"What was the name of your sister?" he asked Uncle Seyed. "The little one, who followed us everywhere? The little one with the beautiful eyes?"

"Jamila," said Uncle Seyed. "She was Jamila."

So that was to be her first name, Jamila, after the little girl who was alive in India when Father was a boy and he and Uncle Seyed had decided to become friends like brothers. And her second name was Shahnaz, which means the Heart's Beloved.

And then I remembered.

"Shah-Jehan," I said. "He can open his tail. I saw him last night, when everyone was asleep."

"You couldn't see in the night," said Rashida. "You dreamt it, baby."

"No, I didn't. It was bright moon."

"You dreamt it, Nimmi," said Father. "A peacock wouldn't open his tail in this country."

"I didn't dream it," I said in a little voice that didn't sound very certain: Father was always right.

"I'll count Jamila's fingers," I said before Rashida could say anything else about the peacock. "*Ek, do, tin, panch,*" I began.

"You've left out *cha,*" said Father.

"Oh, yes, I forgot. I forgot it. *Ek, do, tin, cha, panch.* She has five," I said.

"Everyone has five," said Rashida.

"Show me," said Lal.

And while Father and Ama were showing him the baby's fingers and toes and telling him how to count them, I crept out on to the veranda where I could see the hills.

I counted them quickly. *"Ek, do, tin, cha, panch."* There were only five, not one left over. I was so excited that I felt the closing in my throat again.

"I didn't dream it," I said. "I couldn't dream the pain. I *did* see it, I did. I have another secret now. And only five hills. *Ek, do, tin, cha, panch.*"

They never changed again. I was grown-up.

Australia

Rosemary Dobson

COCK-CROW

WANTING to be myself, alone,
Between the lit house and the town
I took the road, and at the bridge
Turned back and walked the way I'd come.

Three times I took that lonely stretch;
Three times the dark trees closed me round;
The night absolved me of my bonds;
Only my footsteps held the ground.

My mother and my daughter slept,
One life behind and one before,
And I that stood between denied
Their needs in shutting-to the door.

And walking up and down the road
Knew myself, separate and alone,
Cut off from human cries, from pain,
And love that grows about the bone.

Too brief illusion! Thrice for me
I heard the cock crow on the hill
And turned the handle of the door
Thinking I knew his meaning well.

Australia

Douglas Stewart

THE SILKWORMS

ALL their lives in a box! What generations,
What centuries of masters, not meaning to be cruel
But needing their labour, taught these creatures such
    patience
That now though sunlight strikes on the eye's dark
    jewel
Or moonlight breathes on the wing they do not stir
But like the ghosts of moths crouch silent there.

Look, it's a child's toy! There is no lid even,
They can climb, they can fly, and all the world's their
    tree;
But hush, they say in themselves, we are in prison.
There is no word to tell them that they are free,
And they are not; ancestral voices bind them
In dream too deep for wind or word to find them.

135

Even in the young, each like a little dragon
Ramping and green upon his mulberry leaf,
So full of life, it seems, the voice has spoken:
They hide where there is food, where they are safe,
And the voice whispers, "Spin the cocoon,
Sleep, sleep, you shall be wrapped in me soon."

Now is their hour, when they wake from that long
    swoon;
Their pale curved wings are marked in a pattern of
    leaves,
Shadowy for trees, white for the dance of the moon;
And when on summer nights the buddleia gives
Its nectar like lilac wine for insects mating
They drink its fragrance and shiver, impatient with
    waiting,

They stir, they think they will go. Then they remember
It was forbidden, forbidden, ever to go out;
The Hands are on guard outside like claps of thunder,
The ancestral voice says Don't, and they do not.
Still the night calls them to unimaginable bliss
But there is terror around them, the vast, the abyss,

And here is the tribe that they know, in their known
    place,
They are gentle and kind together, they are safe for
    ever,
And all shall be answered at last when they embrace.
White moth moves closer to moth, lover to lover.
There is that pang of joy on the edge of dying—
Their soft wings whirr, they dream that they are flying.

Mulk Raj Anand

THE POWER OF DARKNESS

[*In the autumn of last year, I visited Mangal, the site of
the new dam that has harnessed the course of one of the oldest
waters of the land of five rivers. The sun seemed, in the afternoons, to set fire to the surface of the new canals and made the
earth look like beaten gold. And the pylons seemed to speak to
the sky. And, seeing the wonder of it all, the ejaculation came
spontaneously from my lips, in the homely Punjabi tongue. "In
the jungle has arisen this Mangal!" My speech fell on the ears
of an electrician of the nearby powerhouse. And, as he opened
his mouth and uttered his dictum, in the northern refugee accent,
"Green shoots will soon stand with their roots moistened by this
nectar", I surmised, from the lilt in his voice that he was somewhat by way of being a poet. A little later, I heard him hum a
tune from our famous epic, Hir and Ranjha. And, compelled by
nostalgia, I asked him to sing a little. Instead he began to tell me
the story of Mangal. That tale is told here in the words of Bali
the Bard (for that was his name, I discovered), almost as he told
it to me. And it seems that the recital manner of his telling almost
achieves the dramatic tension necessary to a modern story,
mastering the laws of space and time.*]

"O_F all the gods and goddesses of our country Shakti is the
most supreme. To be sure, everything is Shakti, soul and body,
earth and sky, and the waters that flow from their union. . . .

"But how were the villagers of Kamli to know this truth? For
when the gloom of madness falls upon the soul, so that it turns
to rend and destroy its dearest and nearest, when the light of
dread forebodings covers us with its shadows, whether it be man,

137

woman or child, then who can find in the maleficent presence of fear, his chiefest good?

"And, as the power of darkness blurs the outline of things around us, seeming to free us from the rule of daylight, but really consigning us to hell, when we ourselves beckon the god of the netherworld, Yama, and his doots, we have to close our eyes in order to explore our inner selves and rescue, from the silences, the strength to face a future which we cannot understand. . . .

"Our profoundest truth today, brother, consists in this: that we have a capacity for great works. And if I, Bali, know anything about anything, since I know much about electricity, then these big works are organised schemes, in which the sparks are lit in order to free men from their fetters, to enable them to surpass themselves, and to give all that he has, and what they acquire to his children.

"But how can one show this spirit of light to the dark-minded and the dead in heart?

" 'If it exists,' they said, 'show it to us! How can your electricity vie with Kamli, the mother, after whom our village is named. This giant monster of cement and steel which you are helping to build in your dam is an insult offered to our ancient goddess! For ages she has directed the courses of the sun, the moon, and the stars. And every part of our land is imbued with the spirit of Kamli. And we have had good harvests, plentiful ones, until you refugees came and began to devour our stocks, taking bread from the mouths of our children! And, now these, who are in authority, declare that our village of Kamli is to be submerged in the artificial lake they are constructing. And they want us to move away, before the water fills this construction of the iron age and the canals begin to flow! . . . To be sure, they have given us some compensation and some fallow land, near Chandigarh, where they have built barrack-like structures on the sites where the goddess Chandi manifested herself for the first time when she walked down from the high peaks of the Dhaula Dhar to the plains! Ruffians and scoundrels! Drunk with the wine of power! Respecting neither religion nor our old gods! And to think that the Prime Minister of this faithless age is himself a Brahmin! Look, folks, darkness has come!'

"And though the work proceeded on the huge dam, and the time seemed to come nearer, when the waters of the artificial lake Mangal Sagar were to submerge the little hamlet of Kamli, the villagers, who talked like this, would not move.

"And thus a drama was enacted before our eyes, of which you may see the happy ending but of which you do not know the various acts. Even I can detach myself today and talk of that grim struggle in an even voice, but those were solemn moments, brother, those moments when, for days, we were on the brink of death and destruction, and from which we emerged only because some transcended themselves . . . In those moments of mortal agony, when the lips of these men only framed abuse and oaths and imprecations, I groaned many a time, the cry that we utter in our deepest need, 'oh mother!' . . ."

"Tell me then, oh brother Bali, the story of this struggle," I interrupted.

The bard closed his eyes for a moment as though he was encompassing all the solemn moments of death, all the moments of each act of the drama of the village of Kamli before it was submerged in the lake of Mangal Sagar. And then, he opened his eyes, which were slightly cocked, as though, like Alexander the Great, he drew the wisdom of the heaven with the left eye, which was tilted upwards, and from the earth, with the right eye which was tilted downwards. And he spoke:

"Like a child you are in your curiosity, brother. But if it will fill you with compassion for the human lot, I shall tell you this mythical story and you can draw your own conclusions.

"Once upon a time, and it seems a long time ago, there stood at the bottom of the ravine there, now filled with the life-giving waters of Mangal Sagar, the self-same village of Kamli, of which I have spoken.

"And though it was peopled by seventy souls, all told, there were five men of this village, villains, if you would like to call them such, but men whose words counted for much with the ignorant, and who were able to persuade many to defy the light, for months, on behalf of the power of darkness.

"The head of this group, who was moreover a landlord, owning many bighas of land, and headman of the village was called Viroo. An old man of nearly eighty years he sat upon the land,

and upon his own life, like a leech upon a sick body drinking away the blood without getting any fatter to the naked eye. He had a profligate son, called Prakash, a boy who stole jewellery from his mother's box and sold it in Ambala, but who was nevertheless much loved by his father and utterly spoilt by his mother, being plied with endless long tumblers of whey and copious portions of butter on his spinach and large loaves of maize bread. This Prakash beat up his own young sister, Yashoda, for stopping by the well a little longer than usual to listen to me reciting *Hir* in the distance, and he distinguished himself, during the events of those days, when his village was pitched in a battle against us, by a rascally behaviour that has no parallel in the annals of the Punjab.

"The next in command in the forces of destruction was a goldsmith named Ram Jawaya, a dignitary with a tuft knot that protruded, always, beyond the confines of his small, greasy, black cap, the lashes of his eyes having been blown out by the smoke and fire from the hearth where he melted the jewellery, pawned by the villagers, but whose greedy vision was still unaffected, so that he could see everything evil in all that is good, whose mendacity had remained unabated in the fifty-five odd years of his existence on earth during which his right hand never allowed his left hand to know how much gold he was thieving from the poor or how much land he was absorbing with his penman's jugglery, in the long account book where all the mortgages were recorded. His son, Dharam Dev, was not such a rough as Prakash, the son of the landlord Viroo, but, weak-chinned and pale-faced, this boy was a glib little talker, who constantly twirled his thin moustache in the belief that it was a thick one, though, I am sure, he did this to give himself courage.

"And, then there was the double-dealing, clever young man called Tarachand, who had gone to town and become a B.A. pass, though he had put in for the law and failed to become a Vakil, in spite of the fact that he had sold his mother's land. Some said that he had turned sour, because he could not get a job in the offices of the Sarkar, and that may have been the reason for his virulence. But to me he seemed the kind of man who could have sold his mother herself for his own good and set fire to the whole village if it had suited him, even as he surely lit the flames of the controversy which nearly ruined the fortunes of all the poor peasants.

"There were also two middle peasants, brothers, named Jarnel Singh and Karnel Singh, who had served as Sepoys under the British Raj and retired with the rank of Havildar and Lance Naik, respectively. They had failed to gain any wisdom from their wanderings across the earth and never forgot the two squares of land given to them by the Angrezi Sarkar (English Government) in Lyallpur District, which they had to leave after the partition, even as many of us left everything we ourselves had, north of the Wagha Canal.

"A young boy, named Bharat Ram, the son of the widow Siddhi, who had learnt to be a mechanic in a motor garage in Patiala town, stood aside from all these and seemed to me, in his long silences, to be the superior of this nefarious gang of obstructionists, for he talked sense when he did dare to open his mouth before them, and nearly swayed the villagers on the side of truth. And he it was who came with me, beating the drum, even as I went among the folk singing the songs, and shouting the words, which were to rescue the villagers from the mouth of the disaster that nearly befell them."

"Actually, how did the trouble arise and what happened?" I asked him impetuously in my eagerness to know how the crisis had developed.

"Not so fast, brother," said Bali, the bard. "As the poet Kabir has spoken: 'What cooks slowly matures into a sweeter dish.' And I shall tell you all if you be patient!"

"Go on, brother, go on," I said.

"Actually," he continued, "these people of Kamli did not know, at first, what was going on. They were the creatures of habit, whose chief god was *Dastur*. What was good enough for their forefathers was, they thought, good enough for them. And they did not know where they were going or what they really wanted. And though they followed their customs blindly, they suffered in secret. And then they were amazed that they were caught up in the web of suffering.

"And, yet all the time they were fighting feuds with each other.

"Thus landlord Viroo felt, that the whole life of the village had been poisoned by the goldsmith Ram Jawaya. And goldsmith

141

Ram Jawaya felt, that the cause of the downfall of the whole of the countryside was Babu Tara Chand, B.A., who talked so much, mixing words of Punjabi speech with Angrezi, and putting on kot-patloon to impress all and sundry, and ready to throw all the wise elders on the rubbish heap. The middle peasants, Jarnel Singh and Karnel Singh worked hard on the land and hardly had any time to think, but when they did manage to scratch their heads, they felt that the moment had come when both landlord Viroo and goldsmith Ram Jawaya should give up the headship of the village which these elders had enjoyed in rotation, and allow one of the younger ones among them to become the Chaudhri. And, all of these 'wise' ones distrusted their sons, because the boys were seen in the company of mechanic Bharat Ram, the son of the widow Siddhi, who gave lifts to all his companions on his phutt-phutti.

"And thus the elders stood open-mouthed for the first few months, even as they stared at the glow of the giant lights, which shone during the nights to enable the labourers to keep vigil on the construction of the Mangal Dam. And they muttered curses against the Kali-Yug, during which the laws of nature were being upset by the wiping out of the distinction between day and night. And as they heard the phutt-phutti of mechanic Bharat Ram making frequent trips to the site of the dam, three miles away, with one or two of the boys of the village holding on to him from the seat at the back, they were more furious with this mechanic than even with builders of the dam. And when they realised that most of the villagers got better wages doing labour on the construction than they themselves had ever paid these men for work on their estates, they were filled with murderous rages. . . .

"So they appointed the loquacious Babu Tarachand, B.A., to go and see the Tehsildar of the big village of Mangal and apprise him of the objections of the elders of Kamli against the upset caused by the demoniac construction. . . .

"Babu Tarachand, B.A., went proudly enough to meet the Tehsildar and came back, thumping his chest, at the victory he had secured.

" 'The Sarkar is going to give us money by way of compensation for moving from our houses in this village to a settlement near Chandigarh when Kamli is submerged in the artificial lake of Mangal Sagar that will fill the space between the two hills on our side. And I have secured the promise of the best lands in the basin, at the foot of the Himalayas, for us all! . . .'

" 'Compensation!' exclaimed Viroo.

" 'For leaving our houses?' protested Ram Jawaya.

" 'A settlement near Chandigarh?' inquired Jarnel Singh. 'You mean to say that you, son of an owl, have agreed, on our behalf, that we will move out of our village. . . .'

" 'Hallowed by the incarnation of the goddess herself!' asserted old Viroo.

" 'If the land near Chandigarh is anything like as good as the plots we had in Lyallpur District,' ventured Karnel Singh, 'but what would this literate fool Tarachand know about the qualities of the soil! . . .'

" 'Look, folks, darkness has come,' put in Ram Jawaya. 'He has sold us all, as he would willingly sell his mother, for some advantage which the Tehsildar has promised.'

" 'Uncle,' answered Tarachand, B.A., 'I have not sold you or the village, or myself. I am with you. And I think it is a crime that we should be moved from our homesteads in this village of our ancestors, to the barren deserts of Chandigarh, where a dust storm blows from morning to night, and where no one is buying houses, even of the thickest walls, because nothing can keep away the dust! . . .'

" 'Then learned one,' said old Viroo, 'sit down and forthwith write to the Sarkar to remove this construction, which is blasting away our hills—and let us live in peace.'

" 'To be sure,' added Ram Jawaya.

" 'Han, han,' confirmed Jarnel Singh and Karnel Singh.

"And though Babu Tarachand, B.A., had been tempted by the prospects of going to Chandigarh, where he might be able to bring influence to bear to secure a job in some office, after all, he sat down and did the bidding of the elders and wrote a petition to the Sarkar, protesting against the plan to submerge the village of Kamli in the artificial lake of Mangal Sagar.

"For some time they all waited for the answer of the Sarkar in the most terrible suspense. As you know, brother, at the best of times, our Sarkar bungles with the papers. Perhaps, there are

143

too many of these things called files. But none of the clerks, or officers, of the Sarkar seem to take responsibility. They always pass on the applications with their opinions, on to someone else, who might lose the papers, or may have too much to do to look at them. And so applications are seldom answered or forwarded higher up. So there was some delay in the arrival of an answer to the petition of the elders of Kamli from the Sarkar.

"And, in the meanwhile, as the construction of the dam proceeded, and the earthworks loomed as high as the nearby hills, Ram Jawaya, who had acquired twenty acres of land, in spite of the prohibition against mere moneylenders possessing the soil, went to pray to the goddess Kamli, one night, accompanied by his wife, Dharmi. He put a silver rupee and a coconut before the shrine of the red stone, and prayed that the goddess might make herself manifest and destroy the dam and save the village named after her. And though the goddess did not appear, Dharmi took it upon herself to go at dead of night, evading the big lamps and do magic near the site of the construction, by putting an earthen saucer lamp on the cross-roads with a little rice and sugar around it in the sign of the Swastika. She breathed some secret prayers and repaired home in the dark.

"The next morning the work on the construction proceeded exactly as it had done before the magic was done on the cross-roads.

"Ram Jawaya, whom his wife had told of her magic, ground his teeth in bitterness at the frustration of his wife's design. As Dharmi had taken the wife of old Viroo, named Kala, into confidence, and Kala had told her husband, Viroo, the old landlord swore foul abuse against the giant iron cranes, calling them 'the invention of the devils!'

"The middle peasants Jarnel Singh and Karnel Singh, too, had been thinking of some direct action for ending the dam, which they knew would ultimately submerge their lands in the water and force them, a second time, to go and settle somewhere else.

"Sardar Jarnel Singh said to Sardar Karnel Singh:

"'Brother, we must act, now or never! If only we could get one of those bombs, which are said to carry enough powder to blow up the whole world, we could end this affliction in a moment.'

144

"Sardar Karnel Singh said to Sardar Jarnel Singh:

"'Brother, I know of an acid, which can be put into a little bottle, which itself can be thrown on the head of the big engineer and kill him. So, with the going of the engineer, will go his evil construction.'

"And, though Sardar Jarnel Singh nodded his head affirmatively, he had grave doubts whether the plan of his brother could end the mischief, which was more than the engineer at the dam. Still, he did not dissuade Karnel Singh from thinking what he had said.

"And Karnel Singh, being a man who believed in deeds rather than words, stole up one evening, to the house of the chief engineer Sharma, while this worthy was having his food, completely unaware of his danger. The ex-sepoy threw the bottle of acid on the head of the engineer, and ran away with his tail between his legs.

"The bottle did not burst and, fortunately, the engineer's face was saved from disfigurement.

"This incident led the police to make certain inquiries in the village of Kamli and Sardar Karnel Singh, was handcuffed and taken before the Magistrate, who put him out of touch with his companions, by consigning him in the Ambala District jail.

"There is an old saying in our country that a man may spoil another, just so far as it may serve his ends, but when he is spoiled by others he, despoiled, spoils yet again. So long as evil's fruit is not matured, the fool fancies now is the hour, now is the chance.

"And so the elders, Viroo, Ram Jawaya, Jarnel Singh and Tarachand, B.A., sat in council and decided that the conviction of Karnel Singh must be avenged. They decided to ask all the villagers, who worked on the dam site to withdraw from work. And they exhorted their young sons, Prakash, the scion of the landlord; Dharam Dev, the offspring of Ram Jawaya; and Darshan Singh and Sudarshan Singh sons of Karnel Singh never to go with mechanic Bharat Ram on his phutt-phutti, which kept the whole village awake at night and which was itself a symbol of the evil of the time.

"The peasants in the village, who had been earning good money with their labour on the dam were in a quandry; if they stopped working on the construction, they would lose the money, but if they did not heed the advice of the elders, the goddess Kamli might come and destroy them. So they went to mechanic Bharat Ram, who was foreman in charge of one of the cranes.

" 'I know why you have come,' said mechanic Bharat Ram. 'I have made my choice and will go on working here until the dam is complete. If you wish for the good life, then pay no heed to those oldies and carry on with your labour, put aside a little money, and breathe the air of new times. Otherwise, you can go back to work on the estate of Ram Jawaya, to whom you have already mortgaged your souls and your bodies. . . .'

"Whereupon the labourers decided to continue their work on the dam.

"The headman Viroo, the goldsmith Ram Jawaya, Sardar Jarnel Singh and Babu Tarachand, B.A., were highly incensed at this act of disobedience on the part of the serfs. They assembled before the image of Kamli and solemnly declared, in her name, that, henceforth, they would not share 'hooka and water' with these rebellious village-folk.

"About that time, came the order of the Sarkar that the petition of the elders of Kamli had been rejected and that all the villagers would get compensation immediately for being deprived of their houses, and that they would be given fertile lands to plough after the next harvest and before the water of the artificial lake of Mangal Sagar should begin to flow and submerge the village of Kamli.

"And the Sarkar was as good as its word. And there arrived the Tehsildar of Mangal to distribute one lakh (100,000 rupees) to the villagers, the bulk of it going to the five elders and the rest to the small peasants.

"Never had the elders of this village, far less the small peasants, seen so much cash. Their eyes opened wide at the vision of the silver, and they put their thumb impression on to the papers and received the compensation—Seth Ram Jawaya and Babu Tarachand, B.A., signing their names in the Hindi and Angrezi letters respectively.

"But do you think when their tumbledown houses had been paid for, they would give up the ill feelings they harboured against the dam? To such men as these, the sight alone of greater harvests, on other lands, might have vouchsafed some consolation. As they could see the corn waving in the breeze before their eyes, near Chandigarh, they remained dead at heart.

"A few days after they had put the cash in their boxes, and secured these boxes with strong locks, they went to the temple of Kamli to thank her for the victory she had secured for them, and they begged her again for the boon that the dam, which might deprive them of their lands, might be destroyed by her if only she would assume the form of a stroke of lightning.

"And then they waited for the miracle to happen.

"The sun shone. There were no clouds. So there was no lightning. And the work on the dam now proceeded faster than ever, because the Sarkar declared that the water must flow by the end of April.

"As the elders could not damage anything more than the track which led from the village of Kamli to Mangal with their footsteps, the younger folk tried to intervene on their behalf.

"It seems that Prakash had asked to borrow the phutt-phutti of mechanic Bharat Ram. Since the landlord's son had not learnt to ride the machine properly, mechanic Bharat Ram did not oblige. And this gave Prakash the necessary cue for action.

"Prakash proposed to the weak-chinned son of goldsmith Ram Jawaya, and to Darshan Singh and Sudarshan Singh, sons of Karnel Singh, that they should waylay mechanic Bharat Ram half way from the village to the dam site, beat him up and deprive him of his phutt-phutti. Dharam Dev was not so eager to take part in this ambush, but Darshan Singh and Sudarshan Singh, whose father was still in jail for throwing the acid bottle on chief engineer, Sharma, were more than ready to revenge themselves on the mechanic, who surveyed the world from the top of the crane and was, in their opinion, now so stuck up that he hardly ever joined them in their pastime of poaching for the green mangoes in the villages around.

"The boys all went out, under the light of the stars, on the excuse of doing jungle-pani, and lay in waiting for mechanic Bharat Ram to proceed to his early morning shift at Mangal. They heard the phutt-phutti starting off from the village and got into position behind the bushes from where they could pounce on their victim.

147

"But as mechanic Bharat Ram came, tearing across the track, he sped past them, long before they could rush out of the bushes. All that they could do was to shout abuse after him and eat the dust that he had started up.

"They went back to the village and decided to tell the labourers, who were due to go on the morning shift, that mechanic Bharat Ram had told them the day was a holiday at the dam site and no work would be done. It was certain that if the labourers did not go to work, their pay would be docked, and then these people could be incited against mechanic Bharat Ram on whose information the labourers would have stayed away.

"In this plan, the boys succeeded. So solemnly did they talk to the labourers that the men believed it was a holiday and stayed away from the shifts.

"But, on the next day, they found that they had been deceived and, knowing that their pay would be cut for absenting themselves, they asked mechanic Bharat Ram why he had spread a baseless rumour that there was a holiday on the previous day.

"Mechanic Bharat Ram was a man of few words and merely said that he did not know anything about such a rumour. And the labourers thought, from his parsimonious speech, that he had, indeed, bluffed them all.

"The vicious boys, and some of the elders of the village played upon the suspicions of the labourers and aroused them into a slow and simmering indignation against mechanic Bharat Ram. And when at the end of the month their wages for one day were actually cut, the labourers were incited by Prakash to go and smash the motor cycle of mechanic Bharat Ram, which stood under the shadow of the crane on the ground, while he was manipulating the cranes from the cabin on the top.

"The watchman of the dam arrested the culprits but mechanic Bharat Ram persuaded him to let them off.

"There are many kinds of people in the world, brother, but only two types of characters, because there are two main ways of thinking and feeling. Some people look at everything from the outside, and the others from within. And, while most of the villagers were addicted to the crude lumps of experience, mechanic Bharat Ram saw from the inside. And he believed that the change in men's hearts was more important than the conversion of their heads from the negative gesture to the gesture of affirmation.

"Only the inner change is hard to achieve. And not even his gesture in having the men released from the clutches of the police affected all those villagers. Instead, they only became more enraged, thinking that mechanic Bharat Ram was trying to be a magnanimous Lat Sahib as the elders said.

"And they persuaded the elders to cut him and his old mother Siddhi from hooka and water from the village brotherhood.

"And the womenfolk of the village joined together and invoked the spirit of the goddess Kamli in the temple and declared, on behalf of the goddess, that old Siddhi would die.

"The giant machine on the Mangal Dam worked steadily, however, and it was announced that there were only ten days left before the space on which the village of Kamli stood would be filled up with the waters of Mangal Sagar and the dam would begin to work.

"And, this time, not only the Tehsildar of Mangal, but the Head of the District, the Deputy Commissioner also came, to persuade the villagers to quit their houses and go, in the lorries which had been brought for this purpose, bag and baggage, to the new houses and lands that they had been allotted near Chandigarh. The Deputy Commissioner made a speech, using, for the first time in his life, the Punjabi tongue, and though the villagers laughed out aloud at his accent, they were also somewhat moved by his appeal in the name of the Prime Minister. He said that they should allow the interests of the whole of India to prevail over their own and not cling to their plots in the hamlet of Kamli.

"The sudden silence of the elders showed, however, that they were convinced. Only Sardar Jarnel Singh said:

" 'If you be so concerned about our welfare then why do you hold my brother Karnel Singh in jail?'

"The Head of the District answered immediately:

" 'If that be your only grievance, I shall order Karnel Singh to be released tomorrow and the remaining part of his sentence will be forgiven and forgotten.'

"And, thinking that he had played his trump card and that the villagers of Kamli had been won over, he returned to the Mangal

149

Rest House and sat down in a basket chair to drink his peg of whisky in peace.

"On the next day, when Karnel Singh was set free, there was much rejoicing in the village, and everyone thought that now the elders would call the whole Panchayat together and persuade the villagers to leave in the lorries, which were waiting under the banyan tree.

"But no such thing transpired. Instead, the elders met and claimed the release of Karnel Singh as another victory for the village against the authorities, secured for them by the grace of Kamli.

"At this juncture, the Head of the District was seen to shake his head before the Tehsildar and chief engineer, Sharma, dolefully. And mechanic Bharat Ram, whom they had asked over to advise on the best way of achieving a change of heart in the villagers, sat dumbly with his head hung down.

"At last the Deputy Commissioner ordered his big motor to be got ready and declared that he would have to send many more policemen than were available in Mangal to round up the villagers of Kamli and transport them to Chandigarh by force.

"Whereupon mechanic Bharat Ram made so bold as to lift his head and to say: 'There is only one man who can change the hearts of the villagers, and that man is Bali the electrician, working in the powerhouse.'"

"And how could Bali, the mechanic of the powerhouse succeed where the others had failed?" I asked.

At this, Bali smiled, and, then averting his cock eyes, felt for a packet of Char Minar cigarettes from the pocket of his tunic. As the fluency of Bali's narrative ended in a quixotic smile, and he would not open his mouth beyond testing the end of his cigarette, I was more than ever curious to know of the way in which he could have changed the village deadhearts into the attitude of life.

"Go on, then, brother, don't keep me guessing!"

"The solution was simple," Bali said, after exhaling a large amount of smoke.

"I went up to the head of the district, who had asked me to attend on him the next morning. And I said to the Deputy Commissioner Sahib:

" 'Preserver of the poor, perhaps I can perform the miracle. . . .'

" 'I do not believe in miracles,' said the Head of the District.

" 'Forgive me, sire, but I have chosen the wrong word. Give me a drum and let this boy mechanic Bharat Ram come with me, and I think I can persuade the villagers of Kamli to remove to Chandigarh.'

"The head of the district waved his head sceptically. And the Tehsildar was no more impressed than the Deputy Commissioner. Only Sharma, chief engineer, nodded and said:

" 'Acha, let us see what you can do. Take Mechanic Bharat Ram with you and come back tomorrow with some good news or I will wring your neck for you.' "

"And you went and performed the miracle?" I said.

"To be sure, brother, no miracle did I perform. Only a trick and the job was done."

"But what trick? And how . . . ?"

"Always in life, brother, when words have become meaningless, there is the need to discover a new vital impulse to solve any given problem. And this vital impulse has to be clothed in a new idea. And the new idea has to be put into a new combination of accents, and if these accents come deep from within the belly, which is the source of all movement and speech, then, perhaps, the words arise, in rhythm or song, and may move the listener. This is the truth behind all our poetry. And that is why all our saints and poets, went, tambura in hand, singing the 'name' they had experienced in their hearts.

"And so I kept a vigil that night and felt about in my belly for some new words which may utter themselves, like a cry from inside me.

"And, in the morning, I issued out towards the village, with mechanic Bharat Ram on my side, a drum suspended like a garland around his neck. And while he beat the drum and woke up the villagers, I began to recite my new song.

> "Ohe awake, awake, ohe brothers, awake I sang,
> we have been crushed by our slavery to the soil,
> our houses are crumbling into dust and our roads
> are covered with the thorns, only the empty sound
> of trudging, naked feet, and the naked hearts. . . .

151

"And hearing the drum beats and this wail of mine the villagers crowded around me

" 'The cock-eyed bastard, disturbing our sleep early at dawn!' muttered Prakash.

" 'The filthy electrician Bali!' said Darsham Singh.

" 'The son of a pig!' said Sudarshan Singh.

" 'But sons, he seems to speak the truth,' said Karnel Singh.

" 'He certainly has a lilt in his voice!' said Jarnel Singh.

" 'I have heard him sing Hir!' said Dharm Dev. 'Ohe sing Hir to us.'

"I did not sing the song of Hir, but repeated the words of my new song.

" 'Ohe we have heard that,' said old Viroo. 'Now proceed further and sing the song of God, early in the morning, and make this village blessed, so that the evil construction there may disappear and our harvests flourish.'

" 'Ohe, han, sing the auspicious song of Kamli, so that we may be blessed with riches!'

" 'Acha, I shall sing to the goddess,' I said. And I began to sing a song on the spur of the moment:

> "Oh, divine bestower of food inexhaustible,
>   be gracious unto us and give us your blessings,
>   thou Shakti, who incarnated herself as Kamli
>   in this village, and who has now incarnated herself
>   as the power emanating from the giant dam of
>   Mangal. . . .

" 'Sacrilege!' said old Viroo.

" 'Blasphemy!' said Ram Jawaya.

" 'The fellow is a liar!' said Babu Tarachand, B.A.

"But I sang my song:

> "Oh, divine bestower of food inexhaustible,
>   who incarnated herself as Kamli in this village,
>   and who is the saviour herself in liquid form at Mangal.
>   Mother, who is energy incarnated into the dam, walking
>   magnificently and slowly you will come,
>   and will release the electricity,
>   and new leaves will blossom at your feet,

and mango groves will burst into shoot,
and flowers will have a wonderful scent,
and bees will hum and murmur,
and birds will burst into sound,
and mild and fragrant breeze, will come
stunning the surface of the waters of canals,
and the stalks of corn will flutter,
and there will be enacted festivals
landscape
and all hindrances will be removed,
and the tide of the waters of Mangal Sagar will wash
away all the strains. . . .

" 'Ohe wah wah!' shouted Karnel Singh.
" 'Ohe Bale! Bale!' chimed Jarnel Singh.
" 'He is cockeyed, but seems to have a good voice!' said Ram Jawaya.
" 'A poet and don't know it!' said Babu Tarachand, B.A.
"Ohe, boys, sing with me in chorus, to the tune of mechanic Bharat Ram's dholak (drum).

"Oh, divine bestower of food inexhaustible,
be gracious unto us and give us your blessings,
thou Shakti, who incarnated herself as Kamli
in this village and who has now incarnated herself
as the power emanating from the giant dam of
Mangal. . . .

"And lo and behold! the boys sang with me in chorus. And then the village folk. . . . And the elders joined in slow embarrassed accents, but they forgot themselves, as the drum beat up the rhythm of the song. And as they accepted the tune of my lilt they also accepted the words. And they followed me to the Head of the District and agreed to move to Chandigarh. For, they really believed that the goddess, who had incarnated herself as Kamli in their village, had now reincarnated herself as electricity in the new dam."

Jibananda Das

THE BIRDS

SLEEP will not seal these eyes;
on a night of spring
I lie in bed awake
—far into the night.
There the noise of the sea
I hear; the skylight is overhead;
the birds chat with one another.
Where do they fly from here?
The fragrance of their wings is everywhere.

A flavour of spring pervades my body
and my eyes refuse to sleep;
through a window starlight creeps in;
the sea-born breeze
refreshes my heart.
They are sleeping all around.
Whose time for anchoring is it
on this side of the sea?

On that shore of the sea—on the far shore,
        On some arctic mountain,
          These birds used to dwell.
           Blizzard-chased
They have swooped upon the sea in hordes,
    Just as man swoops towards death's unconsciousness.
        Brown—golden—white—under sparkling
          wings
            They bear their lives
         In breasts like rubber-balls
          They bear their lives
—Just as the sea bears miles and miles of death
         As a similar unplumbed truth.

Somewhere life exists—the taste of life remains;
Somewhere there are rivers—not merely bitter sea-foam;
In those hearts like balls,
This much they know.
Leaving the cold behind them
They reach out to hope.
Then they wing away somewhere.
On flight they talk to their dear ones
—Of what do they talk?
It is time for their first eggs.

After much search amid the salt of the
sea
The smell of land has emerged,
Love and love's children,
And shelter,
A flavour—deep—deep.

Sleep will not seal these eyes
on this spring night;
from there the noise of the sea I hear;
the skylight is overhead;
the birds chat with one another.

Sitor Situmorang

MOTHER'S PILGRIMAGE TO PARADISE

The setting of this story is a mountainous area adjoining Lake Toba where a Lutheran community, engaged in fishing and vegetable growing, exists in a predominantly Islamic country.

MY mother at last died, one year after she had contacted a disease of the chest. At sixty-five her worn out and shrivelled body could no longer resist the relentless onslaught of the bacilla in her lungs. Medicines were rare and food hard to come by in the village, tucked far out of the way amongst the distant hills, not to say proper nursing care. And deep in my heart I was rather relieved when she died, for the agony she had to endure was too much to bear.

I was there by her side when she died but my presence came all by chance. Twice in the last few months before the fatal day I had received a cable. "Mother seriously ill, come," said the first one. I went immediately. But mother recovered later on. And the villagers gathered round her. "Look! Soon you will be well again. It was only the longing for your son," they whispered to comfort my mother, she for whom death had ceased to be a terror. This I could feel from her gaze. She and father, who was even more advanced in years, had between them nothing left in this world that was worth living for. My brother and I, their only two sons, lived away from them. The big house was empty and looked deserted. The ricefields were neglected. Only a tiny patch was cultivated, just enough to provide subsistence to my parents. They roamed the big house, mother once told me, as if it were one huge grave. And people had ceased to make their habitual calls, too. What was there to sit and talk about between a senile old man and his wife whose end was so near?

When a second cable arrived, I did not go. Somehow, I felt

that mother would keep alive for at least another six months. So instead I sent her some woollens. Mother's reply had been written on dictation by another, because she was illiterate and it was addressed to my eldest son telling him how jealous grandpa was. "Send some clothing for him too, of lakan,[1] as you did last time" it pleaded. And, as if to authorise this request the letter was decorated with father's very thumbprint. So a coat followed.

Now the third cable had come. This time I had some sort of premonition urging me to go. When I arrived at the village, all by myself, father greeted me with a disappointed look: "Why, only you!"

For years, my younger brother had given no indication of his whereabouts. At supper that evening father turned to me: "Haven't you been on good terms with your wife lately?" and I could feel the sullenness in his voice as he took himself off. "Travelling is expensive, father!" I still tried to advance. But he was not mindful of my argument and disappearing into the darkness he managed to say the last word: "After your mother dies, I shall not live much longer; and I have yet to see my grandchildren." Mother quietly smiled.

When I saw her the following day it never occurred to me that she would soon pass away. I began to feel myself a little disappointed at having come all the way in reply to the call; and nearly did I make for home again to my work in Java but, after some hesitation, I finally decided in favour of staying. It so happened that the new year was approaching which means that there were not many days left to Christmas. I knew mother would be only too happy if I would spend Christmas with her. With father, however, it was different. I think he never really realised the significance of his baptism which he had received when he was already forty. He still used to recite a mantera[2] whenever he or any member of his family got into extraordinary circumstances. Should one of his buffaloes fall victim to a tiger in the open fields among the hills he would burn a twig in the darkness of the night, chanting the proper manteras the while. This, he believed, would bring a slow death to the ferocious animal.

[1] Heavy cotton material.

[2] An incantation attributed with a supernatural power.

Mother was quite the opposite. Not only had she known no superstitions, but also she was a regular figure at the church; and such was she that the congregation, living as it did amongst a people who were largely irreligious, owed much to her for its unity. It is true that she was also known for her medicinal concoctions but these were prepared without the aid of manteras and, anyhow, the only thing she did was to spit into them.

During service the best place at the church was always reserved for father. It was a heavy solid chair facing the congregation. The people looked up to father as royalty even before the coming of the company and missions. That position was his by rights and so each time he attended church he would sit there in his chair lolling sleepily until the service was over.

On the second day of my visit the local padre called at our place. He knew that mother would not be in a condition to attend church service on Christmas Eve and so he had arranged for the congregation to celebrate the occasion in our house. Mother nodded her agreement in a manner as if there was nothing unusual about it.

Somehow, the idea did not appeal to me but I did not express my disapproval. I learnt that some people had been welcomed to spend the week-end in our house a few times before. These visits somehow gave to me the suggestion of a funeral procession. I recalled the sermons I had listened to in the past when I was only a child. The congregation listening in stupid and open-mouthed fashion while father lolled in his seat. The hymns, throaty and out of tune—human bodies seldom washed, reeking with sweat and dirt. And then the usual after-service gossips in front of the church. All these were brought vividly to my mind again. Of course, I had never noticed these things in quite the same way when a child. For then, there was the churchyard which to a boy is always and ever full of surprises. There were the shady kemiri tree, and the various fruit trees which crowded the yard—djambus, nangkas and mangoes; and the inviting stands of sugar canes in the adjoining garden of the padre. On Christmas Eve, the left-over candles were always mine for the taking. This was a privilege of mine other lads never disputed.

On taking leave the padre invited me to go with him to his house. As I had nothing much to do in that quiet little village I readily accepted. Besides, I was rather anxious to see the church which I had not visited for such a long time, ever since I had left the local primary school twenty years ago.

The way we took led through the village and some paddocks. It wasn't long before the padre took me to task: "Why didn't you come to church when you visited the village some months ago? You stayed well over a week, didn't you?" Whereupon, to evade the question, I enquired about things around the village. The padre changed the subject and questioned me about conditions in Java, the situation in Djakarta, and the possibility of war in Formosa. Did I think the present cabinet would last? Casually, I gave him all the information he wanted, and thus we finally entered the front garden of the church.

My first reaction was surprise. The church and the padre's house, how small they seemed to me now! The garden had apparently shrunk. The kemiri tree was not as tall as I thought, after all, nor was the spire which was still topped by the weathercock cut out of tin. But nothing else had changed. It was the same old wooden church. The same shabby looking thing! After a while, we entered the church, and I saw that it was still used as a school part of the time. Only now I counted a greater number of desks, and in one corner of the garden was a temporary shed. "There is room for three hundred pupils in the church and the shed together" the padre informed me. "We have four teachers, one is qualified," he added. I cast my eyes over the walls where numerous drawings done by the pupils were hanging. One was high up in a corner, of a buffalo shielding its master against the attack of a tiger. It was my drawing.

We were interrupted by the loud calls of the padre's wife who indicated that coffee was ready. "Coming," the padre shouted, and his voice reverberated over the hillsides. He paused to look the church over while his dog came playfully licking my foot. The whole atmosphere was pervaded with tranquillity which even the loud exchange could not disturb.

Over his coffee the padre later suggested that I take up the duty of reciting the Bible on the Christmas Eve. "Your mother would be very happy if you did," he said. I fixed my gaze on the torn picture hanging on the wall opposite—the picture of Christ on the Cross—as I politely declined: "No padre. I'd rather

159

M

not. We might better leave that for the elders to do." "The elders have to look after the congregation," the padre argued, "They have to light the candles, sing the hymns, and keep a watch on the children. The choir has to be conducted also. We have been practising your mother's favourite hymn: In the hands of God!"

I didn't like the whole management but remained silent. The padre seemed to take this silence as signifying consent on my part. "There will be cakes for the children," he beamed. "Old Hotang was kind enough to give a very substantial contribution. Do you recall him?"

Thus I set out upon the return walk with a sense of emptiness and misgiving. I could already see the people gathering in our house. How would mother take it, and where would she be put during the service? Her condition obviously would not permit her to sit up for long hours. Would she perhaps be able to sit through by reclining? With these thoughts I got home to find mother squatting on the floor in the centre room. She was preparing a drink with the condensed milk I had brought with me.

And finally came the long awaited Christmas Eve. Father got himself cleanly dressed early to retire to a solitary corner of the big hall and began to pound for himself some betel in his small silver mortar. Mother was being attended to by two girls I hardly knew. They led her to the divan which was perched against the wall on the far side of where father was sitting. The Christmas tree had been collected from the forest and was now standing in one corner, the candles still to be lit.

After making sure that mother was lying comfortably, the girls left to attend to themselves. There was only an hour left for the service to begin. I retreated into the seclusion of my room and planting myself on a chair, it wasn't long before I fell to musing. Now and again mother's cough interrupted the hiss of the petromax. I sat there in solitary contemplation, I don't know for how long, probably some half hour. But when I became conscious of myself again I noticed that mother's coughing had ceased. Nor could I hear the familiar noise of father's betel mortar. Perhaps he was now chewing the mixture between his toothless jaws. And the petromax hissed even more persistently. I sauntered out to see if everything was ready; father was still in his corner, and then I caught sight of mother lying on the divan under a cotton cover. "The old woman has fallen asleep," I thought, tip-toeing up to her for a look. I studied the lines on her face; the eyes set deep in the sockets; and the cheeks sunken. Then, further down, her chest. It looks very much like that of a dressed fowl, I thought. But, suddenly, I became aware that it was still. I touched her forehead and then lifted her eyelids. She was dead! For an instant I felt a lump sticking into my throat but it was only an instant as it was submerged in a strange sense of relief that descended on me. Instinctively, I looked at father who did not seem to be aware of anything amiss. How should I break the news to him? The guests would be coming soon; I pulled up the sheet over mother's face. It wasn't long before I could hear the first arrivals in front of the house. The padre and the elders, followed by the rest of the congregation. They flocked into the big hall and seated themselves down on the floor, cross-legged and conscious of the solemnity of the occasion, first filling up the space along the sides and corners; then gradually, casting shy glances about, they filled the centre as well.

"Is mother asleep?" the padre asked as he handed me the Bible.

"Yes."

"That's all right," he said. "When it's time to sing her favourite hymn we'll wake her up."

Then he began to put the congregation to order, the elders helping with their allotted tasks. At last, the hall was crowded with people. There was hardly a space left, save in a small circle where father was sitting. The school-children were grouped near the divan, their backs to mother, and facing the Christmas tree which stood at the opposite corner. The candles, of various colours, were lit now and they drew admiring "a-a-ahs" from the children. I stood there near the divan, tense, Bible in hand, and feeling awkward like a new preacher faced with the ordeal of his first sermon.

The service began with a prayer. And father was still busy pounding his betel mixture. Then came hymns, followed by my Bible reading. Was that really my voice? Hymns again. I lost all awareness of time, but I could feel the air reverberating:

"when Jesus came to Bethlehem in Judea. . . ."

The padre tiptoed to me and suggested that it was time to wake my mother up. Her favourite hymn was about to be sung!

I nodded and without any sign of suspicion he went back to his choir. But before it started he turned towards me with an enquiring glance, and once more I gave him a nod. Then it floated out: "In the hands of God! . . ." The words were lost to me. It was a hymn I had never heard before. Besides, the children near the divan and along the doorway were getting restless and had started chatting among themselves. Father, I noticed, had stopped pounding and was now staring at the Christmas tree with its candles flickering in melancholy.

The padre prayed: "O Lord, Thou Almighty and Merciful; to Thee we deliver our mother. In Thy care she dwells the earth, into Thy care she will return. Let her find refuge in paradise!" After the singing of Silent Night the service came to an end with a final prayer. Food was then served while the padre and the elders gathered around father. As he went across the room, the padre playfully pointed in the direction of mother: "Look, how soundly mother sleeps. We'll leave something for her to eat." I slipped into my room to put the Bible on my desk but returned soon to see the crowd.

"Come and sit near us," beckoned an old man. "Let's have a yarn. What's news in Djakarta?"

I excused myself and went out. Let them find out themselves about mother, I thought. But when I returned after some while I found that nobody seemed to have bothered mother in her sleep. One by one the guests departed and mother was still sleeping her peaceful sleep.

Later, after everybody had gone, I told father that mother was no more. For a moment he stopped pounding his betel mixture, as if paralysed, then he quietly asked me to call my uncle in. I took care to put out all the candles before I set out.

Some days later, when mother had been buried according to both custom and faith, I found my father standing in our spacious garden. He motioned me to follow him to a corner spot. I had no idea of what was in his mind, but when I came walking beside him he enquired: "Have you any money?"

The sudden question startled me and I wondered what he was up to but still I asked how much he needed.

"A thousand, two thousand, should be enough," he replied.

"What for, father?" I asked again, still following. We walked some distance before father stopped. He raised his arms and planted his hands on my shoulders. And, fixing his eyes on the lake down below he said: "I wish to be buried here. I want you to build a beautiful tomb for me. Of concrete. When I die I want you to move mother here, too."

"Why here, father?" was all I could say.

He released my right shoulder and turned to face the soaring mountain as he explained: "From here I can always have a clear view of the downs and the lake." I was silent.

The lake down below sparkled in the mid-day sun. Father moved away from me. I could see the padre struggling up the garden. "I heard you're leaving to-morrow. I hope you'll have a safe and pleasant trip!" he said as he approached me. After a pause he added: "You shouldn't be sad, you know! You see how much we here loved your mother. No one in this district was loved and respected as much as she was. And now she is with God!"

"Yes."

"Yes, I know that you are also a believer, although you intellectuals don't go to church any more. I have always been convinced that you follow in Christ's footsteps"—the padre seemed to be talking to himself—"Isn't it true?" he continued. "How is it possible for man not to believe in God! How is it possible that there should be no paradise!" he mumbled with something about him that reminded me of a goat.

"Quite. You're right padre," I responded, "naturally there is a paradise." The padre went without saying another word.

I walked up to the Christmas tree which was now nothing but dry twigs lying disconsolately in the garden. With one matchstick I managed to light it and soon it was all in flames, just like it used to be when I was a boy. The ashes scattered, and were swirled crazily by the wind in the direction of the bluish lake down below.

J. Moeljono

PEMUDA

I who was so anti-soldier once
Sit as a commander now
Playing with the lives of men.
How strange
Here in the bamboo grove
Without hate waiting
For the enemy . . .
—Friend? He whose comrade full of spite
—(Like so many of them)—
Has violated, killed and plundered?
Fire still smoulders in the fields
Where food had stood ripening.
What I experience part of me becomes;
I cannot detach myself from the whole.
So I fight, then loiter and snipe again.
How strange
To kill those ignorant
Over a word, an ideal.
Myself I was thrown into the fight
As a dice.
A stranger in the hamlets
I mix with the villagers,
Resigned, poor cattle.
Their weal and woe
Is in my heart,
But rice and rest I cannot give.
They will say in Jogja
He sacrificed his life.
If I die under the sun
They will take a solemn oath:
"Fight till the bitter end."

English has become the fashion
Yet Eliot after Du Perron!
But then in battle one dead the more
One dead the less
Does not matter in this glorious age!
With life uncertain everywhere
We gamble for a better lot.
Do not they do the same
With the world and God
From Stalingrad to Trumanstown?
L'après-midi d'un faunc.
How strange
To sit without aim
Without hate!

Indonesia

Chairil Anwar

DUSK IN THE HARBOUR

AT this hour there is no one seeking love
Among the godowns or in the old houses, nor yet
    among the stores
Of ropes and masts. Grounded ships and boats
Lie there abandoned hoping to be moored.

Rain precipitates the night. Faintly comes the rustle
Of kites' wings; and the soft sounds of day
Are hushed swimming to meet the end of sight.
    Nothing moves.
Land and sea lie sleeping and the waves dissolve.

Nothing moves. Nothing—only I, strolling
Along the headland, my vanquished hopes within me.
And as I reached the end—Good-bye!
The last sob smothered upon the beach.

165

S. W. R. D. Bandaranaike

THE HORROR OF MAHAHENA

*I*T was evening. I had had some strenuous sets of tennis at the club, and now, having returned home, I was stretched luxuriously on the lounge-chair on the veranda, after a refreshing warm bath, with a cool drink by my side and the evening paper in my hand.

I glanced through my newspaper. The sports news was uninteresting, no serious crimes had apparently been committed in the previous twenty-four hours, and the editorial contained some incredibly dull and ill-informed views on the sterling balances of the country.

I heard with relief the tinkle of the postman's bell. Among the letters there was one that bore the postmark of Mahahena, and the envelope was addressed in the neat, small handwriting of my cousin Leela.

Leela had done well at school, played a good game of tennis, and was very good looking. After she left school, she drifted into the usual life of our society ladies. She became a member of all the fashionable associations for social work, went to the August races in beautiful saris, and was duly photographed every year, attended regularly the insufferably dull parties given by leading politicians, and never missed the cinema.

At one time I was very much in love with her, and hoped she would eventually make up her mind to marry me, until that remarkable character Ananda Livera, appeared on the scene.

Ananda was a first-rate athlete, and had obtained a first class in science at the 'Varsity. He could have, if he chose, reached the front rank in politics or the bar, or even in the Civil Service —if in a moment of aberration he had sat for the Civil Service examination.

He did none of these things. He preferred to plant in the

wilds of Mahahena and shoot big game. Then, two years ago, he descended on Colombo in one of his rare visits to the capital, met Leela, fell violently in love with her, married her within a week, and disappeared with her to the solitude of Mahahena.

I was roused from my reverie by a familiar voice.

"I never thought, Richard, that you possessed the feminine trait of holding an envelope in your hand and dreaming, instead of opening it and reading its contents."

I looked up in some confusion, and saw John Ratsinghe standing in the portico, and looking at me quizzically with his eternal Jaffna cigar in a corner of his mouth.

I had not heard him approach, but then John had the feline habit of moving without a sound.

"Come in, John. Come in!" I cried with a laugh. "You will give me a heart attack one day with these silent, secret ways of yours."

I tore open the envelope and was soon absorbed in the extraordinary letter it contained.

My Dear Richard,

I do not know what you must be thinking of me! It is not that I have forgotten my old friends, but I was so busy at the start, and later have been so worried, that I was unable to write to you all for a long time. Dear Richard, I am in great trouble, and I know you will help me, if you can. Some mysterious and horrible deaths have occurred in this area lately. Within the past three months the bodies of a girl and two young lads were found in the jungle. There were, it seems, marks of violent struggles in each case, and the throats of the victims were mangled and torn. But there was, strange to say, hardly any blood on the bodies or the ground nearby. The cause of these deaths remains a mystery, in spite of all the efforts of the police and others. I believe they even got down some C.I.D. men from Colombo, who made enquiries for a number of days in vain. Ananda has been taking a great interest and helping the police in every way. I know he, too, is very worried, though he tries not to show it. The villagers are in a panic, and all sorts of wild stories are being spread. They say that the Riri Yakka is responsible for these

167

atrocities. I do not know what to think. I am not at all well myself, and am on the verge of a breakdown. Now, Richard, I have been reading your accounts of the exploits of your friend, Mr John Ratsinghe. Perhaps he may be able to help us? Do please bring him here for a few days. I do not want Ananda to know that I have written to you, as he may think I have been needlessly fussy. Just send me a wire that you are coming for the week-end with a friend. Ananda will be pleased, as he always likes company. You can come next Friday. Please, please do not fail me.

Yours very sincerely,

Leela Livera

I read this letter twice over, and handed it in silence to John. I watched him as he perused it, and could see that he was interested, even excited: he was chewing his cigar, and shifting it from one side of his mouth to the other—always a sure sign of interest in him.

"Most intriguing, Richard," he said, handing the letter back to me. "Quite a number of interesting possibilities. I suppose we had better go."

"Splendid! I shall send off that wire at once. What time on Friday can we start?"

"I have a small case in the magistrate's court on Friday morning," he replied. "We can leave after lunch about two. Will that suit you?"

"Oh yes. I shall call for you at your bungalow about two on Friday."

John Ratsinghe lay back in his seat with his eyes half closed, as we sped south to Mahahena on Friday afternoon.

He seemed to be dozing. Only once did he rouse himself to ask for Leela's letter, which he studied closely. It was past five when we reached the village. We turned into Mahahena Estate through the imposing gates at the entrance, and drove through the coconut plantation leading to the bungalow. We soon came in sight of it, situated on an elevation overlooking the sea. The evening sun had stained the white walls and pillars with a rosy glow.

Leela welcomed me effusively, and Ananda was no less cordial. I introduced John Ratsinghe to them, and at the mention of his name, Ananda's eyes lit up with interest.

"You are both very welcome," he said. "I am especially glad to see you, Ratsinghe. I have heard a great deal about you, and have often wanted to meet you. We lead rather a dull life here," he added with a laugh, "but I hope you won't be too bored."

"Not at all," murmured John politely. "In a place like this, I cannot imagine anyone being bored."

The boy, Elias, carrying our bags, preceded us with a cheerful smile, upstairs to our rooms. These appeared to be comfortable and airy, and were luxuriously furnished. They adjoined each other, and provided a glorious view over the sea. After tidying ourselves we went down to the garden, where tea was served.

"This is my ideal of a garden," remarked John, looking about him appreciatively. "A well kept lawn, a few flower beds, and large, shady flowering trees."

"That's what I always say," interposed Ananda, beaming with pleasure, "though Leela does not agree with me."

"I always like plenty of flowers in a garden," said Leela.

"Too much colour and beauty are apt to be cloying," returned John. "Now look at that rose. If it were surrounded by a profusion of its kind, the effect would be lost. I believe in individual beauty, and not in mass loveliness."

He walked up to the flower, a large, cream-coloured rose, which bloomed in solitary glory. He took it gently in his hand, and murmured: "What a lovely thing a rose is. And yet it will fade and die so quickly. What a waste of beauty and fragrance."

"I see you are a poet," said Ananda laughing.

"Oh, no," retorted John. "Richard is the poet. I am a most humdrum person."

"That rose is a rare variety," said Leela. "It is called . . ."

"Stop," interrupted John. "Please don't spoil everything by telling me its botanical name. I am sure it must be something, something, *gloriosa*. I hate these jaw-breaking Latin names. After all, what does it matter what it is called?"

We all laughed. The feeling of strain and tension, which I

169

had sensed in both Ananda and Leela, seemed to ease, and we chatted pleasantly, till the sun sank in a glory of gold and crimson, and the sky darkened into violet.

After dinner we made up a four at bridge. Both Ananda and Leela were preoccupied and played badly. John, who is a good player, hates nothing more than an inattentive one, and I could see a look of relief on his face, when after a couple of rubbers, Ananda rose from the table.

"I hope you will excuse me," he said. "It is time I went on my usual round: I have a look round every night to see that the watchers are up and about their duties."

We went up, and John came into my room in a few minutes puffing happily at one of his foul cigars.

I leaned out of the window, drinking in the beauty of the scene outside. There was strong moonlight, as it was only three days before full-moon.

"What a lovely, peaceful night it is," I said. "Surely this is not a place where dreadful deeds are done."

"That's just where you are mistaken," he rejoined. "You take life from books, without trusting to your own experience, and your own eyes and ears. In real life, the true horror consists of the frequent juxtaposition of peace and violence, good and evil, the ordinary and the extraordinary. A night like this gives me the creeps far more than a violent storm would."

As though in justification of his words, at this moment there reached us through the still air the sound of howling, mournful and desolate, in the distance. It was taken up by another and still another, till the air vibrated and throbbed with it.

John turned and looked at me enquiringly.

"It is only a pack of jackals," I announced with some satisfaction at my superior knowledge. "After all, jackals must be fairly common in these jungle areas."

"Jackals?" he said. "I see. I expect the jackal in our country can be taken as a substitute for the wolf in others. You will probably recollect, Richard, that the wolf is an animal frequently mentioned in the vampire legend. It is a sort of familiar of the vampire."

The howling continued for some minutes, the sound now

receding, now approaching, with a persistence and intensity that was quite unusual in my experience.

Suddenly it ceased.

We smoked awhile in silence, till again the quiet of the night was rent by a cry of the most extreme fear and dread that I had ever heard.

"In heaven's name, what's that, John?" I cried.

"Obviously a human being, this time," he said quietly. "Come on. Let's go down."

We went downstairs, and saw a group of servants huddled in the hall, and talking in frightened whispers.

"What's all this about?" demanded John.

"We do not know, sir," replied the boy Elias.

"Where's your master?"

"He has not returned yet."

We discussed what should be done, and decided to wait until Ananda returned. About twenty minutes later, we heard the approach of hurried footsteps, and Ananda burst into the hall, dusty and perspiring.

"Did you hear that cry?" he asked us. "I heard it while going round the estate, and rushed back to pick up some servants and go to investigate."

"We heard it all right," replied John. "Where did it come from, do you think?"

"It is difficult to judge distances by sound on these still nights," he said. "It was certainly not on the estate. It might be anything from a quarter to one mile away. You two had better come with me. Let us take my car and go up the main road. The cry seemed to come from that direction. Elias, bring my double-barrelled gun and some S.G. cartridges. Ask the driver to bring the car."

"I hope Leela has not been alarmed," I said with some anxiety.

"I don't think so," replied Ananda. "She has not been able to sleep well lately, and the doctor has prescribed a sleeping draught which she takes every night. However, I shall go up and see." He returned in a few minutes and announced with relief that she was sleeping soundly.

We crowded into his Hillman, the three of us behind, and Elias and another servant in front with the driver, and started off.

"I did not want to worry you with our little troubles on your short holiday, Ratsinghe," Ananda remarked as we went. "But as you happen to be here, I might tell you that there have been some queer happenings in this area recently. I only hope that the cry we heard does not mean that another tragedy has occurred. I sincerely hope you can be of some help to us in unravelling these mysteries."

"I shall of course be delighted to do what I can," said John and was about to question him further, when he cried out to the driver to stop. We had gone only about a quarter of a mile. Ananda jumped out of the car and went to the drain by the road and peered into it. We followed him, and saw a huddled form, lying in the drain. Ananda pulled an electric torch out of his pocket, and switched on the light. We saw the body of a young man lying on his side.

"I thought I saw something in the drain. That is why I stopped the car," he explained.

We gently turned the body over, and found that the man was dead. The throat was severely mangled, and the face was convulsed in a look of dreadful fear. There appeared to be no other injuries.

"We heard a pack of jackals," I said. "I wonder whether they are responsible for this."

"It is possible," Ananda replied. "There are a lot of jackals about just now. They seem to be famished, and are much bolder than usual."

"There are no other injuries except on the throat," John observed.

"Remember this is by the roadside," said Ananda. "The jackals may have been frightened away by some sound they heard. I know this boy. He is called Bempy, and he lived with his parents about a mile further on. Will you wait here, while I go in the car and bring the police inspector, and also inform the parents?"

John and I agreed, and Ananda went off on his errand.

"Well, well," said John. "We are now in the thick of things." He stooped over the body and examined it carefully. He was clearly puzzled, but refused to express any opinion.

Soon Ananda returned accompanied by a police officer, two constables and an old villager.

"This is sub-inspector Edirisinghe," Ananda introduced his companion. "Edirisinghe, these gentlemen are Mr Richard Perera and Mr John Ratsinghe, who are staying with me for the week-end."

We shook hands.

While the inspector examined the body, Ananda called up the old man.

"This is the boy's father," he informed us. "Silindu, tell us what you know." "Aiyo! sir," said Silindu, in a broken voice, "I know nothing. Bempy was a witness in an assault case, and went this morning to the Indura magistrate's court to give evidence. As you know, it is about fifteen miles away. I was not worried that he was getting late to return. I thought he might stay at Indura for the night and return in the morning."

"Did you not hear a cry?" asked John.

"Yes. I did, but did not pay much attention to it. I was thunder-struck, when Livera Hamu came and told us that Bempy was lying injured."

"I am afraid he is dead, Silindu," said Ananda gently.

"Not . . . not like the others?" faltered old Silindu.

"We are not sure," said Ananda. "But it may be so, Silindu." The old man broke into loud lamentation. "Aiyo! aiyo! Is there no way to save us from this curse? We shall all have to leave the village and go far away."

The inspector, having finished his examination of the body, came up to us.

"I shall want your statements, gentlemen," he said. "I shall leave a P.C. on guard here. The doctor will come early in the morning, and the inquest will be held later in the day. I shall notify you the time as soon as possible."

It was now nearly 1 a.m. I, for one, was very glad to tumble into bed when we got back.

I confess, with some shame, that I slept soundly and dream-lessly, haunted by no nightmare visions of vampires or other monsters. I was awakened by a loud knock at my door, and Elias

173

came in with a steaming cup of tea and a cheerful smile on his face.

"What time is it?" I asked sleepily.

"Seven o'clock, sir."

"Are the others up yet?"

"I have taken a cup of tea to Mr Ratsinghe. Master went out early, to be present when the doctor examined the body of poor Bempy."

"What do the village people say about these deaths, Elias? I understand there were three other similar deaths earlier."

"They first thought it was some wild animal. But now many say that it is the Riri Yakka. They are preparing to perform a *thoila* ceremony to appease the demon."

He left my tea and went out. Just then John came into my room. He was dressed, and puffing vigorously at a Jaffna.

"John," I said, "Elias has been telling me that the people think the Riri Yakka has caused these deaths and that they are preparing to perform a *thoila*. You remember, Leela also said something about this in her letter. What exactly is the Riri Yakka?"

"The Riri Yakka in Ceylon corresponds in many respects to the vampire legend of Central Europe and the Balkans. The ancient verses, referring to this demon, say that he was the son of a king of a land to the south of Lanka and a *Yakkini* called Lethali. When he grew up, his craving for human blood was so insatiable that he appeared before the Lord of the Demons and demanded permission to satisfy his lust. This was granted, and since then he has ranged this land picking his victims from time to time, now here, now there. He is supposed to have the power of taking eighteen different forms, one of which, it is interesting to note, is that of a bat a span and six inches in size. The verses also prescribe the *thoila* ceremony to appease and exorcise the demon. It is no surprise to me that the villagers should ascribe these deaths to the Riri Yakka."

I was soon dressed, and we went down. Leela was already down and we went into breakfast. She was looking pale and ill.

"Richard," she said, "I have heard all about what happened last night." She began to cry quietly. "When will this nightmare end? Mr Ratsinghe, you must, you must, help us."

174

"I know what a strain it must be for you, Mrs Livera," John said gently. "But please be brave. Everyone is doing his best, and I promise you that I shall do all in my power."

"Forgive me for breaking down," she said with greater composure. "Please count on my help, too, Mr Ratsinghe, if there is anything I can do. It is a great comfort to have you both here at this time."

"That's the right spirit, Leela," I returned, assuming a cheerfulness I was far from feeling. "You can count on John."

"What delicious hoppers," remarked John. "I prefer hoppers to anything else for breakfast. Mrs Livera, I'll tell you the best way to eat them: you must have them with butter, cheese, sambol and plantains."

"What a mixture!" laughed Leela. "But I shall certainly try your recipe." We all did, and found it excellent. But I noticed John looking at my cousin from time to time with a slightly puzzled frown.

When we had finished breakfast, he spoke to her in a casual tone. "By the way, Mrs Livera, you look very pale and ill. Besides my other qualifications I am something of a physician as well. Besides the worry you must naturally be feeling, are you ill in any way?"

"I don't think so," she said doubtfully. "The doctor says there is nothing the matter with me. My nerves are in pieces owing to these troubles, and I cannot sleep well at nights. The doctor has given me a sleeping draught, but sometimes I have hardly the strength to get out of my bed in the morning. I feel so weak. And then, there are some tiresome insects from whose bites I have been suffering lately, even the mosquito net does not seem to keep them out. My throat is still sore with their bites."

John stiffened into sudden interest.

"Throat," he said. "May I have a look?"

Leela obediently bent back her head, and John, rising from his chair, stooped over her, and closely examined what appeared to me to look like some slightly inflamed marks of an insect bite. He came back to his seat without a word, and his face had a strangely drawn and haggard look.

"I wonder if you mind my smoking one of my cigars?" he asked. "It is an incurably bad habit of mine, Mrs Livera."

175

N

"Not at all," she replied. "My father used to smoke them continually."

"Oh, there's Ananda," said Leela, as we heard footsteps in the hall. "Come along, Ananda, and have some breakfast."

"You lazy people," said Ananda to John and me, taking a seat and helping himself to a hopper. "I was up at six and went to the autopsy. There were no other injuries besides that on the throat. The jugular vein had been severed. The inquest is at ten. Both of you are wanted by the inspector. I told him I would bring you along."

John was in a thoughtful mood, and spoke very little. We went to the inquest. The inquirer into sudden deaths was a small, elderly man called Weerasinghe. The proceedings did not take long. Ananda, John and I gave evidence briefly: we mentioned the cry we heard, the discovery of the body, and the information given to the inspector. We added that we had also heard the howling of a pack of jackals. The inspector and Silindu also gave evidence.

The doctor, the local D.M.O., stated that he examined the body, and found injuries on the throat; the jugular vein had been severed. The injuries seemed to have been caused by the teeth of some animal. There were no other injuries.

The inquirer, in his finding, held that death was caused by some wild animal, probably a jackal. He called up the inspector. "This is very unsatisfactory, inspector. This is the fourth death that has occurred in the past three months under similar circumstances. The precise cause of these deaths has not been discovered, and no effective steps have been taken, as far as I can see, to prevent such happenings in the future."

"We are doing all we can," replied the inspector. "We are organising nightly patrols. The S.P. has sent a number of P.Cs. who, with village volunteers, will patrol the village every night. We have also offered a reward for every jackal that is destroyed. I think sir, there will be no more of these deaths."

"I hope not," replied the inquirer.

We started on our way back. John was in one of his silent moods. Only once John roused himself to ask Ananda: "Let me see—today is Saturday, full-moon is on Monday. Have you observed that the other deaths occurred about full-moon time?"

Ananda thought for a moment.

"Why, now that I come to think of it, I believe they did," he replied in surprise. "What made you ask?"

"Just an idea," said John, and relapsed into silence. We returned in time for lunch. At lunch, Ananda told us: "The villagers are having a *thoila* tonight. Something about the Riri Yakka. I think it all rot, of course, but it may be interesting to see. Would you people like to go?"

"I should like to see it very much," John said. "And I am sure Richard would, too. I have never seen such a ceremony before."

"We shall have to leave about five-thirty," said Ananda. "The *thoila* starts at six. It will go on till six in the morning, but we need not wait all that time."

We went up to our rooms after lunch. John, pleading a headache did not come down for tea.

"All the servants and the estate workers want to go to the *thoila*," said Ananda as we set out. "I think they might go, Leela. I have told Elias to remain in the house. He is, of course, rather disappointed, but it can't be helped." We reached the village, and found most of the inhabitants assembled in an open space.

The headman and old Silindu came up and escorted us to chairs from which we could get a good view of the ceremony.

"You know all about these ceremonies, Silindu," said Ananda. "You had better remain and explain everything to us."

The old man squatted on the ground, and pointed to a rectangular enclosure surrounded with sticks, decorated with tender coconut leaves.

"That is the *vidiya*," he said, "where the *thoila* will be performed. And that," pointing to its entrance, "is the *ile*. The large branches you see planted on either side are *goraka*."

"What is that?" asked John, pointing to a small platform in one corner of the enclosure.

"That," said Silindu, "is the *pideniya*. You will notice a number of jak leaves, folded funnel-wise. They are the *gotu* or offerings to the *yakka*. One contains the blood of a red cock, another five varieties of seeds, the third raw flesh, the fourth raw fish, the

177

fifth rice, prepared in a special manner, and the sixth sweets. There is also a king-coconut."

The villagers, men, women and children squatted expectantly all round the enclosure. Soon, with much din and hubbub, the *kattadiya* entered the *vidiya*. He was dressed in a red cloth and a red scarf was tied about his head. He bore in his hands two blazing torches consisting of rags, tied round sticks.

The drummers, who were outside the *vidiya*, started their weird music, while the *kattadiya* began a frenzied dance. He turned in various directions, chanting in a loud voice.

"He is summoning the Riri Yakka," explained Silindu. "While doing so, he has to turn to the eight points of the compass."

I looked about me. It was a scene I shall not easily forget. In the distance, the deep shadows of night, dappled with moonlight; closer the stronger light of the torches, shining on the eager, absorbed faces of the squatting villagers: the throbbing, insistent, sinister music of the drums, which mingled horribly with the distant howling of jackals in the jungle; the grotesque and passionate dancing of the *kattadiya*, and, dominating all, the rise and fall of his chanting voice. After some time, the chant subtly changed in tone to an incantation.

"He is now muttering the *mantara*, requesting the *yakka* to accept the offerings, and spare the people of this village," explained Silindu.

We listened for a while longer, when Ananda glanced at his watch. "It is nearly ten," he said. "I think we might slip away. The *thoila* will go on till morning."

We made our way quietly to our car, bidding Silindu and the headman, good-bye.

"I hope our troubles will now be at an end," said Leela. "Mr Ratsinghe, do you believe that such ceremonies can be effective?"

"Why not?" said John. "I am not modern enough to despise these old customs. After all, what people have believed in and practised through the ages must have some justification. But, of course," he added with a smile, "a lot will naturally depend on whether the Riri Yakka is the real culprit."

We sat down to a cold dinner. John, who had regained his cheerfulness, talked entertainingly on a variety of subjects. He studiously avoided any reference to the one subject that was

178

really obsessing our minds. After dinner, Ananda called Elias whose disappointed and crest-fallen air we had all observed with some amusement, and said: "Elias, you may go to the *thoila* now if you like."

I was awakened next morning by a thumping at my door, and Ananda burst in. "Richard," he cried, "something terrible has happened. Poor Elias . . . like the others."

"What?" I shouted, springing out of my bed. "What's that you say?"

"Labourers, coming to work this morning, discovered the body of Elias under some bushes on the land. They came running here and gave me the information."

"Have you told John?"

"Yes."

I quickly got into some clothes. John was also ready, and we went to the scene guided by one of the labourers who had discovered the body. At one end of the estate, away from the main road, the body was lying under some bushes. This part of the property adjoined Crown jungle and was rather isolated. The injuries were the same as those on Bempy. We stood, looking sadly at the body. Elias had been a cheery lad and, from the little I saw, an efficient and willing servant. Ananda was obviously very moved.

John suddenly bent down, and looked long and earnestly at the face. He got up with a grunt, but said nothing.

Reverently we covered the corpse with a cloth and retraced our steps to the house in silence.

"I do not know how to break the news to Leela," said Ananda. "She will be terribly sorry."

"Leave it to me," replied John curtly. "Ananda, ring up the police, and also inform the boy's parents."

As Ananda went off to carry out these requests, Leela came downstairs. She looked from one of us to the other quickly and said: "Is there anything wrong?"

"Mrs Livera, please come here," said John, taking her gently by the arm. He led her to a sofa in the sitting-room. I followed them, but remained discreetly in the background.

"You remember you promised me to be brave," he reminded

179

her. "I know you will keep that promise. It is the only way you can help me."

"I shall try to," she responded, with trembling lips. "Tell me what has happened."

"Elias has been found dead. Like the others. I am desperately sorry this has happened, Mrs Livera. But I promise you that this is the end. I swear to you by all that is holy that this curse shall cease."

I looked curiously at John. Never before had I seen him in such deadly earnest; never before had he said such a thing, while he was still working on a case. His face was lined and haggard, and his mouth was set in a hard line.

"Mr Ratsinghe," said Leela. "I trust you implicitly. I shall do whatever you say."

"Thank you," said John, his face relaxing.

"I would only ask you to continue to trust me. Do not be surprised at anything I may say or do: just fall in line with any suggestions I may make."

That Sunday was a sad day for us all. The enquiry was held without delay, as well as the autopsy and the inquest. The body of poor Elias was handed over to his relations that evening for burial. At dinner Ananda told us: "I am organising a jackal hunt for tomorrow morning. I shall see that none of these foul beasts are left in the jungles round here. Would you two like to come?"

"Richard always enjoys a hunt," replied John. "I do not shoot but I shall gladly come with you."

Next morning we were out at dawn. Ananda had mobilised his labourers and a number of villagers to act as beaters. He lent me a gun and we all walked together into the jungle that lay behind the estate.

"The jackals are not likely to break cover into the estate," Ananda informed us. "There is fairly open scrub land on the other side of this jungle belt. Richard and I will take up our stand at suitable points. The beaters will give us fifteen minutes to get there, and then start beating from this end."

We walked briskly through the jungle and, in about fifteen minutes emerged into fairly open, scrub country. There Ananda asked one of his men to lead me to a certain point, while he himself went off in the opposite direction.

I soon reached the place that had been indicated to me, and took up my stand behind some bushes. John, who had attached himself to me, made himself comfortable on the ground and lit one of his Jaffnas.

Before long I heard the sound of the beaters in the distance, advancing through the jungle. A slight rustle on the fringe of the thick undergrowth attracted my attention. Two jackals broke cover, and with a right and left I got both. Soon I heard two shots from Ananda.

As the beaters approached us, two more jackals trotted out. I bagged them both. I heard two more shots from Ananda's direction. I saw five or six more beasts break cover, but they were too far away, and I did not fire. Eventually the beaters emerged from the jungle, and were delighted when they saw the four animals stretched out on the ground.

"You have done well, sir," said one. "Let us go and see how Ananda hamu has got on."

We went in the direction of Ananda, and saw him coming towards us.

"I got three of them," he shouted. "What about you?"

"I bagged four," I replied with pardonable pride.

"As for me, I had far more fun, watching a hawk wheeling in the sky," remarked John. "I expect he is waiting impatiently for our departure, to start his breakfast on one of the jackals."

As we returned through the forest, John suddenly uttered a cry of pain. We all stopped. He held up his left hand and we saw a few drops of blood trickling down a finger. "I brushed my hand against some sharp thorns," he said.

Ananda looked concerned. "My dear fellow," he said, "some of these thorns are poisonous. Let me suck out the wound." He applied his lips to the injury. "There," he said. "It will be all right now. Just dab it with a little iodine when we get back." John swayed, as though he were dizzy.

"What's the matter?" I asked.

"I feel rather faint," he muttered, "let's rest for a few minutes."

He sat down on a fallen tree trunk, and we stood by, lighting cigarettes.

181

"Don't tell me you are one of those people who faint at the sight of a few drops of blood," bantered Ananda.

I must confess that I blushed for my friend. "Probably a touch of the sun," I hastened to explain. "John is not much of an out-of-doors man, you know."

After a few minutes, John declared that he felt better, and we returned without further mishap.

At lunch, John took us all by surprise. "I had forgotten all about some rather important work I have in Colombo. I am awfully sorry, I shall have to run up there today. There is nothing much I can do here at present, in any case. I should think that the patrols that have been organised, and your destruction of the jackals, to say nothing of the *thoila*, should have the desired effect. If there is any further trouble, Livera, please let me know and I shall come at once."

There was a look of dismay on Leela's face, but she said nothing, no doubt remembering her promise to John earlier.

"If you must go, I suppose it cannot be helped," said Ananda. "But we were hoping you would stay a little longer. I can, of course, see your point that perhaps it is a stalemate at the moment. I shall certainly let you both know if there are any further developments."

"Don't you think, Ananda, that it will be a good thing for Leela to get away from here for a short holiday. She does not seem well, and these happenings are obviously affecting her nerves," I ventured.

"I quite agree with you," said Ananda. To my utter surprise, John seemed to be displeased at my suggestion.

"I think it would be better for her to remain," he said. "At least for the present. If she went away now, she would probably worry far more than if she were here. Later she might consider it, if necessary."

I said nothing, though I could not help feeling that the reason he advanced was rather weak.

We set out soon after lunch. I was bursting with curiosity, but knew by experience that it was no use questioning John, until he chose to explain. When we had gone about thirty miles, he suggested we should turn into the nearest resthouse.

"I thought you wanted to get to Colombo as soon as possible," I said.

"Oh, there is no hurry," he replied airily.

There was a resthouse a few miles further on. When we got there, John calmly asserted that he would like a siesta, and asked the boy to take out our bags.

"You are a most exasperating fellow, John," I said. "Why on earth you take a delight in all this mystery, I cannot understand."

"For the good reason, Richard," he replied gravely, "that I don't know myself what is going to happen. I am taking a great risk, and making a dangerous experiment."

After that there was nothing more I could say. I stretched myself on a lounge-chair on the veranda, and tried to read a book. My mind, however, was seething with doubts and speculations, and I could not at all concentrate on what I was reading.

About four, John emerged from his room, looking indecently cheerful, and refreshed. We had our tea and went for a stroll along the beach. I was in a fever of excitement, and though John tried to keep up a conversation, I was in no mood for small talk. He, too, soon relapsed into silence.

After dinner, we sat about for some time pretending to read the evening papers. I could see John looking at his watch from time to time.

Suddenly he got up. "Ten-thirty," he said. "People go to bed early in the country." He paid the bill, the bags were put back into the car, and we started off.

"Tell the driver to turn back, Richard," he said. "We are returning to Mahahena."

When we reached Mahahena, he ordered the car to draw up on the side of the road, about a quarter-mile from the entrance to Mahahena Estate. He opened his bag and took out of it an electric torch and a short rubber truncheon.

"I never carry a revolver," he observed. "I find this much more useful."

The driver was asked to put out the car lights, and await our return.

"Come on, Richard," he said.

We entered the estate, and, avoiding the drive, approached the house.

"I noticed a ladder in this out-house," he whispered. "We shall need it."

We found the ladder, and I shouldered it.

We then stealthily drew up to the house. There was, fortunately, no one about.

"Out patrolling, no doubt," John said laconically. We moved round the house, John scanning the windows of the rooms upstairs carefully. Suddenly he stopped, and motioned to me to place the ladder against the wall. He ascended first, and I followed. When he reached the window, opposite which the ladder had been placed, he fumbled with it, and it opened with a slight click. He put his leg over the sill, and dropped soundlessly into the room. I followed, and found that we were in Leela's bedroom.

She was in bed and her rhythmic breathing showed that she was fast asleep. John looked about, and seeing a curtain, which screened a wall-cupboard, beckoned to me, and we both concealed ourselves behind it. After a time we heard footsteps. John stiffened and put his hand on my arm. I heard the door open quietly, and the footsteps advance into the room. There was a pause, and then a slight gurgling sound. John flung the curtain aside, and sprang forward. I caught a glimpse of a figure bending over the bed.

It turned its head, and my hair stood on end as I saw the face of Ananda in the moonlight. His lips were curled in a snarl and his mouth was dabbed in blood. John brought his rubber truncheon down on his head with a thud, and he collapsed in a heap on the floor. John bent for a moment over the still sleeping form of Leela.

"She has not taken much harm," he said with relief.

He searched about the bed. "Ah, I thought so," he said, picking up something and putting it in his pocket.

"Come, Richard, help me to carry him to his room."

I took Ananda by the shoulders, John took him by the legs, and we carried him to his room and laid him on his bed.

John sat down in a chair, pulled out his handkerchief and wiped his face. I noticed idly that it was streaming with sweat. He then extracted a cigar from his pocket and lighted it. I stood by benumbed and dazed, my mind in a whirl of confusion. Ananda was breathing stertorously.

After a few minutes he groaned and sat up. He glanced at us wildly, and passing his hand over his face, looked at it. It was stained with blood. Some realisation of the position must then have dawned on him. He buried his head in his arms and sobbed bitterly.

It is a terrible thing to see a man crying. After a while, the sobbing ceased, and Ananda looked up at John.

"I suppose you know all," he said in a strangled voice.

"Not all," John said gently, "but a great deal. How did you get this craving for human blood?"

He thought a moment. "I was once after a wild buffalo," he began. "I shot it after a long and tiring stalk. While the shikaris went to cut a pole on which to sling the head, I took out my hunting knife to sever the animal's head. As I cut, the blood began to pour out. I was very thirsty. More in fun than otherwise, I drank some of it. It seemed to me delicious. After that, whenever I was not observed, I used to drink the warm, fresh blood of animals.

"Once when I was shooting alone in the jungle, I saw a lad picking firewood. An overwhelming impulse seized me. I caught him in my arms, and buried my teeth in his throat. It was soon over."

"You were responsible for all these deaths here?"

"Yes."

"What about Elias?"

"After we returned that night, I thought of taking my usual round, to see that everything was all right. You remember I had given Elias permission to go to the *thoila*. As I went out I saw him going. Again the craving came over me. I knew that there was no one about, as the others were all at the *thoila*."

"And now," said John with some hesitation, "about your wife?"

Ananda covered his face with his hands. "Oh, it was terrible," he moaned. "I loved her passionately, and often when the craving was on me, I thought of shooting myself, rather than doing her the smallest harm . . . But I was careful not to hurt her much . . . only a few drops of blood."

185

"You used a needle, in her case, didn't you? I found this on her bed." John pulled a needle out of his pocket.

"Yes."

Ananda raised his head with sudden resolution. "And now," he said, "there is only one thing to be done. Please ring up the police."

John rose slowly from his chair and placed his hand on his shoulder.

"There is another way, Livera," he said. "There are others to be considered in this matter. You are a big game hunter. Sometimes it is a dangerous sport."

When we reached Colombo I dropped John at his bungalow and went on home.

Two days later, when I opened the morning paper, a headline caught my attention.

Death of Well-known Sportsman

Information has just been received of the tragic death of the well-known sportsman, Mr Ananda Livera. It would appear that he went out after a rogue elephant. Although he fired a number of shots at the beast, none of them succeeded in bringing the elephant down. The animal is then said to have charged him and crushed him to death.

I called for my car and, taking the paper, rushed to John's bungalow.

"Sit down, Richard," he said calmly. He settled back in his chair and carefully lighted his Jaffna. "And now, for the long-due explanations I owe you.

"When I read Mrs Livera's letter to you I was very interested. Clearly this was a case out of the ordinary. I kept my mind open, however, even to possibilities of the supernatural. The three deaths that had taken place earlier could hardly yield any really valuable data, but we were fortunate in the occurrence of a case on our very first night at Mahahena. The death of Bempy shortly after the howling of the pack of jackals provided a complication. I had to consider seriously the possibility that, after all, the jackals had been responsible for these deaths. The fact, however, that the body was not eaten at all was significant. I can hardly imagine a ravenous pack of jackals behaving like that. The explanation that they may have been frightened away before they started feeding was rather weak. But the strongest point was the absence of blood, although the jugular vein had been severed. It would appear then, that whatever caused the death, it was not likely that the jackals did so, and that it was some creature that only drank the blood.

"What we knew about the previous cases confirmed this view. Now, what is the animal that does this? The vampire bat is supposed to, but no bat could have caused deaths like these. I began to wonder whether the vampire or Riri Yakka of the legends was really abroad at Mahahena. But I was loath to accept any such theory, if a natural explanation was at all possible. It struck me that there were still probably human beings who ate human flesh. Why should there not be human beings, who drank human blood? If that were so, then a rational explanation was possible, without the need for any supernatural trappings.

"I then set about considering who it might be. The so-called insect bites on Mrs Livera's throat helped to narrow the field greatly. When I examined the 'bites', it was clear that they were not caused by any insect; they looked rather like the punctures caused by the needle of a hypodermic syringe. Her paleness and weakness were indications of loss of blood. It was not too far-fetched to think that her condition was not unconnected with the other happenings.

"It was then someone connected with Mrs Livera, and having access to her. My suspicions began to turn in the direction of Ananda. He was out at the time Bempy died, remember; he also had the easiest access to Mrs Livera, particularly at night. Remember further that she was taking sleeping draughts, and would not know what had happened. Elias' death still further confirmed these suspicions. I looked at his face closely, because I saw there, not the appearance of fear we noticed on the face of Bempy, but one rather of wonder. It was possible to think that his assailant was one he knew well.

"My suspicions became certainty at the jackal hunt. I deliberately gashed my finger, to try a little experiment. It worked, Richard. You did not notice, but I did, that when he sucked out the blood from the wound, he did not spit it out. Rather strange, especially as he had just told us that the thorns might be poisonous. I also saw the look of gloating on his face as he sucked out

187

the blood. I was now certain, and the certainty was horrible. It is that which made me feel faint.

"What was I to do? I had to bring home the guilt to him, and that quickly. If I taxed him with it, he would probably have denied the charge flatly, and I had no means of proving it. I had to catch him in the act. It was here that I took a grave risk. I deliberately used Mrs Livera as a decoy. Monday was full-moon day. I elicited the fact that these attacks occurred during this time. The moon, Richard, affects some people, and animals, as we know. Well, the craving was likely to be still strong in Ananda. He could scarcely look abroad, as everything was now on the qui-vive, and the area was being patrolled. But Mrs Livera still remained. You know what happened after that."

Vance Palmer

JOSIE

*I*T was drowsy in school that afternoon. We woke up only when the teacher stopped talking and went out on to the veranda to speak to a boy who had ridden up on a bicycle. Those who could see from the back seats said it was young Paton, who worked in the brickfields near the station. Young Paton, Josie's brother! There was a buzz of whispering, a scuffle among the class standing round the blackboard, all wanting to get a look out of the window. No one was tall enough without standing on the teacher's chair.

When he came back he had taken off his spectacles, and his eyes had the pale, uneasy look we always noticed in them when the inspector was about or someone's father was coming to speak to him.

"You can go back to your seats," he said to the class on the floor.

And then, rapping with his cane on the table and calling for silence, he began in a queer voice that seemed to come from the back of his throat, "I have some sad news for you, children. Death—it is a solemn thought—death has visited our little community for the first time since this school was opened. You will be grieved to hear that your little playmate, Josie Paton, passed away this morning. There will be no more school this afternoon. Those of you who haven't had your homework already set can leave it till Monday."

There had never been such quiet in the school before. No one wanted to move; no one wanted to look round. Even the small children in the front desks sat as still as if they were holding their breath to listen to the clock tick. We had nearly forgotten about Josie. She had been taken off to the township hospital three weeks before because the nurse said there was no room for anyone sick down at Paton's. She would be away till the next holidays, they told us.

It wasn't till we had marched out and were getting our bags from the hooks on the veranda that our voices came back, and then only in whispers.

"It's dip. The nurse said it was dip."

"She never. She on'y said it might be."

"They can't tell at first. You get a sore throat and then it swells."

"I know. It swells till you can't swaller, and then you choke."

"Dip! It ain't catching, is it?"

"Not catching? Oo, listen; he says it ain't catching!"

Everyone wanted to go past Paton's on the way home, yet not to go too near. There it stood by the edge of the railway, a little slab-sided place, with no gutters on the tin roof and a chimney half brick and half wood. There was a dog-leg fence round it and a pepper-tree drooping over the wood heap. No garden. Paton was a ganger on the line, and grew his vegetables on a patch inside the wires, like the other navvies. They brought home sacks of them when they came home from work. And they all lived in bare little houses like this one of Paton's, with no paddocks or yards, though usually there were a few spindly lemon- or peach-trees at the back.

Most of us had passed the place that morning, but now a change had come over it. It had grown quiet and strange; even the fowls, rooting in the dust, looked as if they might know something we didn't. An axe stood fixed in the chopping block near the door. The broken shutter over the front window seemed like a squinting eye.

And though the place was shut up we had a feeling that Josie was somewhere inside. Lurking there as she had a way of doing under the school veranda when the teacher had given her leave to go out. How well we remembered her sitting in the sand, letting handfuls of it filter through her fingers as she hunted for the ant lions that squatted at the bottom of their little pits, and ready to make a face at anyone who caught her!

"Where's Josie Paton?" the teacher was always asking. "Didn't she answer the roll this morning?"

And one of us would be sent out to look for her.

No one had ever liked Josie very much. There was her moony look, her way of cleaning her slate with her tongue, the silly grin she always gave when she was found picking at the lunch in other girls' bags. Often there was a fight about sitting next to her in class. They said she had things in her hair. And more than once she had had ringworm.

But it seemed wicked to think of all that now. Josie would be lying still and cold in her room at the township hospital, her eyes closed and her face turned to wax. Yet not all of her would be there. That was what made you feel uneasy in thinking about her. When anyone died, they said, the spirit was set free. And Josie's might be somewhere about, able to overhear not only what you said, but what you thought. It might be in the house, this spirit; it might be flickering about through the air like a yellow butterfly. There was something creepy about the Paton's place, with the broken shutter giving it a watching look, and the fowls staring one-eyed at the closed door.

All that afternoon the thought of having to die clung to us as we played about the cow-sheds and down by the creek. Never before had it come so near, though we had all heard about Bob Sheddan, the butcher's offsider. He had been frightening to meet when he was drunk, his eyes all bloodshot and his horse dancing round as he laid about him with his whip, cutting the cattle coming out of the railway trucks. But they said that before he hit the ground he had muttered "God be merciful to me a sinner," and that had saved him in the end.

"God be merciful to me a sinner." For months afterwards we had been haunted by these words, wondering fearfully whether we would have time to get them out if the worst happened. They were always on the tip of our tongues: they came back to us every night before our eyes closed: sometimes we gabbled them beneath our breath when we were running to take off from the high bank at the swimming-hole or preparing for a jump from the leaning tree behind the school.

And they were in the air about us now as we trailed round the paddocks, waiting for the long afternoon to pass, waiting for it to be time to bring in the cows and get ready for tea. There seemed so many ways in which death might trip you up. Every black snaky-looking stick in the grass made your heart jump;

191

O

the sleepy draught-horses by the bails looked as if they might lash out suddenly and catch you in the stomach.

Overhead, when you lay in the grass, the sky seemed empty and far away. Eternity? What did it mean? Was there really another life that went on for ever and ever, without change? And would there be a meeting-place where you could find your family and the people you knew, or was there a risk of being left wandering by yourself as you sometimes were in dreams? If you tried to think about it you felt the world flowing away from you: you were left in some soundless place where you were cold, frightened and hopelessly lost.

And that was not the worst. There were the woodcuts in the illustrated Bible with the red cover—a world grey-black instead of dazzling white. Wicked people sitting on thunderclouds adrift in space; pits of darkness you looked down upon from the peaks of bare mountains; hordes of grinning figures with the wings of bats and the feet of goats.

They did not bear thinking about, those pictures. No, you would lie awake all night listening for sounds in the dark if you kept thinking of them. It was better to rush about heedlessly, jumping over every patch of grass where a snake might lie hidden, giving the heels of the draught-horses a wide berth, and keeping the magic words ready on your tongue, "God be merciful to me a sinner." After all, lots of people did grow up to be old, and your chance was as good as any.

That evening, when tea was finished, mother called us out to look at the sky. It was filled with small clouds the colour of tinned salmon, massed together lightly like plucked feathers, but parted in the middle to leave a path of pearly blue. Far, far away into another world that path took you. The sun had just set, and there was a gentle look about everything—the cropped paddocks, the cows lying by their penned calves, the soft trees touched with gold.

No one wanted to speak. We were thinking of Josie—Josie squatting in the dust under the school steps; Josie letting the spit run down her slate in class; Josie lying now, white as wax, her hands folded on her chest, in a room that smelt of lilies.

And above were the soft clouds, parted in a pearly-blue opening, as if they had been brushed aside by a feather, letting the faint stars show through. Beautiful, it looked, shedding an awe upon the heart. It was the path, mother said, made by the angels' wings as they carried Josie up to heaven.

We felt sad and tender about Josie. We were glad the angels didn't know as much about her as we did.

Australia

Francis Webb

THE SUN MADE

THE sun made for my childhood's eyes a temple
Heaped with pure offerings, a history
Of kind white lambs absorbed in games, the simple
Hide and seek of flower or pride of tree.

Clouds came to him, flowers wasted pale and old,
Lambs bled and bleated, storm railed bitterly
At colours—yet I rode the travelling gold
Of lightning, bleeding, weeping, singing, free.

A candle. Words of the judges have undone
My humble secret. Let it be said aloud
That while I wrestled with the sum, the sun,
Mortality came to him like a cloud.
I confess connivance, weeping, on my knees:
My heart sang with you, Aristophanes.

James McAuley

SECRET SONG

Only your ear could trace
　　My spirit's inmost tone;
Meanings that words efface
　　Were caught by you alone.

Only your love could find
　　In that dark destined lot
To which I was assigned
　　The password I forgot.

Only your voice could touch
　　So lightly on my pain
As not to rouse too much
　　What might not rest again . . .

Saadat Hasan Manto

BLACK SHALWAR

BEFORE coming to Delhi, she had lived in Ambala Cantonment, where the tommies were a good source of income to her. She was in great demand. Almost every night, some home-sick tommies, sodden with drink, would come to her and seek solace in her arms. She would dispose of as many as eight or ten of them in a few hours, and earn about twenty or thirty rupees. She preferred the tommies to her countrymen. She could not, of course, fully understand their language, but this was more to her advantage. If they asked her for some concession she would reply, "Sahib, no andersten." And if they handled her roughly, she would abuse them in Urdu, "Sahib, you are the son of an owl, ek dum! . . . you are a bastard . . . andersten . . . ?"

Her vituperation would flow in soft pleasant vernacular, without any suggestion of anger, for she was a good business woman and the tommies would gape at her without understanding the occasion or meaning of her utterance; but to appease her, they would nod their heads in agreement and laugh. And Sultana would feel that the tommies were really the sons of owls!

In Delhi, not a single tommy had come to her. It was now three months since she had migrated to this great Indian city. She had heard about its seductive grandeur and about the Big Lat Sahib who lived in it, but abandoned it in summer for the cool hills of Simla.

Sultana had come with high hopes, but had received only six customers in the last three months and had earned, God forbid that she should tell a lie, only eighteen and a half rupees. Not one of the customers had agreed to pay more than three rupees.

Eighteen and a half rupees in three months and she paid twenty rupees a month as rent! Her landlord had described her type of house as a "flat" and she added this word to her stock of English.

The first time she used the lavatory in the flat, Sultana discovered a gadget she had never seen. She had a backache that day and when she finished she found a chain hanging by her side. Remembering the landlord's boast that this was a luxury flat, she caught at the chain to help her rise. Suddenly, there was a metallic clang, something gurgled ominously above her and the next moment a column of water cascaded down and formed a roaring whirlpool under her. She screamed.

Khuda Bux came rushing out of the adjoining room, where he had been busy sorting out photographic chemicals and asked, "Who screamed—was it you?"

Sultana placed a hand on her frightened heart. "What sort of lavatory is this?—What's that hanging like an alarm chain in a train? I had a backache and thought I'd take its support to rise but as soon as I touched the damned thing, there was such a commotion that it scared me out of my wits."

Khuda Bux laughed and explained the working of the flush system to Sultana.

Who Khuda Bux was and how he came to live with Sultana is a long story. He belonged to Rawalpindi, where he matriculated and learned how to drive buses. For four years he drove buses between Rawalpindi and Srinagar. Then he seduced a woman in Kashmir and brought her to Lahore. There he failed to find employment and forced the woman to sell herself, to earn a living for both of them. This went on for about three years till the woman eloped with someone else. Khuda Bux came to Ambala in search of her and found Sultana instead, who liked him and let him stay with her.

Sultana began to prosper, and being a superstitious woman, she attributed this to Khuda Bux's coming into her life. She began to value him all the more.

Khuda Bux was hard working and liked to be busy all the time. He made friends with a photographer who operated near the railway station and soon he had learned the trade. He took sixty rupees from Sultana and bought himself a camera, a screen and the essential chemicals and set himself up as an independent photographer.

He was successful and after some time he moved to the cantonment area, where the tommies swarmed to him. He got to know several of them and after a month, persuaded Sultana to shift to the cantonment also. This proved to be a lucky move, for soon many tommies became permanent customers of Sultana, and her income doubled.

She bought ear-rings, had eight bangles made out of five and a half tolas of gold, furnished her apartment and replenished her wardrobe. But one day, suddenly, Khuda Bux decided to move to Delhi and Sultana could not refuse because of her faith in him. Besides the material benefit which she hoped would result from her migration to Delhi, Sultana also looked forward to being near the shrine of Hazrat Nizam-ud-Din Aualia. She planned to visit the shrine frequently for her spiritual salvation. She sold all her immovable assets and came to Delhi.

Sultana did no business during her first month in Delhi. She consoled herself with the thought that people are always shy of a new shop. But another month went by and she had yet to receive her first customer. She became anxious and said to Khuda Bux, "I can't understand what is wrong—we've been here two months now and no one has shown up. I know business is dull these days, but it can't be as bad as all that!"

After five months, Sultana found her income still less than a fourth of her expenditure. She got very worried. She sold her gold bangles one by one. When Sultana was handing over her last bangle to Khuda Bux, she said, "Let's go back to Ambala—there is nothing in Delhi. This city has not brought me any luck. Let's go back and make good our losses. You go and sell this bangle and I'll pack. We can catch the night train."

Khuda Bux took the bangle from Sultana and said, "No, my dear, we won't go back to Ambala. We'll soon strike a lucky patch in Delhi and all your bangles will be back on your wrists. Have faith in God. He is all knowing. He'll look after us."

Sultana kept quiet. It hurt her to look at her bare arms, but what could she do; Khuda Bux and she had to keep body and soul together, somehow.

Khuda Bux began to keep away from the house all day, and

197

she felt neglected. She had made friends with some women in the neighbourhood, whom she could call on, but she did not like going to their flats every day and spending hours there. Gradually she restricted her calling. She stayed at home, alone, all day. At times, she would chop betel nuts, at others recondition her old clothes, or stand in her balcony and watch, with a vacant look, the activity in the railway yard across the road.

The railway yard extended along the road over a wide area. A conspicuous building in it, situated to the left of Sultana's flat was a goods-shed, choked almost to its corrugated iron roof with crates of all shapes and sizes. The rest of the yard was laid with rail-tracks, which glistened under the sun, reminding Sultana of the blue veins bulging under the shiny skin of her hands. The engines, gasping and puffing, bustled to and fro all the day, shunting wagons. In the mornings, Sultana would gaze upon the mist-covered yard from her balcony and see thick smoke billow skywards from the engines, like a heavy man rising unsteadily to his feet. Clouds of steam would hiss across the rails and dissolve into the air in the twinkling of an eye.

Sometimes a solitary wagon would clatter down the track after being pushed by an engine. And she would feel that her life was like the run of the wagon; that she had been pushed on to the track of life and left to move with her own momentum, without any control over herself, with other people acting as pointsmen and diverting her to some destination—where that was, she had no idea, but she knew that one day she would stop at a strange place, utterly foreign to her.

Sultana wanted to escape her quaint thoughts, which she attributed to some sudden defect of the mind. She began to avoid going to the balcony, and said to Khuda Bux several times, "Please, take pity on me. Don't keep away from home all day—I am sick with loneliness." But he always mollified Sultana by replying, "My dear, I'm trying to put through a deal—It's a matter of days, and God willing I'll cash in shortly."

Full five months had gone by and neither Khuda Bux nor Sultana had cashed in on anything substantial so far. Moharram was at hand and Sultana did not have any money to order herself a black costume for the occasion. Anwari had already got a smart shirt of Lady Hamilton material, with sleeves of georgette.

To match she had a black satin shalwar, which had the lustre of collorium. Mumtaz had bought a black georgette sari and had told Sultana that she would wear a white silk petticoat under it as that was the latest fashion. She also showed Sultana a pair of dainty black velvet shoes she had bought to complete the costume of mourning.

After seeing the preparations by Anwari and Mumtaz for Moharram, she came back home in a pensive mood. The desire to have a complete black costume for herself was troubling her like an internal sore. She found herself alone in the flat. Khuda Bux was out as usual. She lay down on the durree with her head resting on a thick bolster. She remained in this position for a long time, till the high bolster strained her neck. She got up and walked out of the room, to the balcony, determined to divert her thoughts and get rid of her depression.

In the railway yard, there were several wagons, but no engines. The road had been sprinkled with water and was no longer dusty. Men were already moving up and down the road, looking at the women on the balconies, making a choice and furtively mounting the stairs to their flats. Sultana saw someone looking at her and she smiled back automatically. At the same moment an engine entered the railway yard and she forgot the man, watching the engine's progress. It wore a black dress! Sultana turned her eyes away and looked at the road again. The man she had smiled at had not moved. He stood near a bullock-cart still looking up at her with the same hungry look he had first given her. She beckoned him. He examined the building for a moment, and then with an almost imperceptible gesture asked Sultana the way to her flat. She leaned over and pointed out the stairs that would lead him to her. The man paused for a moment then crossed the road and mounted the stairs with great alacrity. Sultana took him to the outer room and as he sat on the durree, she asked, "Were you afraid to come up?"

"What gave you that idea. What was there to be afraid of?"

"I only asked, since you seemed to hesitate. . . ."

"You are mistaken. I was looking at the flat above yours. A woman there was sticking out her tongue at a man. The scene intrigued me, then a green light came on and I began to look at that—I find green very soothing to the eyes."

199

He began to look round the room. He got up. Sultana asked, "Are you going?"

"No. I want to look round—come, show me your flat."

Sultana took him through the three rooms one by one. The man inspected the flat without making any comment. When they returned to the room from which they had started the man said, "My name is Shanker."

Sultana looked at him carefully for the first time. His features were plain, but his eyes were unusually clear and lustrous. He had an athletic build, and his hair was greying at the temples. He wore grey trousers and a white shirt, with its collar turned up.

Shanker made himself at home on the durree and Sultana felt as if she and not Shanker was the customer. She became nervous and said, "What can I do for you?"

Shanker stretched himself out on the durree and said, "What can you do for me?—I thought it was the other way round—Was it not you who called me?—Tell me, what can I do for you?"

Sultana was struck dumb.

Shanker sat up, "Oh, I understand—there's been a mistake, you've got the wrong idea. I'm not the type that pays anything. I charge a fee like a doctor—whenever I'm called a fee has to be paid."

Sultana could not help laughing in her confusion. She asked, "What sort of business are you in?"

"Same as yours."

"How?"

"What do you do?"

"I—I—I don't do anything."

"I also don't do anything."

"This doesn't make sense," said Sultana, irritated, "You must be doing something."

Shanker replied composedly, "You too must be doing something."

"I damn myself."

"I do the same."

"Let's both damn ourselves."

"But, I never pay to have myself damned."

"Talk sense—I don't dole out charity."

"I too am not a volunteer."

Sultana stopped—"What's a volunteer?"

"A damn fool!"

"Oh! well, I too am not a damn fool."

"But that man Khuda Bux who lives with you is certainly a damn fool."

"Why?"

"Because every day he goes to a fakir for luck—and he doesn't know that the fakir's own luck is like a rusty lock that can't be opened."

Shanker laughed.

Sultana said, "You are a Hindu and you have no respect for our holy men."

Shanker smiled, "There is no Hindu-Muslim problem in places like these. If our leaders came to this place, they too would behave like decent people."

"What nonsense are you talking about—Tell me, do you want to stay?"

"Yes, but on the terms I have already stated."

Sultana stood up, "Then you can take your leave."

Shanker rose to his feet slowly, and putting his hands into his trousers pockets, said, "I pass this way frequently—if you ever need me you can call me up. I am a very useful person."

Shanker went away and Sultana, forgetting about the black dress, began to think about him. Her experience with him had for the time being, lessened her worry. If he had come to her in Ambala, where she was well off, she would have taken a different line with him. She might even have gone to the extent of throwing him out of her house, but here she was lonely and had liked talking to him.

When Khuda Bux came home late in the evening she asked, "Where have you been all day?"

Khuda Bux was very tired. He said, "I went to Old Fort. A fakir is camping there—I go to him daily in the hope that he'll do something for us!"

Sultana was bent upon observing Moharram in the orthodox way. She said to Khuda Bux in a plaintive voice, "You're out all day and I feel shut up in a cage. I can't go anywhere and have no one to talk to. Moharram is at hand. Have you given any thought to it? I want a black dress and there isn't a broken cowrie in the house. We have sold the bangles one by one—What are we to do now?—How long will you continue running after holy men? God has turned His face away from us ever since we came to Delhi—I think you should start some business of your own, it will be something to fall back upon."

Khuda Bux stretched himself out on the durree and said, "But I'll need money to start business. For God's sake don't talk of things that are impossible, they depress me all the more. I can't bear them. I really made a blunder in bringing you here from Ambala, but, it was God's will—whatever He does is for the good. It's possible he's only testing us and may soon——"

Sultana cut in, "Don't depend upon God alone, do something yourself—you must get me some black satin for a shalwar. I don't care if you have to beg, borrow or steal; but I must have that cloth. I have got a white silk shirt and that white ninon dupata you gave me last Devali—I can get them dyed black. All I need to complete my costume for Moharram is a black shalwar and you've got to get that somehow. Maybe you see me dead if you don't!"

Khuda Bux sat up. "Now, stop all this. How am I to get you satin for the shalwar? I haven't even money to buy myself poison!"

"Do what you like," said Sultana, "But get me four and a half yards of black satin."

"Pray to God that He may send you some customers tonight."

"So, you won't lift a finger to help me?—if you want to, you can certainly raise enough money to buy me the satin. Before the war, satin was about twelve annas a yard; now it must be about eight annas more—and how much will four and a half yards cost?"

"Oh, all right," said Khuda Bux, "I will try and do something." He rose to his feet. "Now cheer up, while I get something to eat from the hotel."

The food came and they ate it without any relish, and went to sleep. Next morning Khuda Bux went to the fakir at Old Fort as usual, and Sultana again found herself alone in the flat. She remained in bed for some time and after that she dragged herself about the flat till lunch. She then collected her white shirt and dupata, went out and gave them to the laundry on the ground floor, to have them dyed black. After that she returned to the flat and began looking through dog-eared film magazines and booklets of film songs, which she bought every time she went to the cinema. She fell asleep, and when she woke up it was past four; this she calculated from the wedge of sunlight that had slowly pushed itself as far as the drain, that ran along one side of the terrace. She had a bath, changed into her evening clothes, wrapped a shawl round her shoulders and took up her usual position on the balcony. An hour went by. It was evening and lights began dotting the locality. The air became chilly, but Sultana did not feel the cold. She kept on looking at the road, which was full of cars and tongas, streaming past. Suddenly she saw Shanker. He looked up and smiled at her. Automatically she smiled back and waved to him. He immediately doubled up the stairs to her flat. Sultana did not know what to do. She had not meant to call him up to her flat; her hands and lips had acted on their own. She followed Shanker into the outer room, where he sat down on the durree arranging the bolsters around him like Dutch-wives. He felt completely at home. She also sat down, but could not think of anything to say. Shanker said, "You can summon me and throw me out a hundred times, these things never annoy me."

Sultana's confusion increased. She said, "No, no stay by all means—who asked you to leave?"

Shanker smiled, "Then you accept my terms?"

"What terms?" Sultana asked, and smiling, she added, "Do you want to sign a marriage contract with me?"

"Marriage," said Shanker, "Neither you nor I shall ever marry anybody—these institutions are not for the like of us—forget about them. Let's talk of something else."

"For instance?"

"You are a woman—say something that will amuse me—my dear, business is not the only thing that matters in the world."

Sultana who, mentally, had already surrendered, said, "Come to the point; what do you want from me?"

"What others have wanted."

"Then what's the difference between you and the others?"

Shanker sat up. "You and I are the same; but I am different from others. There are many things which one should be able to understand without asking."

Sultana tried to think this out for a moment and then said, "I have understood."

"Well then, what next?"

"You win—I don't think anyone has ever agreed to such a silly proposal as I have."

"You shouldn't be ashamed of it, you are not going to degrade yourself, as you have been doing, without remorse, in the past. Do you know, there are women who just cannot believe that creatures of your type exist, but how wrong they are—your name's Sultana, isn't it?"

"Yes, it's Sultana."

Shanker rose to his feet, smiling broadly, "My name's Shanker. These names are funny things—come, let's go into the other room."

When Shanker and Sultana returned to the outer room they were both laughing at something. Shanker soon wanted to leave and Sultana said, "Shanker, will you do something for me?"

"You first tell me what it is?"

Sultana said, hesitatingly, "You'll say I'm trying to get my fee out of you——"

"Come on, say it——"

Sultana braced herself, "It's like this, Moharram is approaching and I haven't any money for a black shalwar—You've already heard about all my troubles—I've got a shirt and a dupata—I'm having them dyed black."

Shanker said, "You want me to give you some money to buy a black shalwar?"

Sultana hastily said, "No, I don't mean that—if possible get me a black satin shalwar."

Shanker smiled, "I hardly ever have anything in my pocket. Anyway, I'll try to do something. You will get the shalwar on the first of Moharram—Now cheer up!" Shanker looked at Sultana's ear-rings and said, "Can you give me your ear-rings?"

Sultana smiled, "What will you do with them—they are silver and hardly worth five rupees."

"I only asked for the ear-rings, not their price—will you give them to me?"

"Here take them." Sultana handed over her ear-rings to Shanker. When Shanker had left, she regretted her action.

Sultana did not believe for a moment that Shanker would keep his word. But at eight on the morning of the first Moharram there was a knock at the door. She opened it and found Shanker, with a package under his arm. He handed it over to Sultana and said, "Here is a black satin shalwar—try it on—probably it's a little long for you—I am going now."

Shanker went away without another word. His trousers were baggy, his hair ruffled, as if he had come to Sultana straight from bed.

Sultana opened the newspaper wrapping. The shalwar was just as she wanted it to be, like Anwari's.

Sultana was very happy and was sorry that she had doubted Shanker's word.

In the afternoon she got her shirt and dupata from the laundry. They were dyed a beautiful black. She put on her complete Moharram costume. There was a knock at the door. She opened it and Anwari entered. She surveyed Sultana's dress and said, "The shirt and the dupata seem to be dyed, but this shalwar is new—when did you have it made?"

Sultana said, "The dressmaker brought it this morning." She looked at Anwari's ear-rings and said, "When did you get these ear-rings?"

"I got them today," said Anwari.

And suddenly they could only stare at each other, without saying a word.

"Faiz"

FREEDOM'S DAWN

THIS leprous daylight, dawn that night's fangs have torn,
—This is not that long-looked-for break of day,
Not that clear dawn in search of which our comrades
Set out, believing somewhere there must be
In the empty heavens the stars' last halting-place,
Somewhere a shore for night's slow-washing tide,
Somewhere an anchorage for the ship of pain.

When they set out, following youth's secret pathways,
Those friends, how many a hand plucked at their sleeves!
From panting casements of the land of beauty
Soft arms invoked them, flesh cried out to them;
But dearer was the lure of dawn's bright face,
Closer to them hung her robe of shimmering rays;
Light-winged their longing, feather-light their toil.

But now, word goes, the war of day with darkness
Is over; wandering feet have found their goal.
Our leaders wear changed faces; festive looks
Are now commended, discontent reproved.

And yet no physic offered to unslaked eye
Or heart unsatisfied works them any cure.
Where did that sweet breeze blow from then—where has it
Gone, while the lamp by the road has never flickered?
Night's heaviness is unlessened yet, the hour
Of mind and spirit's ransom has not struck.
Let us go on, our goal is not yet here.

Taufig Riffat

BEAUTY SLIDES LIKE THE SEA

BEAUTY slides like the sea from rock-face.
Those who were graceful, the pointed-at,
And the tanned assertive warriors
Now stare in wonder at hostile mirrors,
Fingertips charged as their hearts were once.
Even the hermit in his cell is dumb:
He has no substitute for beauty.

The gutter of tears now overflows
The lanes of that ruined city, their pride.
Time shrugs his shoulders and wipes his hands.

P

N. V. M. Gonzalez

THE MORNING STAR

THE sailor went back to the outriggered boat and returned with a lantern. It lighted up the footpath before him and his flat un-shod feet. He walked in a slow, shuffling manner, the lantern in his hand swinging in rhythm.

"Can't you walk faster?" the old man shouted from the coconut grove.

Instead of saying something in reply, the sailor shuffled on, neither hastening nor slowing his gait.

"You're a turtle, that's what," said the old man.

As the sailor approached, the lantern light caught the entrance of the makeshift shelter. Then the oval of light completely en-gulfed the shelter, which was shaped like a pup tent and built of coconut leaves woven into loose shingles. A matting of coconut leaves was spread on the ground, and walking across it, the old man hung the lantern from a ridgepole at the far end. A woman sat in one corner, her back half-turned to the entrance.

"Now, if you aren't stupid. Quite like a turtle, really," the old man said to the sailor.

"Ha?" the other said, with a twang.

The old man had expected that; there was something wrong with the sailor's tongue. "And how about the jute sacks and the blankets?" the old man said. "Didn't I tell you to get them?"

"Ha?" came the sailor's reply.

"Stop it!" said the old man, angrily. "If you weren't born that way, I'd give you a thrashing." He waved him away. "Be off! And while you are at it, bring over some water. There's no saying whether we'll find drinking water hereabouts. Would you care for supper, Marta?"

"No, thank you," said the woman in the hut.

"It'll be best to get some food ready, though," said the old man. "We've salmon in the boat."

The sailor had shuffled away, the coconut fronds on the ground rustling softly as he stepped on them.

"Bring over a tin of salmon. And also the pot of rice we have on the stove box," the old man called after the sailor.

From somewhere a bird uttered a shrill cry; and the old man spoke to the woman again. "If you'll step out of there just a while, Marta. . . ."

"I am quite comfortable here, Uncle," she said.

"But you should be walking about, instead of sitting down like that."

"It seems better here," said the woman. But later she said: "All right."

"I'll build a fire," the old man said.

The bird's call came again, in a note of wild urgency. "That's the witch bird. I can tell for certain," the woman said. "They take newborn children away."

"No, it's not the witch bird," the old man said.

He gathered some dry leaves and twigs and in a minute had a fire blazing.

"Still, it's a fine time for having a baby, Uncle. Isn't it?"

"It's God's will," the old man said. Marta was laughing at herself. "We'll do the best we can. Walk about, stretch your legs; hold on to a coconut trunk over there, if it hurts you so."

"I'm quite all right, Uncle," said Marta.

The fire crackled, and the old man added more leaves and twigs. The blaze illumined the large boles of the coconut palms.

The clear sky peered through the fronds of the palms but there were no stars. The night had a taut, timorous silence, disturbed only by the crackling of the fire.

The woman walked up and down, not venturing beyond the space lighted up by the fire. She was a squat, well-built woman. Her arms and legs were full-muscled, like those of a man. If she had cut her hair and worn trousers instead of a skirt, she would have passed for a man. Her distended belly and large breasts would not have made any difference.

The old man watched her with unending curiosity. Like him, she wore a field jacket, the sleeves rolled up, being too long.

209

Her skirt was of a thick olive-drab material, made from fatigues that some American soldier had discarded.

"Is that his name printed on there?" the old man asked.

In the firelight the letters "Theodore C. Howard" could be read in white stencils on the back of the drab green jacket.

"Oh, no, Uncle," said Marta. "This isn't his. He gave me three woollen blankets, though."

"That's fair," said the old man.

"What do you mean, Uncle? Please don't tease me," said Marta.

"Well, others do get more than that. For their labour, I mean. You worked as a laundry woman?"

"Yes, Uncle," Marta replied. "But afterwards we lived together. Three weeks. We had a hut near Upper Mangyan. You could see the whole camp of the Army from there." With her hands, she held on to her belt, a rattan string, as she spoke. "It pains so, at times. Well, I washed clothes for a living, Uncle. That's what I went there for."

"Did you earn any money?"

"No, Uncle. I'm never for making money. He said one day, 'Here are twenty pesos,'" she said with a laugh. "He had a way of talking to me and never saying my name, as though I had no name. The others, the ones I only washed clothes for, had a nickname for me. 'Sweet Plum', I remember. That's how they called me. 'Sweet Plum.' What's a 'plum', Uncle? They say it's a fruit."

"I don't know," said the old man. "In our country, we have no such fruit."

"He would not call me 'Sweet Plum', even. And, as I said, he wanted to give me money. 'What for?' I said. And he said, 'For your mother.' But I have no mother, I told him so. 'Well, for your father and brothers and sisters.' But I have no such folk. I told him so. I said, 'Keep your money. I love you, so keep your money.' And he was angry, and he swore and then left the hut. I never saw him again, but he left me three woollen blankets."

The old man listened to the story with great interest, but now that it was over he made no comment, beyond getting up and thoughtfully tending the fire.

"No, Uncle. You're wrong to think I ever earned money," Marta said. She walked a few steps and returned to the fireside. "By the way, Uncle, how much does it cost to go to San Paulino in your boat?"

"That's where you live?"

She nodded.

"For you, nothing. Not a centavo."

"I can give you one of my woollen blankets."

"The trip will cost you nothing."

"Of course, you'll say, 'What a foolish woman she is! To think that she does not know when her time comes!' But truly, Uncle, the days are the same to me. The nights are the same. I can't count days and months. Maybe, Uncle, I'll never grow old. Do you think I'll ever grow old?"

The old man did not know what to say. A soft chuckle, and that was all.

"And I am going home. Am I not foolish, Uncle?"

To humour her, the old man said: "Yes, you are quite foolish. A good thing you found my boat, no?"

"I feel lucky, yes," Marta said. "I must leave, that is all. Maybe, it isn't my time yet. The long walk from Upper Mangyan, and then three days on the beach, before finding your boat. . . . Maybe, this is only the seventh month. How long is nine months, Uncle?"

The old man wished he could give a good answer. "Nine months," he said finally.

"I understand. You old men know a lot. Now, don't laugh, Uncle. I've been married before, and this man I married was an old man, too. May he rest in peace. Oh, it pains so! Here, right here!" She indicated the approximate location of the pain.

"Walking relieves it, so they say."

The leaves crackled softly on the ground as she trod upon them with her bare feet. She went back and forth, and talked on as if to amuse herself.

"Now, this man was a tailor. You see, I worked as a servant in a rich man's house. And this tailor said, one day, 'You don't have to work so hard like that, Marta. Come live with me.' Ah, you men are tricky. Aren't you, Uncle?"

"Sometimes," the old man couldn't help saying. "Some men are, I must say," he agreed readily.

211

"This tailor, he saw how industrious I was—and, I dare say, I am. Because God made me so; with the build of an animal, how can one be lazy? There's not a kind of work you men can do that I can't do also. That's a woman for you! My tailor was pleased with me. I was a woman and a man all in one, and he was so happy he stopped becoming a tailor and took instead to visiting with neighbours, talking politics and things like that." She stopped, and then as if suddenly remembering something: "But he left me no child. Oh, he fooled me so, Uncle!"

"Well, you'll have one soon, I must say," said the old man.

"As I was saying, I lived with this old tailor. He was a widower and had been lonely, and now he was kind to me. But he died of consumption—he had it for a long time—the year the war started. I went back to the rich man's house where I had worked before. When the Americans came back I said to this rich man, 'I am going away. Only for a short time, though. I hear they pay well at the camp of the Army, if you can wash clothes and do things like that. When I have enough money, I'll come back.' That's what I said. Oh, oh! It hurts so!"

"It's time the sailor returns," said the old man. "Does it pain much?"

"Ah, but pain never bothers me, Uncle. Didn't I tell you I am built like an animal? This tailor, he used to beat me. I didn't care. I can stand anything, you know. I chopped wood and pounded rice for him. I was quite sorry when he died. That's the truth, Uncle."

She stopped and laughed, amused more than ever perhaps at the way she had been talking. The old man looked at her quizzically.

"And you'll bring this baby home to San Paulino?" he said.

"Why, of course, Uncle. It'll be so tiny, so helpless—you know. Why do you ask?"

The old man hesitated, but in the end he decided to tell her: "There are places—in the city, for example—where they'll take care of babies like that. . . ."

"But can they take care of him better than I? That's impossible, Uncle," the woman said, excitedly. "Oh, it hurts so!—I do like— oh!—to look after him myself. . . ."

212

The firelight caught her faint smile. She had a common-looking face, but her eyes were pretty and big and smiling.

She had stopped talking. The sailor appeared in their midst, saying, "Ha!"

"Warm the salmon in the fire," said the old man.

He took the jute sacks and the blankets into the shelter and prepared a bed. Outside in the light of the fire, the sailor opened the salmon can with his bolo and began drinking the soup in the can.

"Can't you wait for me?"

The old man crawled out of the hut, annoyed partly because the sailor had begun to eat and partly because Marta was groaning.

"Don't wail there like a sow," he told her gruffly.

Then he sat before the pot of rice that the sailor brought over.

"A sow doesn't wail so, Uncle," said the woman innocently.

The old man said nothing in reply. He and the sailor ate hurriedly, making noises with their mouths.

"Ha!" said the sailor, in that helpless way of his, looking in Marta's direction.

"She doesn't care for food. She said so," the old man explained. And to Marta, he said: "If it's too much to bear, you may go in. We'll keep some of the salmon for you. Afterwards you'll be so hungry."

Marta followed his advice, crawling into the hut. Her head struck the lantern that hung from the ridgepole, and for a while it swung about, the oval of light dancing on the ground.

"I'll be with you in a minute," said the old man. "Why you've to let me do this, I don't know." It seemed he had become a different person from the *uncle* Marta knew a while ago; he felt the change in himself.

"Uncle," the woman called from in the shelter, "what's a man called when he does a midwife's business?"

The old man was washing his mouth with water from the container the sailor had brought from their outriggered boat. When he was through, he said: "You horrible creature! I'm now sure of it! You've fooled me. You planned all this. . . . You are more clever than I thought. . . ."

There was silence in the shelter. From afar the night bird called again, clearly and hauntingly. The sailor, calling the old man's attention to the bird, said, "Ha, ha!" He pointed with his finger at the darkness, but the old man did not mind him.

The silence grew tense, although there were soft noises from the shelter, noises that the movement of feet and arms and body made upon the matting, as if a sow were indeed lying there to deliver a litter. The lantern glow fell full upon the woman's upraised knees. She had covered them with a blanket.

"Uncle!" she called frantically.

Before going in the old man looked up at the sky. There was a lone star at last, up in the heavens. He could see it through the palm fronds. He'd like to remember that. He wished he could see a moon, too, and that he knew for certain how high the tide was at the beach; for, later, he'd recall all this. But there were no other signs. There was only this star.

"I'm so frightened, Uncle," Marta was saying, her voice hoarse and trembling. "And it hurts so! Uncle, it will be the death of me!"

"Stop this foolish talk," said the old man angrily. "Pray to God. He is kind," he said.

His hands and knees were shaking. He knelt beside Marta, ready to be of assistance.

"Oh—oh—oh! Uncle, I want to die, I want to die!" she cried, clutching his hand.

When the sailor heard the squall of the child he said "Ha, ha," with joy. He wanted to see the child, but the old man told him to go away.

"Go!" the old man said waving his arms.

The sailor returned to his sleeping place and lay as before. The night was warm and restful, and soon he was fast asleep.

The old man joined him under the coconut tree, their feet touching and pointing towards the smouldering fire. Through the palm fronds the old man could see the sky growing light, for soon it would be morning. The star peered at him as before, through the thick coconut palm leaves. It had watched over them all this time.

The old man turned and using his arm for a pillow tried to sleep. The sailor was snoring peacefully. The old man could see

Marta in the shelter, her legs flat on the mat and the child in a bundle beside her.

The old man fell asleep thinking of the child, for it was a boy. A gust of wind woke him up, and when he opened his eyes he did not realize at first where he was. He felt glad he had been of help to the woman, and he wondered if in any way he had been unkind to her. He wished he had not called her a sow and had been gentle with her. He sat up and saw the lantern in the shelter.

"Are you all right?" he called, for he heard the woman stir.

She did not answer but sat up, moving in a slow, deliberate way, her shadow covering the child like a blanket.

"It's the witch bird, Uncle," she said in a tired, faraway voice. "Did you hear the witch bird? Now he is dead—Uncle, he is dead!"

The old man lowered the lantern. It had a faint blue flame. The baby beside her was limp and grey like the blanket wrapped around it.

"You're a sow, that's what you are! God Almighty," he crossed himself, "may You have mercy on us!"

"Believe me, Uncle. . . . It's the witch bird. . . ."

The sailor had wakened. He got up and sat hugging his knees and stared at the old man.

"You build a fire, turtle!" the old man shouted at him. "Don't you see it's so dark?"

"Ha!" the sailor said.

José Garcia Villa

THE WAY MY IDEAS THINK ME

THE way my ideas think me
Is the way I unthink God.
As in the name of heaven I make hell
That is the way the Lord says me.

And all is adventure and danger
And I roll Him off cliffs and mountains
But fast as I am to push Him off
Fast am I to reach Him below.

And it may be then His turn to push me off,
I wait breathless for that terrible second:
And if He push me not, I turn around in anger;
"O art thou the God I would have!"

Then He pushes me and I plunge down, down!
And when He comes to help me up
I put my arms around Him, saying, "Brother,
Brother." . . . This is the way we are.

Patrick Ng Kah Onn

THE INTERVIEW

Young Road. There in the little valley stood the shed that once housed the British Council Centre. The stone steps leading down to it were covered with moss and dried tree branches. The walls that once swung open revealing shelves of books to the passers-by were now tightly shut.

He looked dispassionately at the building squatting there below and he smiled wryly to himself. Empty and useless. Just like himself.

The driver shifted the gears and the car whined in an anxious, high-pitched, complaining sound as it ascended the steep incline. Sitting in the back seat, he stared at the nape of the driver's neck. The khaki collar was frayed a little round the edges, but at least the shirt was his own, bought with his own money. How much did he earn a month? Perhaps $90 . . . $100 at the most. . . .

He looked down at the cuffs of his starched, white shirt, his carefully pressed, white trousers, his polished shoes. An exterior. A mere exterior covering a multitude of shame, sufferance, charity, and condescension. Everything that he wore, everything that he had, even his very existence depended on his father. He pressed his lips tight against his teeth and looked out of the window. He could feel that lump rising in his throat.

There were trees beside the road and some buildings behind them but he could not see much except their roofs. A few signboards came into view. "Department of Broadcasting", "Trade Union Adviser", "Department of Aborigines". He had a friend in the Broadcasting Department, but he had not seen him for nearly three years now. He even had to give up his friends, because he could not afford the cups of coffee, the occasional cinema and concert tickets, or those little birthday and Christmas presents that friendship demanded.

217

The hum of the engine had risen to such a high pitch that it seemed it could not possibly continue at that rate without bursting. He held his breath waiting for the driver to change gears. But the car continued up the slope holding on to its shrill note till it was almost shrieking. It must reach the end of its tether! . . . Soon! . . . Soon! . . .

He had already given up his pseudo-existentialist existence. It was impossible holding a one-man mutiny against the world. How full of hope he had been when he set out four years back! He was going to be an artist, paint sensational canvasses that would be talked about the world over. It took only a year for his bank account to dwindle down to a mere third of its original amount. That ought to have jerked him into reasoning, but it did not. He would sell some of his pictures and restore what he had spent. The only snag was that nobody looked at his canvasses, and when some people did, they did not know what they were all about. He began shedding his friends and living like a recluse monk. It was a dismal and unrewarding existence both for his body and his soul. He starved himself. His canvasses became duller, partly because he was using cheaper oils, and only sub-turpentine for his pictures, but mostly because he was sick and tired of that existentialist life.

When his bank account had dwindled to $1.93, he had gone back to his family. He found his father quite tolerant, considering the fact that he had gone against his wishes when he set out to conquer the world of art.

"You can occupy your old room. I'll provide your meals, your clothes, and everything else that's absolutely necessary. But I'll give you no allowance. If you need money to purchase anything, come and ask me, and I'll see if you really need it. One thing I'm certain of . . . I'll buy no painting materials for you, so you can save yourself the trouble of asking for money for anything of that nature."

He had proper meals once more, and his clothes were no longer decorated with colourful patches. His hair which once curled round his collar was now cut once a month. His physical self had improved tremendously since those bread-and-sardine days, but the rot of shame for his dependence and inability to stand on his own two feet, the despairing doubt of whether he was betraying his own true self by giving up painting, had already set in.

The car engine, too, finally reached the end of its shrill endurance and the driver changed the gears, bringing the car to a smooth run over a level. They passed a long building along the open-fronted wards of which were lined rows of iron beds filled with emaciated creatures with hollowed temples, eye-sockets, cheeks and collar-bones. They all wore a sort of white jacket, and they all stared at him as the car passed by them. Sick patients of the Tanglin Hospital. Sick in body only. He was sick in soul too. But he was on his way to seek a cure. The interview would decide.

He had written, in desperation, to the Federation Establishment Officer asking for a job as a clerk. A clerk! He drew down the corners of his mouth bitterly. Some of his friends had gone overseas to study in those respected and famous universities in the U.K., the U.S.A., Australia. He lacked their scholarship-scale intelligence . . . and rich parents.

He opened the elaborately decorated folder lying on the seat beside him, and thumbed through the papers he had put inside. Cambridge School Leaving Certificate (Grade II); Certificate of Study at St John's Institution (Conduct: excellent, Remarks: took keen interest in debates, concerts, plays, and art exhibitions, Sporting Activities: blank); Birth Certificate (1933: by the 29th of December he would already be twenty-three years old with a third of a man's normal life-span gone); and of course the slip of paper which stated his appointment with the interviewing committee.

He looked up from the papers just in time to see the words "Public Service Board" with a red arrow underneath flashing past the car. He leaned forward and tapped the driver's shoulder. The car nosed slowly down a narrow, winding road flanked by small, wooden houses raised from the ground by stumpy concrete pillars. A strange combination. But not stranger than he.

During his hermit days, notwithstanding the drawback of only a Second Grade School Certificate, he had joined the Kuala Lumpur Book Club and had read practically all the books in the Modern Literature section. Eliot, Fry, Graham Greene, William Sansom, Anouilh, Sartre, Mauriac, Duhamel, and even translations from Chaim Grade. He heaved a sigh. No more. No more lazing about with a book. He could not bear asking his father for the library fees every month. So he had given up his membership of the Club.

The driver applied the hand brake as the car glided down the sharp slope. The road ended in a huge square surrounded on three sides by low, brightly painted, prefabricated buildings, all of a similar, modern Scandinavian design. Could that be the Public Service Board where he had to report for the interview? He had always associated Government Offices with old, dark, venerable-looking architecture.

He approached the building with the grilled windows.

An Englishman smoking a pipe and holding a sheaf of papers in his hand was standing beside it.

"Have you come for an interview?" The Englishman took the pipe out of his mouth and pointed the stem at him.

"Yes."

"Then you had better come with me."

They stepped onto a sort of roofed walk which connected the main building to a smaller one, which consisted of a series of small rooms arranged in a straight row somewhat like a school dormitory. Swinging doors painted a bright lemon yellow stood in front of each room. The Englishman pushed open one of the doors and said:

"Will you please step inside this waiting room? We'll send for you when the committee is ready."

He looked round the room. There were eight rattan chairs and two low, glass-topped tables, four chairs round each table. He put his folder on the table in front of him, and waited.

The door swung open again before long and an Indian ushered him to another room. There a fat man sat with his back to the window directly facing him. On his left was seated a middle-aged man biting the stump of a pencil, and listening to the fat man talking.

"Sit down. Sit down," said the older man and immediately resumed his attentive, deliberating pose.

He sat down on the chair with its back to the door. He wondered if it was all right to put his folder on the table this time. He looked across to where the men were sitting. There were large books and papers scattered about in front of them. There were also two *songkoks* (Malay Islamic velvet cap) beside them on the table. He put his folder in front of him on the table.

The older man had now put down his pencil and was smoking a cigarette in a bone holder. The fat man was still talking but he could not understand what was being said. The man was talking in rapid Malay. He looked down at his shoes. The older man now and again said something also in Malay. He heard them laugh and slap their thighs.

Then the older one cleared his throat and said in English, "Well . . . the interview."

He looked up. They were arranging the books and papers in front of them. Then both opened a sort of entry book each, and studied some writing in the first column.

"You've come for an interview for . . . ?" asked the older man.

"The clerical service."

"And your name is . . . ?" again the older one.

He told him.

"Ah! No. 9. Good." The older man helped the fat man find the number in the other's book. "And you've brought the necessary papers with you?"

He opened his folder and handed the chit which fixed his appointment for the interview, and also his certificates across the table.

"That's a very nice cover you have there," said the fat man smiling.

"I . . . er . . . I used it to . . ." he spoke in a bare whisper and left the sentence unfinished.

He felt shy talking about his sketches and notes which used to fill the folder. He directed his attention to the older man who had donned glasses and who seemed to be reading through his certificates.

Without lifting his eyes from the papers, the older man said: "You were born in 1933?"

"Yes, I'll be twenty-three years old in December."

"Where were you born?"

"Kuala Lumpur."

"Where?"

221

"In the Bunsar Hospital."

The fat man chuckled happily.

"And you've been living in Kuala Lumpur all the time?" The older man went on with his questioning.

"No. We had been staying in Singapore for several years, but that was when I was very small. We've been staying in Kuala Lumpur since 1941."

Singapore. A house on the hill. A square-looking Fiat car. High stools in ice-cream parlours. Swings and slides in Katong Park. Ice-cream cones and peanuts at the pier. The sea, enormous and faintly threatening, and full of steamers from all parts of the world.

"You did your schooling at . . . ?" said the older man.

"St John's Institution."

"Ah! The Brothers' School!" broke in the fat man with a soft laugh.

"And you've passed your School Certificate?" said the older one puffing at his cigarette.

"Yes, in 1951."

"1951?"

"Yes."

"And what Grade did you get?"

"Second Grade." Why did he not look at the papers in front of him?

"Besides the School Certificate, have you passed any other examinations? University degrees? Diplomas?"

"No." What would he be doing there if he had university degrees and diplomas? Really!

"1951 is a long time ago. What have you been doing since?"

"I . . . I'm an artist."

"An artist! What pictures do you paint?"

"All types of wall pictures. Oil, Tempera, Pastel. . . ."

Those Robert Colquhoun-Keith Vaughan abominations standing with their faces to the wall in his room. His father had said, "Keep those things in your own room. I don't want them in the hall."

"Have you had any public exhibition of your pictures?"

"No."

Three years in succession he had sent in his paintings to the

Malayan Artists' Exhibitions that were sponsored annually by the local Arts Council, and every year, his pictures were rejected.

The door behind him opened and the pipe-smoking Englishman came in carrying a press-button bell.

"Oh! Am I interrupting anything?" He seemed surprised and out of breath puffing wheezily at his pipe. "I'm sorry, I won't be a moment. I thought it a good idea to leave this bell here so that when you've finished with a candidate you can press the bell for the next one when you're ready. I'm sorry I can't spare you a man. But I think the candidate who's finished with the interview can inform the next man."

"Thank you. That would be excellent," said the fat man touching the bell fondly.

"I don't think you'll be wanting anything else?" said the Englishman looking round the table. "Oh, yes, the ash-trays. I'm sorry about that. Our first day at this new office you know. I'll send a couple in immediately."

Then the man left, puffing furiously at his pipe. Like an engine.

"H'mph. And now let's get back to our interview. Why have you applied for the G.C.S., with the Government?" said the man on his left.

"I don't have any qualifications for specialized jobs, and I thought the clerical service would be easiest for a start," he said.

"You want to give up painting, is that it?"

He nodded dumbly. There was no question of wanting or not wanting. He had to.

"Do you know typewriting and shorthand?"

"No."

"Can you speak Malay?"*

"No. I never took any lessons in Malay, but I speak a sort of Bazaar Malay."

"You should learn to speak proper Malay if you are to get anywhere. Weren't you taught Malay in school?"

"No."

He had studied French taught by the Brothers. Wrong plan-

* A knowledge of the Malay language or "Bahasa Kebangsaan" (the *national* language) is a pre-requisite to employment in the Government service in the newly created Federation of Malaya.

Q

ning, wrong ideas, wrong sets of values that no longer held in the New Malaya.

"Don't you attend any Adult Education Classes where Malay is being taught?"

"N-n-no." He thought of the fees that would cost him.

The fat man laughed.

The older man flicked his cigarette ash on to the floor, then raised his eyebrows and said:

"*Berapa umor kamu?*" (How old are you?)

He breathed in deeply. Malay! That was meant for him! His mind turned a somersault. He seldom had occasion to speak Malay. Even with the driver he spoke in English. He lowered his eyes and concentrated hard on the jumble of forgotten words that were on the verge of peeping out of the recesses of his brain. Then, with a silent click, it came back.

"*Saya berumor dua puloh tiga.*" (I am twenty-three years old.)

"*Dua puloh tiga . . . ?*" (Twenty-three . . . ?)

"Yes."

"Continue. *Dua puloh tiga* what?"

Years! What was that? He pressed his tongue against his teeth. What . . . ?

"*Bulan.*"

"No. *Bulan* is month."

"I . . . I . . . don't know."

"Of course you do. Now, what's day?"

"*Hari.*"

"Week?"

"*Minggu.*"

"Month?"

"*Bulan.*"

"Year?"

"*TAHUN!*" He almost shouted the word.

The fat man laughed again.

"Good. Now, say the sentence again," said the older man.

He repeated the sentence adding "*tahun*" at the end.

"*Kamu ada berapa adek beradek?*" (How many brothers and sisters have you?) said the older man.

Brothers, sisters. What was that . . . ? Then he said slowly one word at a time, the words that were filtering back.

"*Saya . . . ada . . . tiga adek perempuan . . . dan dua adek . . . laki laki.*" (I have three sisters and two brothers.)

The two men went into a huddle and whispered something in Malay very fast. Then they wrote something in their entry books. When he had finished writing, the older one turned to him again.

"You paint, you don't typewrite, you don't write shorthand, and you speak Bazaar Malay." He paused to light another cigarette, then, "Do you take part in any sport?"

"No, I'm afraid I don't know how to play any games."

"Not even badminton?"

"Not even badminton."

"Don't you get tired and bored with just painting?"

"Well, I . . . read a little."

He used to read a little anyway.

"Ah! Do you read the *Week-ender?*"

"No."

"*Humour? Tit-bits? Esquire?*"

"No. I don't go in for that type of reading. I prefer . . ." He shut his mouth. *Respectable Prostitutes* and *Ladies Not for Burning. Rotting Hills* and *Prospects of Seas. Love Among Ruins* and *Cries Out of Depths. Thieves' Carnivals* and *Orpheuses' Descendings.* And *Orpheuses* in calf-bound volumes in John Lehmann's editions. He bit his lower lip.

"Why, you should read the *Week-ender, Tit-bits, Humour,* and *Esquire.* They are very nice magazines."

He smiled weakly.

The older man whispered something to the fat man, who grinned and turned to him and said:

"I understand that you artists live very fast lives. Do you go to the cabaret?"

"No."

He had never been to a cabaret in his life. Why did the man form that opinion of artists? He looked at the men sitting there. The older man was absorbed in looking at his own finger nails. The fat man's face glistened with oily sweat.

"Are you married?" said the fat man.

"No." Why did the man ask him that all of a sudden?

"Do you intend getting married soon?"

"No."

225

They wrote something in their entry books.

"Well, that's all," said the older man capping his pen. "Now, will you go to the room where you were in just now and ask the next person on the list to come and wait outside? Tell him not to come in till he hears the bell. You can go after that. We'll inform you of our decision later."

He got up. Was the interview really over?

"Can I have my papers please?"

"Oh, sorry, here they are," said the older man. "Oh, yes. . . . Don't tell the others what we've been asking you. We want to test each person on his own ability."

"Of course." He put his papers into the folder. He hesitated for a moment. Then he said softly, "Good-bye."

The men seemed to be waiting for him to leave the room.

"*Selamat Tingal.*" (Stay well), he said loudly.

The men stared at him, surprised.

He left the room quickly closing the door behind him. He could hear their voices raised talking in rapid Malay. The interview was over.

He turned left at the corner of Young Road and stepped onto the footpath along Jalan Raja. The main thoroughfare in Kuala Lumpur. Heavy, incessant traffic. Exceptionally heavy it seemed that morning. He wrinkled his nose at the exhaust fumes of a lumbering lorry, and looked ahead to the left of him. He could see the new British Council building with its gorgeous architecture and semi-oriental roof on top of the hill at Bluff Road. There was a streamer with Romanized Malay in red letters strung high across the road. The exhibition of pictures by Malay artists. He had read about it in the newspapers before he left the house that morning. Admission free. Yes. He must see that before he went home.

J. Kasem Sibunruang

THE GOLDEN GOBY

"*F*ATHER, how is it that you are so late? . . . And where is Mother?" asked Uay, when she saw her father coming back alone from fishing. But her father did not answer her; he did not even look at her, but went directly to his second wife's quarters, where soon Uay heard him laughing and joking with his two other daughters.

The fisherman, Sethi, had two wives, of whom the first, Kanitha, had a daughter called Uay. The second wife, called Kanithi, had two daughters, Ay and Ee.

For several days, the husband had had many things he wanted to discuss with his second wife and had resented the constant presence of his first wife. Then the previous day, the two wives had quarrelled and the husband had reprimanded the first wife rather severely. But the next morning, in order that the second wife should not be too proud of her victory, he took the first wife along with him when he went out fishing. But in spite of his good will and his sense of justice, her presence weighed upon him.

It came to pass that, on that day, he caught nothing but a tiny little goby. "This woman brings me ill luck," thought the fisherman, and he threw the fish away.

"Please, do not throw it away! I'd like to take it back to my child," said Kanitha, but the husband did not say anything.

Presently the same fish came into the net again, and again the husband threw it away. Seeing that it was the same fish he had caught, Kanitha again asked her husband to keep it, saying:

"You see, my husband, this fish wants to come with us," and she laughed, suspecting not the hatred the man felt against her. "After all, we are not so well off, we never can offer a toy for our child. This fish costs you nothing, and still you refuse it. . . ."

It was a hot day and the fishing was fruitless . . . "Why does this

227

ungrateful woman reproach me so?", thought the angry fisherman and he struck her with all his strength. The struggle did not last long; Kanitha missed her footing and fell into the water.

"Pah, feminine tactics!", said the furious husband to himself, shrugging his shoulders.

Tired, angry with everything and especially with himself, the fisherman did not attempt to save his wife at all. He started home . . . "After all, good riddance to bad rubbish, there will be no more quarrelling under my roof. . . ."

"But Father, where is Mother?", asked the unfortunate Uay. To these repeated questions, the father finally replied:

"Listen, my child, think well, and stop bothering me with your silly questions:

> *To a beautiful palace under the sea*
> *Has gone thy mother away from thee.*
> *Come, dost thou not give way to weeping,*
> *In three days' time she will float back sleeping."*

At this instant, the daughter of the first wife realised the truth, she understood the sinister sense of the riddle; she had heard that when one is drowned, the body sinks down first, then floats on the surface for three days, then sinks again. She also knew that the corpse of a woman floats on its back while that of a man floats face downwards.

The poor girl insisted no more. She cried silently over her fate and lamented her mother's death. Scoldings and whippings from her father and especially from her step-mother she endured bravely. Outraged, but resigned, Uay ceased to give way to her grief. She bore the cruel yoke silently.

Now that Uay was deprived of her mother, she had to do all the hard work for the whole household. But she hurried through her work without complaint. As soon as she had a spare moment, she would run to the river. But, alas, nothing was to be seen. Days passed and there was no sign of her mother.

One day, as Uay was looking into the clear water, she saw a strange little fish; it glittered under the water, as if made of gold. Uay wiped her tears away, and for the first time diverted from her grief, she spoke aloud: "My poor little fish, I wish I had something to give you to eat. . . ." To her great astonishment, she heard the fish say: "My little Mouse, I am your Mother. . . . Listen to me and try to understand: I was killed cruelly, so the gods showed mercy and have granted me the power of speech. . . ."

According to superstition, the last vision before death has an influence upon the form one takes in the next reincarnation. Kanitha's thought was fixed upon the goby; so once dead, she took the form of a goby.

Uay's gladness knew no bounds. She took the fish in her hands, fondled her and told her all the details of her wretched life. But time was short, Uay had to run home lest her absence should be noticed. At night she crept into the garden and dug a little pond. . . . You can never tell, you can never be too sure of the current . . . nor of the fisher's net . . . and the thought had filled her with anguish. . . .

Now that Uay had taken the fish into her pond she was almost happy again; she came to feed her and spent long hours playing with and talking to her mother. . . .

Now Uay had a new job: she had to take care of the ducks; she had had no rice for her fish, so she reserved the tender morsels which were given her for the ducks.

Unhappily, one day, her step-sisters caught her speaking into the pond, and they duly reported to their mother, who guessed the truth and ordered her elder daughter Ay to catch the fish. The mother then sent Uay to look after the cows near the forest. Uay was sad and worried. What would happen to her golden goby during a whole day's absence? She fidgeted uncomfortably all day long, asking the animals not to wander too far off: she would like to get home as soon as she could. The animals understood her entreaties and stayed within sight.

In the meantime, Kanithi and her daughters took the fish out of the pond and prepared a delicious dish which they ate triumphantly. They took care to get rid of all traces. They gave the bones to their cats and the rest was thrown into the river. However, while they were preparing the fish, one of the scales fell to the ground. A duck saw it and picked it up for Uay who had been so kind to him.

Uay hurried home when the sun was low in the west. She ran to the pond and called her goby, but in vain. Desperate, she went

229

to her pet animals. The dogs and the cats looked at her silently. But the gods had mercy on her and allowed the duck to have the power of speech, not only did it give her the scale, but also told her the whole story. . . .

Grieved and bewildered, Uay bore her sorrow silently. She went about her work humbly, taking care not to show her feelings. She was resigned to her fate now; she put the beloved scale in a corner of her handkerchief and it consoled her to feel it next to her heart. One day she took the cows further than usual into the forest; there was a quiet, peaceful spot that pleased her a great deal. "I shall bury mother's relic here," said Uay to herself. "It is far from the house and nobody would think to come and harm it." Thus she buried the fish scale there and felt much better for having laid it to rest.

Now she was quite content to go about her work. She took the animals to the forest as soon as the house work was done. That seeming contentment, faint as it was, puzzled the step-mother and she sent her two daughters to spy on Uay.

Days and weeks went by, and it came to pass that at the spot where Uay had her mother's little tomb, there grew two plants called Makheua Proh (a kind of egg-plant, with delicious green fruit and hard seeds). These two plants, with their thick green leaves, bore a great quantity of fruit. The joy of the motherless Uay knew no bounds. But, alas, it was short-lived, for soon her two sisters found the plants and uprooted them, eating the fruit and throwing the rest into the river.

Here was more sorrow for the poor girl. She asked no questions, she did not even cry, but sat dumbly under the "sai" (banyan) tree. Silent, patient, her young heart heavy with pain and disappointment, she watched the cows grazing. The animals had pity on her; they never went out of her sight and their silent presence kept her company. But when it was time to take the animals home, Uay cringed at the thought of facing the cruelty of her step-mother and the two other girls. Her father took no part in the game. He had washed his hands of the whole business; but his very silence hurt Uay's affectionate young heart.

To her surprise, she had one friend; it was the duck. It followed Uay everywhere. When Uay went to the river to wash the dishes, she found the duck by her side, and as soon as they were alone, the duck gave Uay some of the Makheua seeds she had kept in her beak and told Uay about the whole incident.

The next day, when Uay took the cattle to the woods, she went a little further and buried the seeds. . . . She left the place reluctantly and after a few steps looked back. Lo! there stood at the very spot two beautiful papal trees.* One of the trees had golden leaves and the other silver ones. Uay came back to them, put her scarf on the fertile soil, and made obeisance over it three times: to her, this was doubly sacred.

Now a king named Thao Phrommathat came to hunt in the forest and saw the beautiful papal trees in this deserted spot. He thought that somebody must have been taking care of them, and ordered inquiries to be made. Thus Uay, young and beautiful, was brought into the royal presence.

The monarch fell in love with her and, not long afterwards, Uay became his queen.

The king graciously ordered that the trees be transported to the palace; but in spite of every effort, even with the help of elephants, it was impossible to move these sacred trees. Uay then prostrated herself on the very ground in front of the trees, saluted three times and said in her heart, "My mother, if you refuse to go to the palace, I will not leave you. These trees are all that I possess in this world. Please hear me, and answer my prayer." She then took hold of the trees with both hands, and out of the ground they came. . . .

This was the most happy period in Uay's life so far. Unfortunately, it did not last long. Her step-mother heard about her new life and worked out a plan with the aid of a witch, for she meant to make her own daughter queen at all costs.

Accordingly, Kanithi sent for Uay, pretending that her father had been taken very seriously ill. Suspecting nothing, Uay hurried to her old home. She was met by her step-mother at the door and she followed her to her father's room. But, alas, the prepared floor opened under her and she fell straight into a vat of boiling water. Calmly, Ay took her dead sister's garments and, thus attired, went to the palace.

Following her mother's sound advice, the sagacious girl pre-

* The papal tree under which Buddha meditated and found the Noble Truths. It is a sacred tree.

tended that she was ill and must keep to her own room. The king came to see her, but only in the semi-darkness, so he did not detect the deception. Besides, Ay had put a magic pomade on her lips and thus enchanted the king. But the latter was a man of strong will and not easily overpowered by any spell. Soon he became sad and distrait.

Uay, drowned in the boiling water, took the form of a parrot in her next reincarnation. She flew into the palace grounds and perched near the window of the king's bedroom. The sacred trees had now withered. The parrot kept singing this refrain:

> Sire, your trees are dying,
> Soon you will be crying.
> The fates have snapped the thread.
> You'll find your true love dead.

The king paid no attention at first, but as the bird sang on, he realised the truth and asked the bird to tell him the whole story. Then he ordered a golden cage to be made for the parrot and put it in his bedroom. Before he could do anything more, however, an urgent royal duty called him up country; a white elephant was seen up north and he had to go and hunt this animal of good omen. But it grieved him to leave the bird alone in his palace.

The false queen suspected the bird's influence over the king, now that the king was absent; she gave the bird to the cook. The latter plucked the bird, which pretended to be dead. The cook left it and went into the garden to pick some vegetables. In the meantime, with a supreme effort, the bird forced itself into a mouse hole. When the cook came back into the kitchen and found no bird, she was so frightened that she did not dare tell the truth to her queen. She just bought another parrot and prepared everything just as had been ordered for the royal dinner. The queen was very pleased with the cook and gave her a scarf as a reward.

The mouse was full of compassion for the unfortunate bird. He nursed the bird and took care of her until she was well enough to seek another and safer place. Then he took her to the other opening that he had made and which led to the forest, and bade her safe journey.

All by herself and deprived of wings, weak and forlorn, the parrot made her way slowly through strange places. She was exposed to many and varied dangers. Once a serpent was on the point of eating her, but fortunately, the serpent itself was attacked by a big bird and thus she was saved. Her strength was almost exhausted, when she came upon an anchorite. He took pity upon her and put her near the fire, the sacred object of his meditation. Suddenly the bird vanished and a beautiful young maiden rose from the flames: it was Uay, to whom the gods had granted a new life. Full of gratitude, Uay prostrated herself at the feet of the holy man, asking permission to serve him till the end of her life. But the old sage whose life was dedicated to prayer and solitude, thought that it would be wiser to create another human being to keep her company. So he drew a picture of a small boy five years of age and gave it the breath of life, this boy was named Lop.

Uay was very happy now. Restored to human life again, she now spent her time with Lop gathering fruits for the hermit. Many a time, she thought of her royal consort, especially when the child asked about his father and his kinsfolk. Then she would explain to the boy. "Lop, you are my child, and I am the child of this holy man. Your father is a king." But the lad wanted to know more about his royal father. Curious, the boy said: "Mother, let me go to the palace."

"My child," she replied, "would you know how to take care of yourself? Many dangers lie ahead of you." "The gods will protect me, Mother; you always say that the gods look after their creatures," insisted the boy. "Let me go to see my father, Mother. All the good that you have done shall be like a shield for my protection. I do want to see the trees with leaves of gold and silver, if they are still there, and I do want to see my father."

Lop's entreaties and insistence finally persuaded Uay to let him go to the city. She put around his neck a garland of flowers on which she inscribed the story of the white elephant hunt, the usurper's crime, the flight of the wingless bird, the resurrection and the creation of the boy.

Lop went to the city; he enjoyed himself tremendously, not noticing that people stared at him, wondering: "Whose child is this? What a queer chain he is wearing!" and so forth.

Soon this news reached the king and Lop was brought into his royal presence. The monarch asked the boy to tell about his errand, and the boy said he wanted to see the miraculous trees.

233

Great was the king's surprise, but greater still when he saw the garland round the boy's neck. The king could see the interpretation on the garland. He asked the boy questions, and the boy did not disappoint him, for young though he was, he was also very intelligent, and soon the king knew of Uay's existence; and he went to her in the forest.

When the holy man saw the king, he knew that both happiness and grief were in store for Uay; for it was written that when she saw her husband again she would lose what she cherished most. Lop would turn into an image again as soon as he was seven years old and that would be in three days' time. The hermit called the girl and told her what the future held for her. He then entreated her to leave the forest; her duty was to follow her royal husband.

Thus Uay left the hermit and came into the city. The people celebrated the queen's happy return for seven days and seven nights. The half-sister and her cook were brought to trial and they confessed their crimes. They were not killed, but put into prison.

Uay had suffered a great deal, but her meditations had made her more compassionate and less vindictive. She realised that a bad action must not be answered by another bad one. Evil must be overcome by good. It is better to stop the circle of reincarnation. After much pleading, she obtained a pardon for the two guilty women. But it was too late for her half-sister, Ay poisoned herself while she was in prison.

Uay's father had been cruel to his own flesh and blood and the step-mother had killed Uay for the sake of Ay. The king ordered that Ay's body be sent to Sethi in a jar. The parents were very proud of their daughter being a queen. They boasted so much about her. Now, when they received a present from the palace, they believed that the queen, their daughter, had provided meat for her family. But soon they realised with terror that their crimes were discovered, and they fled into the deep forest.

Now there came at this time a wise man to the kingdom of Thao Phrommathat. The king received the holy man royally. He asked him to explain to them the cause of Uay's misfortunes, for Uay had done no wrong to her fellow creatures. This was what he told them:

"In one of her previous lives Kanitha, Uay's mother, had separated a chicken from its mother; she took the hen to the gods and gave the chicken to her own child to play with. But the chicken cried and ran after its mother and fell into a pot of boiling water. Thus Uay was separated from her mother and killed in the same way."

"But," asked the king, "when she became a bird and was on the point of being killed, why was she saved?"

"In one of her previous lives, she was a vulture, Ay was a chicken. The bird of prey was taking the chicken up to its eyrie, but she let it go by accident, and that is why Uay was saved."

"Most noble father," asked the king, "why did Sethi kill his first wife?"

"Sethi once took the form of a talkative parrot and was cherished by its owner. In that same reincarnation, Kanitha took the form of a cat, living in the same house as the parrot. The cat was jealous of the parrot and, when the owner was absent, she killed the bird. That was why he hated her and let her drown.

"Every act has its consequence and repeats itself reciprocally until one party realises the essence of life and ceases to return evil for evil. Then little by little we eliminate our own reincarnations and come to that blissful joy of pure serenity which saves us from this dreary and vicious world."

The king and Uay forgave Sethi and his wife Kanithi. They asked the culprits to leave their hiding place and to come and live at court.

The king and Uay spent the rest of their lives virtuously and lived together in perfect harmony till the end of their long and peaceful lives.

Achdiat K. Mihardja

HAMID

*A*T moments like these Hamid badly needed his wife—or somebody who similarly admired him and would praise him when, as now, he wanted to tell about the speech he had made at the meeting.

It was three weeks now since Mimi had gone to Bandung about an inheritance, so that Hamid had had to live like a bachelor, with only Salim to bear him company and manage the household.

It was almost sunset. Bathed, and in pyjamas still warm from the iron, Hamid enjoyed the freshness of the afternoon breeze. He dragged out to the terrace his favourite sagging-seated rattan chair, and snuggled his fat body down into it.

His thoughts still on the meeting, Hamid was only partly aware of the pedicab drivers out front, chatting, cleaning their lamps, ringing their bells, or saying something to passing maid-servants or working girls to make them blush. When, occasionally, some sentence registered on Hamid's mind and startled him from reverie, he was shocked, and shivered as if frightened. How dirty-mouthed, how crude and coarse they are, he thought. He hated them. But he hated himself too for having, a week ago, praised them before a branch meeting of his party as heroes of freedom. Why was President Sukarno once so generous in praise of these rude men? What did he know about them? Palace and hovel are too far apart. But he, Hamid, knew all, for they lived behind his house.

The sun set; the evening drum sounded. Hamid turned on the lights and hastily performed his ritual washing in the bathroom. He prayed: *Allahu Akbar! Allahu Akbar!* Evening prayer finished, he ate—little, and without appetite. He was fed up with Salim's cooking—fried bean cakes again. He lighted a Skipper cigarette, playing with the blue smoke that spiralled delicately upward.

He felt, as often since Mimi had gone away, a lonely deserted feeling in the house. He was a voluble person who loved to spend evenings on idle chitchat, and was restless and bored when alone. A week ago he was still easily able to allay this feeling: jump into the office car, and glide off to a friend's to talk or invite him for a spin about the city, to Pasar Senen, Glodok, Jatinegara, Zandvoort, or anywhere, until the gas was almost gone.

But since the car had been damaged in a collision a week ago, he mostly just stayed at home, terribly bored. He sometimes invited Salim for a chat, but Salim was so talkative that Hamid could scarcely get in a word, and he often overstepped the bounds distinguishing friend from employer—as if he were addressing his friend Abdul, or his younger brother Otong, or his sweetheart Omah, rather than his employer Hamid, who gave him food and wages.

Furthermore, Salim was too fond of comparing the "normal" Dutch period with the present, harping on how in the old days he could eat, buy clothing, see every new film with his sweetheart, whereas now . . . Hamid thought him a deserter from the holy national struggle, and were it not that he pitied Salim because he could not return to his native village, now controlled by Kartosuwirjo, the Darul-Islam leader, would have chased him from the house long ago.

What to do, then? Since overtime regulations became valid for senior employees, Hamid never brought work home: it was more advantageous to continue working after hours in the office. And, save for newspapers and picture magazines, Hamid didn't like to read. Nor was he a journalist or author who liked to write at home for a newspaper or on a book.

"Isn't Tuan going out this evening?" asked Salim. Hamid did not reply.

Under the Dutch, Hamid had been only a clerk second grade: now he was a category C senior employee—a real "six-C-er". It was political activity which had won him the post, to which his party's representative in the cabinet had forthwith appointed him. The moment this had occurred, Hamid had gone straightway to the shrine of Luar Batang to present the *Kulhu* and

Fatihah to the soul of Sheik Abdul Muhji. After strewing flowers, he had caressed and embraced Jagur, the holy cannon, a Portuguese trophy. And that evening he had dined at home with the Minister.

Hamid's speeches were clever—"remarkable", said his friends in the party. And they were not the only ones who enjoyed listening; Hamid himself did. He had once frankly confessed this to Mimi, who had replied, "Ah, dear, as happy as you are to hear yourself, you are not half so happy as I." The answer consumed Hamid with happiness: he embraced her, his eyes blinded by tears of joy.

This evening, as always, Hamid felt elated about his speech— as if he could still hear his voice and feel his gestures as he stood on the rostrum. The glowing reception of today's speech had been especially wonderful. The audience applauded noisily after he analysed and attacked "Tjiliwung Culture" as rampant in certain Jakarta social strata which liked dancing at Garden Hall, at the Hôtel des Indes, at the Airport, and so on.

All this proved, he believed, that Indonesian social groups were dominated by a character crisis caused by "the aggression of Western culture", pioneered by the Dutch who wanted to colonize Indonesia again, assisted by henchmen who favoured retention of the Dutch language in high schools and the university. This aggression must be stopped because it damaged and frustrated the national character. Dancing, swimming, and worse . . . The government itself, calling itself national and based on the philosophy of the Pantja-Sila, the Five Principles, had permitted this, and in the schools made boys and girls study and participate in sports together. Did all this not contravene the culture of the East? Where was the nation going? Did the national government want to make us lose our way, as the colonial government had done? Was this what our country sacrificed, fought, and died for?

Suddenly Hamid jumped from his chair. He could not bear to sit alone any longer. He sensed it was disloyal to criticize the government, because his party participated in it. He quickly went into his bedroom and changed to complete street clothes. But at the last minute he took off his tie again.

"Salim, Salim," he called. "I'm going out. Close the front and side doors. Don't you leave the house. Don't think that, just because I'm out, you can go have fun at Omah's house."

The clock said 7.45. He hurried out, and jumped into a pedicab.

"Let's go, Bung!"

"Where to, Boss?" asked the driver, who was borrowing a cigarette from his friend.

"Anywhere." The driver looked surprised.

"Eh, well . . . to Tanah Abang, then."

"Okay, Boss!" The driver jumped to his seat and pedalled them off, his palm-leaf cigarette crackling and sputtering. "Going to enjoy yourself, Boss?"

Hamid at first pretended not to have heard, then: "I'm looking for *saté*, Bung. I haven't eaten Tanah Abang *saté* for a long time."

Amat's pedicab squeezed skilfully among the crowding vehicles. At each near-collision, Hamid shouted a warning. But Amat always answered:

"Experience, Boss. Don't worry . . . ten years of pedalling . . . in an office I'd have been promoted by now." In a quieter street he enlarged on the theme. "Never had an accident, Boss. I'm not like those other showoffs. They're less careful, less experienced. They're nervous, too, so naturally they have accidents. But not me. Has our pedicab even grazed another vehicle? Just say 'bismillah' once and we are safe."

And with that, for no apparent reason, the pedicab suddenly swerved to the left, tilting so that Hamid, hat askew, fell into the footrest section.

He shouted again, this time very angry: "Watch out, you fool! Do you want to kill us?"

"Experience, Boss, experience . . . Don't you worry."

They were silent some time. Then Amat said: "Haven't taken the Missus to market for a long time. Is she out of town, Boss?"

"She went to Bandung," Hamid snapped.

"Oh, to Bandung, Boss?"

Amat then had to push the pedicab up a hill. He was panting. But the moment he got on the down-grade, he began again:

"Uh . . . Boss, in Tanah Abang I know a . . ."

239

R

"Know what?"

"Someone who's just come from Sukabumi. Wah, she's quite a dish, Boss. Terrific. She's a lovesick widow, too, Boss. You know what that is!"

Very angry, Hamid snarled loudly: "What do you think I am?"

Amat was embarrassed by the outburst. A miscalculation. This fish didn't grab the bait. He decided not to say another word. At the corner by the movie theatre Hamid got out and silently handed Amat two *rupiahs* and a half.

"Allah! Only a *ringgit*! You can't be serious! I pedal till I'm half dead, and only a *ringgit*! Have a heart and give me some more." Hamid ignored him and disappeared into the throng, followed by Amat's highly audible insults: "If you don't have any more, don't take a pedicab, you shameless so-and-so." The watching people laughed.

As always, Tanah Abang was jammed with humans moving as restlessly as ants. Street vendors were laying out mats on which to spread cloth, ready-made clothing, teapots and cups, medicines, hair-combs, pins, and the like. Above their merchandise, Petromax lamps hissed. The vendors tried to outshout one another:

"Step up, Bung! Step up, Tuan! Come on, Madam! Select first, then bargain. Don't pay before you buy. You're sure to be satisfied. If you don't buy, you'll regret it. Hurry, hurry, hurry!"

With voices already hoarse, and dripping with perspiration, they shouted through megaphones. From coffee shops and restaurants radios were going full blast. Here, Nji Upit-Sarimanah, singing the Sundanese song, "Bintang Gurilja"; there, Dimin singing "Kerontjong Merdeka." On another radio, someone was speaking, and some words stopped Hamid: the subject was his own favourite—the character crisis—and it was a woman speaking. Her voice was unfamiliar, but he agreed with her speech. From time to time he nodded and smiled to himself. He wanted to listen till the end, but his feet were repeatedly stepped on; to protect them, he had to let himself be swept along in the tide. Not far away was a rice house that featured goat *saté*. When he had ordered twenty large pieces, he noticed that fortunately the same woman's speech was on that radio too, so, while he waited, he listened, nodding and smiling agreement as before.

After eating, Hamid again went along with the human sea. Usually he was unhappy when alone, with no friend to talk to; but this time, elated by the surrounding gaiety, he felt that alone he could better absorb all that was occurring about him.

This was the arena of ordinary life, the common people of the palm-leaf-wrapped cigarette and the hairknot greased with coconut oil; far from the world of "Soir de Paris" and the "Karel I" cigar. But it was a world still pure and unsoiled, not yet ensnared in artificiality. Hamid felt deep satisfaction in seeing it mill before his eyes. He watched especially to see whether, among the women, any were scantily clad, as on the dance floor at the Garden Hall or the Hôtel des Indes. He also kept an extra-sharp lookout to see whether, among the inhabitants of the shacks and muddy alleys, any embraced in public.

Hamid was like driftwood on an ocean swell. Sometimes he would watch someone bargaining for a piece of cloth; sometimes listen to the spiel of a patent-medicine hawker. He asked himself why these people, who were not outdone by even President Sukarno in the art of haranguing, didn't use this skill to become a leader like "Bung Karno" or like him, Hamid.

Then he suddenly suspected that it might be more advantageous if he, Hamid, used his skill at speaking in the trade of patent-medicine selling. But this thought was quickly shoved aside by another: that the position of a patent-medicine salesman was not so high as that of a senior official like himself. The highest ranking patent-medicine salesman would not have had a journalist waiting to interview him as had occurred ten days ago to Hamid.

Unwittingly Hamid was being swept toward an open place where men and women in pairs were noisily dancing under the light of a smoky three-wick kerosene lamp on a pole. A drum boomed, a wooden flute tootled the song "Kembang Beureum", and, at certain intervals, a gong clanged while a woman's voice, already hoarse, tirelessly sang the verses:

> Short cane reed, tall cane reed,
> Cane reed leaning over the pathway.
> I love to stay, I love to visit,
> I love to meet people as I go along.

241

Hamid pushed his way to where, by standing on his toes, he could see over the shoulder of a tall man. Five taxi-girls were dancing. The three still without partners stood in front of the musicians, facing the spectators.

By turns the girls sang erotic songs. All were young, some still children of thirteen or fourteen. Some wore green, yellow or red imitation-silk pedal pushers, while their *kains* were folded, reaching midway on their thighs. Their jackets were tucked into their *kains* which were gathered with their sashes, the ends of which hung down free on either side. Red or yellow glass necklaces and bracelets decorated their necks and wrists. Their face powder was thick. Some did not wear pedal pushers, but the usual batik cloth instead. Some also wore, instead of a jacket, a *kain* sash around their torsos which only half covered their breasts. Several also had white handkerchiefs tied round their heads.

The pushing from behind had shoved Hamid out in front of the tall man, where he could see more clearly. Two of the remaining three taxi-girls now had partners. The singing and dancing grew more eager. The girls lightly moved their arms, while their hips writhed and their waists undulated, arousing their partners to passion and more zealous dancing. Their feet kicked like those of a colt round its mother, their backs arched and crouched, their heads swayed from side to side when the gong sounded.

Hamid pushed till he was right in front, with a full view. Suddenly he saw one of the dancers kissed on the lips by her partner. Hamid was startled. Insolent, he thought. Yet his heart pounded, and he felt a certain welling upward.

The man continued to kiss the girl's lips, cheeks, and neck, pressing his body closer and closer to hers, while his right hand caressed her breasts. How brazen, seethed Hamid. But he kept staring wide-eyed, and that certain feeling welled up even stronger, choking him. He swallowed hard.

Just then he felt someone pushing from behind. A girl's breast brushed his arm. The fragrant odours of "Saripohatji" face powder and of a sweet *tjempaka* flower tucked in her hairknot made that certain feeling reach the boiling point. He glanced sidewise at her: young, and pretty. Her nose was pointed, her mouth tiny, and her black eyes sparkled. The moment they met Hamid's, she smiled.

His heart beat faster. The girl pressed her body more tightly against him. His nervousness was great, but the throbbing emotions in his breast were stronger. Suddenly his uncertain groping hand found the girl's. As he grasped it, an electric current coursed through his body. While he caressed the hand, his eyes continued to stare at the embracing couple. After several moments, his hand was suddenly pulled and a soft voice invited:

"Come, Sir."

They entered a narrow dark alley. Hamid could not bear it any longer. Ani suddenly found herself locked in a tight embrace, pressed against a fence. Her lips were kissed and her cheeks bitten. She squirmed, trying to free herself, but Hamid pressed her even harder against the fence.

"Don't, not here, Boss, not here," Ani cried out, wriggling like an eel to free herself.

Hamid came to his senses; with his body quivering he freed Ani and picked up his cap, knocked to the ground by her flailing hands. They walked on without saying a word.

"Having a little fun, Boss?" asked a man's voice. Hamid snatched his hand from around Ani's waist. He felt as if his blood had stopped circulating. His face was pale in the light of the lamp covered with red paper hanging in front of a dilapidated shack. For he had immediately recognized the voice as that of Sanusi, the journalist who had interviewed him on the character crisis. Hamid felt completely humiliated. Ani's tug at his sleeve pulled him out of his daze.

"Come on, Boss, please go in."

Hamid felt his feet treading stairs, but suddenly he wrenched his arm from Ani's hand:

"No, I'm sorry . . . I . . . I . . ."

He nervously pulled out a twenty *rupiah* note and thrust it at her. Surprised, Ani mocked him:

"Boss is a big spendthrift. Won't there be a shortage in the household money?" She laughed piercingly. Her stab struck deep. A grade C official and popular leader, short of household money? How impertinent, how insolent. Hamid grew very angry.

He snatched the smaller note from her fingers and threw a fifty *rupiah* note in her face.

"Why are you angry, Boss?" she asked as she bent to pick up the note. At its size, she laughed.

But Hamid had hurried away to catch Sanusi. He was no longer visible in the dark alley.

"Did you see a man in a sports shirt and grey trousers just now?" Hamid asked of a man broiling *saté* in front of a shack with a green lantern.

"He just went into that alley, there."

"Thank you," said Hamid and hurried to it. He saw Sanusi entering a shack with a red lantern. At Hamid's shout, Sanusi, startled, looked round.

"Uh, Bung," Hamid stammered, "uh . . . don't tell anyone, huh? . . . don't . . . uh . . . put it in your column . . ." Sanusi burst out laughing "And . . . uh . . . I didn't do a thing, did I, huh?"

Sanusi laughed louder. He guffawed. An understanding laugh, but it made Hamid lose courage. Why did Sanusi laugh so? Was he crazy?

"Don't worry, Boss. I'll take care of it."

"Oh, thank you, thank you." Hamid felt relieved to have escaped the danger. He turned to leave.

"Oh, just a minute, Boss. Just leave it to me, but of course, you know . . . between the two of us. If not, well . . . " and Sanusi shrugged his shoulders.

The despicable scoundrel, thought Hamid. He pulled out another fifty *rupiah* note and shoved it into the hands of Sanusi, who examined it under the light from the red lamp. He laughed mockingly.

"Fifty *rupiahs*. Ha ha!"

His sports shirt twitched with his laughter. This rotten journalist, thought Hamid. He pulled out another banknote.

Again Hamid received only laughter in reply:

"Ha ha, ten more . . . a high official . . ."

Hamid was now too angry to care what happened. To hell with it, let Sanusi write it up in his gossip column, he wasn't scared. He wanted to punch Sanusi's flat nose. But he did not act on the urge. He quickly turned and walked away from

Sanusi, who was still laughing, with the two banknotes in his hands. Sixty *rupiahs*, chuckled Sanusi to himself. Manna, manna from heaven. Sixty *rupiahs* in two minutes, without lifting a finger. Out of this world. And, smiling, he entered the shack.

At a main street, Hamid jumped into a pedicab: "Kembang Street, Bung."

Still greatly upset, Hamid wasn't able to forget it all: the dancers embracing, Ani, Sanusi. He completely and utterly hated that Sanusi. He felt like killing him. But his anger gradually gave way to fear. He felt as if the world were closing in on him. He was afraid that, just at this time of character crisis, Sanusi might mention him in his gossip column anyway. Because he hadn't bribed him enough, judging from the way Sanusi had laughed.

In his confusion, Hamid almost wept. But he was suddenly relieved by the thought of going to Sukotjo, a tough sergeant-major, a former guerrilla fighter. He could help him. It was easy to get Sukotjo to do something. With a hundred *rupiahs*, it would all be settled. Let him threaten Sanusi, and, if necessary, yes, if necessary . . .

Hamid felt calm again. Tomorrow he would go see the sergeant-major. Tonight it was too late. He felt greatly relieved now. His reputation as a leader, as a high official, and as a person of good character, would be protected.

It was already past eleven when he got out of the pedicab in front of his house. Eee . . . he was startled. Why was the light in the front room still burning? Was Salim still up? Hamid rapped at the door.

"Salim, Salim, open up!" The door was immediately opened. Mimi! "Why, Mimi, when did you get home?"

His nervousness was such that he was wiping his shoes on the doormat as if they were thick with mud.

"Early, dear, at eight o'clock. You must just have left when I came. The bus broke down at Puntjak. Where did you go?"

Hamid's nervousness increased. Unable to think instantly of an answer, he tried to conceal his discomfiture by blowing his nose as if he had a cold.

"To a meeting, Mimi," he got out after several blows. Mimi smiled and pulled him into the house.

Before going to sleep, Mimi told her husband how proud she was of his interview with Sanusi.

"I read the interview to Mother, dear."

Hamid smiled and playfully bit Mimi on the chin.

Throughout the night Mimi slept contentedly nestled in Hamid's embrace. And, as usual, a knowing smile played lightly about her lips.

Indonesia

Chairil Anwar

TO GADIS

AMIDST
The green leaves
The light and open fields,
Innocent children just able to crawl,
Sweet-singing birds,
The fresh, invigorating rain.
A young nation rises that can just say "I"
And then
The crisp dry wind, the scorched earth,
The swirling sand blown back,
The evacuated land.
We are wedged in
And forced to shrink, grow small,
Able to move a step only now and then.

Let us free ourselves, our souls, become
A winging dove,
Fly
And know the fields without meeting and
        without
The consummation of the flight.

Sitor Situmorang

CHARTRES CATHEDRAL

WILL He speak in the still night
When snow falls and birds are all whitefeathered?
Sometimes one wants to surrender,
To find the shelter of bare prayer.

Oh, God, never again can we meet in prayer
Together with the congregation of the faithful.
Here I brought love in my love's sad quiet eyes.
The living day and judgment day were joined.

She wept bitterly that Easter Day
When we went on pilgrimage to Chartres;
Her prayers were a film over the colours of the stained
    glass.
And Christ was crucified with my final desperate words.

And that night before the cock crowed,
Before the people of Chartres left the fair,
She wept among the leaves of the declining night
While my thoughts, memories, went wandering in the rain.

To motherhood, to wife and child, and to the figure of
    Jesus.
The heart struggled between adultery and faith.
My love is one, her God is one,
Living and the end of life united.

This was the story of our love
Which began in the flower fair
In the early morning around Notre Dame de Paris
In the flowering season, the season of dreaming eyes.

247

This was the story of that Easter Day
When all nature was pursued by restlessness,
By temptation, adulteries, love and the city;
Because of her, because of me and the faith of a wife.

And that night in bed at the lodgings
The holiness of the song of the church of faith
Brought together the curse of passion and the compassion
    of God
The beckoning of faithful love and the clasp of woman.

Such
The tale of Easter
When the ground was wet
Tears of sadness
And flowers blooming
On the soil of France
On sweet soil
When Christ was crucified.

John Morrison

GOING THROUGH

*I*T can mean one of two things. Either you're being admitted to the Union—the Waterside Workers' Federation of Australia —or you're, well, just "going through". In plain English: knocking off before time, beating the whistle, sneaking away in the last few minutes and leaving your mates to put on beams and hatchboards while you make sure of a seat in the waiting bus. An unfortunate identity of terms. In one instance, you're a good fellow— or supposed to be—in the other you're both ends and the bight of an unmitigated name.

In this case, we're all good fellows—or supposed to be. Three hundred of us, all in our Sunday best, crowded into the narrow lane alongside the hall on a bright afternoon in mid-winter. Three hundred Second Preference men all agog at the prospect of becoming Federation men in the next few blessed hours, of walking the Dock Road next week with the magical little blue button in our lapels, of standing up for work in the sacred inner precincts of the Compound, of getting good ships and being in on the big money. It's been a long road for most of us, a road measured in years, in workless weeks, in bitter struggles "on the outer" for all the wretched scraps of jobs that were turned down inside: sulphur, superphosphates, soda ash, freezer, double-dump wool. We've cursed the Federation from Hell to Booligal for all the muck they've tossed out at us, but there isn't one of us here who isn't licking his lips over what's going to happen next week. It'll be worth it all, if only for the joy of presenting our insolent backs to the first foreman who picks up for wool on Monday morning—"Take it out to the bloody Seconds!"

There'll be plenty to succeed us, with licences still going at 12/- the dozen and no difficult questions asked.

Nothing to do now but yarn, smoke, and study each other,

249

while waiting for routine business to be got through inside. They've been at it for nearly an hour. Rumour has it that they're debating a motion that a car be provided for the Vigilance Officer. We'd like to be in on that one. Second Preference men on rock at Yarraville and wheat at Williamstown have always had to fight their own battles.

The door at the top of the short flight of wooden steps remains closed, but every window, high in the brick wall above our heads, is open a few inches and plenty of noise comes out. Union meetings of wharfies are forthright if nothing else. Someone who has just been around to the entrance in Flinders Street informs us that the hall is packed, that they're standing in the aisles. Against a ceaseless undertone of murmuring voices and shuffling feet one man is endeavouring to make himself heard:

"Always blowing our bags about conditions . . . our own officers . . . pushbikes . . . flat out like lizards . . . Twenty-one Dock . . . singing out for him at Port Melbourne . . . be a bloody Mandrake. . . ."

Another voice calls him to order, but he bellows on in a gale of laughter, stamping feet, and yells of encouragement.

Next meeting we'll be concerned with all this domestic business; today we aren't. We want them to get it over quickly, to get down to the only really important item on the agenda: "New members".

We watch each other. Interesting to observe how clothes transform men. Sometimes I have to look a second time before recognizing a fellow I've worked alongside for days on end. Nothing in common except the big hard hands, and some quality not easily definable in the endless variety of faces. Most of us are talking, but with little enthusiasm. Our minds are on something else. Without actually listening, we're alive to every sound that floats out through the windows. We glance persistently at the door at the top of the steps. Once, when it opens and an official puts his head out for a moment, the whole crowd ripples into life. But he is gone before any of us gets a chance to ask him a question. We feel colder than ever then. We stamp our feet, and look enviously at pedestrians passing to and fro across the outlet into Flinders Street. We could go out there and keep warm by walking up and down, but the habits of the pick-up are too strong on us. We're afraid we might miss something.

Here and there a bit of malicious gossip colours the conversation. All of us know men who have no hope of going through, who in attempting to do so are running a risk of insult, even of physical hurt. Men of whom it is whispered that they once scabbed in some other industry, gave information against a fellow-worker, or bribed a foreman for a job on the waterfront. Some of them betray themselves by their demeanour, like Colin Lamond, to whom my mate, Tiny Stoll, draws attention.

"Get an eyeful of Col over there. The bastard doesn't know whether to go on with it or go home."

I nod, with distaste, but with a little pity also. A situation like this goes so much deeper than one man's wretched weakness. But Col was well warned, and he must have known that a day of reckoning had to come sooner or later. He stands alone, keeping in the background, a big powerful man of middle-age, wrapped in a new fawn belted overcoat that must have set him back fifteen guineas. He can afford it. There are many ways of getting into the big money without waiting for a union ticket, and Col has exploited them all. Time and again he has been seen on jobs that were certainly never picked inside. The strain of excessive working hours shows in his drawn face and tired eyes. And something else—indecision, a grim, urgent thoughtfulness. Not for him the joy of an approaching rich reward. Plenty of Federation men also know him by sight, and it will need only one shout of "Sniper!" and Lamond will be lucky to get out without being knocked down. He has a problem to solve all right, and not many minutes left in which to solve it.

"If it was me I'd give it away," I say to Tiny.

"He's got Buckley's chance."

The door at the top of the steps opens wide and an official comes out on to the landing.

"All right, you fellows. We're going to take you in alphabetical order. All the A's, B's, and C's come up to the front."

The surge of eager men is partially arrested. We sort ourselves out amid a chorus of familiar cries, so that the narrow lane takes on all the colour and excitement of a Compound lock-up.

"They're racing!"

251

"Three o'clock start and back after tea!"

"Freezer with hooks!"

"Get down off the fence!"

The last sally strikes a popular note. Even the official smiles. We won't hear that one after today. I glance at Col Lamond. He hasn't moved. He's stroking his chin now, and staring up at the official as if he hated the very guts of him. Just one whisper of a challenge coming out by those windows and he'll go to water.

The first half dozen men mount the steps and pass in. The door closes. We settle down to more waiting, more gossip. All the gossip with a tang of the waterfront. Of ships, of cargoes, of foremen, of waterfront ethics—mostly of waterfront ethics. There's a special morality here which is not easy for outsiders to comprehend.

I'm reminded of an incident that occurred only last week when I went into the Clyde for a drink with a Federation acquaintance. My mate introduced me to an old-timer who had been drinking alone.

"Tom Hendry—meet a young cobber of mine, Jim Lamble. He's coming up for admission on Sunday."

I shook hands with Tom Hendry. He had a hearty grip, wise grey eyes that rested thoughtfully on mine for a moment before he spoke.

"You'll be all right. You never did nothing wrong, did you?"

Anything wrong? Startled, my mind flew immediately to all the old familiar paternal precepts: stealing, lying, swearing. . . .

He released my hand, picked up his half-emptied glass from the bar counter.

"You know what I'm talking about, don't you? You never scabbed, or anything like that? You never did any sniping?"

"Not on your life!"

"You'll be all right, son."

The tremendous assurance of it! I'd be all right. What matter if I had strangled my blind mother. . . .

They aren't wasting much time inside. All of us know the procedure from hearsay, and although only a few words are distinguishable we can tell by the rise and fall of voices just what is going on at any given moment. Every time the door opens to

admit more men—six at a time—we know that the last batch is
even then facing the assembled members. We can hear the
powerful voice of the President as he introduces each individual,
and the muffled responses of proposer and seconder as they
pop up in the body of the hall.

"George Eaton . . ."

"Proposed!"

"Seconded!"

"Arthur Emberson . . ."

"Proposed!"

"Here!"

And the short tense silence which, at the end of every group
of introductions, follows the President's: "Anybody know anything against any of these men?"

Finally the outburst of clapping hands and stamping feet
which tells the nervous recruits that it is all over, they are
through: ". . . admitted to membership of the Waterside Workers'
Federation of Australia."

Even those of us with easy consciences are caught up in an
atmosphere of suspense. This isn't at all like joining the A.W.U.
or other trade unions with which we are familiar. "Federation",
always a name to be spoken with respect, becomes suddenly
portentous. We've been thinking of this day in terms of more
and better jobs, bigger pay envelopes; it is borne in on us now
that that is only part of it, that there are obligations less
tangible and far more profound than the mere observance of
job conditions.

The lane takes on something of the alertness of a dentist's
waiting-room. We talk less, listen yet more eagerly, stare foolishly
up at the windows as if images as well as words were floating
out. No challenges yet, but in those awful pauses we become
part of the solemn tribunal inside. It's beginning to haunt
Lamond. His name, like mine, is half-way through the alphabet,
which means that he'll go through all the torments of a challenge
twenty times before mounting those steps. He hasn't moved a
muscle in the last ten minutes. He still leans against the wall,
hands thrust deep into overcoat pockets. A small space has been
left clear immediately in front of him, and he never lifts his
eyes from the bluestone roadway. No doubt, ghosts of all the

foremen he has ever bribed, and all the Union men who have ever questioned his presence on a job, are passing there before his worried gaze.

Four o'clock. On the K's, and still no challenges. It's becoming tedious. We've got tired of the strain of listening, of standing stiff-necked with pricked ears, of watching the processions of newly-fledged unionists troop down the steps with smiling, relaxed faces.

They sound as if they're getting a bit bored inside, too. The voice of the President has fallen to a monotonous recitation, time allowed for a challenge has dwindled to a few seconds, and the final roar of applause cuts in each time even as approval is being moved. No doubt it's cold in there also, and they're in a hurry to be finished and get home to tea and fireside. The light of the sinking sun has long since receded from the top of the over-hanging wall. The air takes on the nip of imminent frost, while out in Flinders Street a thin mist settles over the polished road. Faces among the Seconds are pinched and blue.

It is something in the nature of an anti-climax when the first of the L's are called and I climb the wooden steps. Six of us. We want to run up, to bound up two at a time, but we restrain ourselves and go up with becoming dignity.

We find ourselves in a large room full of cupboards and stacked chairs, and with three doors. The one we're interested in is covered with green baize. The official marshals us, checks off our names on a sheet of foolscap, tells us we are to go in in single file and identify ourselves to the Secretary as we pass on to the stage. Lamond, as I had anticipated, is next to me. He is the only one of us who doesn't look cold. His lips are tightly closed, his face very pale. There is something of the trapped animal in the glance he throws around him. When, to cover his nervousness, he lights a cigarette, I notice that his hands are trembling.

In an odour of dust and old paper we stand listening. We can hear everything now. The last of the K's are on the stage, introductions are over. The voice of the President, now only a few feet away, intones the familiar formula: Anybody know anything against any of these men?

"Yes . . . I do!"

There have been many little silences this afternoon, but none like this one. We heard the President quite distinctly, but only now became aware that he was speaking against a murmur of hundreds of lowered voices. All this now ceases. The official who is with us gives an excited exclamation, steps over to the green door, and unashamedly places his ear against it. Lamond catches me watching him, drops his eyes to the floor, then suddenly lifts his head and gives me a defiant stare.

We can see nothing, but we know that everybody at the other side of the door is looking to where a man has stood up and is pointing at the stage.

"I want to ask that man a question."

"Which man?" asks the President. "Name him."

"The third from the left. The bloke in the black raincoat."

We can count each footfall as the President approaches the bloke in the black raincoat.

"Yes, that's him. Ask him . . ."

"Thomas King . . ."

"I forget the second name, but it's him all right. I only knew him as Tom." It is as if the two voices are speaking in an empty hall.

"What d'you want to ask him?"

"I want to ask him first: Did he ever live in Rennison Street, Richmond?"

We do not hear the reply, but the man must have indicated agreement.

"And you worked for Gagen's Timber Company in Burnley?"

Perhaps five seconds—then the voice of the President:

"Go on, you can answer that one."

"Tell him to speak up!"

"Stir him up! This ain't a quiz . . ."

Shouts of impatience are rising from all parts of the hall. Again we do not hear the reply, but the man must have said something, because silence falls again and there comes the third question:

"You was at Gagen's when the timber workers was out in thirty-two. Now what I want to know is: Where did you go to work then? Because . . ." The shouting starts again, but the interrogator claps on steam, "because you never stopped work-

255

S

ing. You took a job at Rickson's in Camberwell Road, didn't you. Now, didn't you?" The victim is probably trying to make some kind of answer, but he must know he's lost. He's been a bundle of nerves all the afternoon, like Lamond. Now, with several thousand keen eyes watching his every change of expression. . . .

Amid a rising tumult, the accuser goes on:

"Have a good look at me, Tom King: I lived only three doors down from you. You used to come home every night after dark, with your work togs in a bag. Everybody in the bloody street was on to your form!"

"Order! The member must make his charges . . ."

"I'll make 'em all right, don't you worry. I had mates starved in that strike, and that animal . . ."

"Order! If the member . . ."

It's all over, though, and nobody knows it better than the President himself. The unfortunate man must have made a gesture, of confession, of despair, of fear, because the rising wave of noise suddenly breaks. I'm not personally involved, but the violence of it horrifies me. It is as if those men had been confronted by the very spirit of a dreaded pestilence. There is a prolonged crashing of chairs as half of them jump to their feet.

"Scab! . . . Scab! . . . Scab! . . ."

"Out with him!"

"Throw the bastard down the stairs!"

Close to us there is a sound of hurrying feet, and the green door is flung open. The roar of angry voices hits us like something solid, but our eyes are not on the cave out of which it comes. They are on the President, standing at one side, one hand holding wide the door, the other plucking, quite unnecessarily, at a hurrying black raincoat. He wears the expression of a man breathing tainted air. He speaks to the other official:

"See him off, Sam. Tell him not to go out by Flinders Street. Some of them are silly enough . . ."

A few minutes later we are called, and only then do we realize that we are but five. Lamond has taken advantage of the confusion to do the only sensible thing.

". . . against any of these men?"

Almost over. How strangely disturbing it is, this great pit filled with shadows and white faces! God pity the man in the black raincoat; it must have been dreadful in eruption. It's quiet now, but frighteningly quiet. I have nothing to be afraid of—on the contrary, many of those men down there are already my friends —but the sweat suddenly breaks on my forehead. I've been suffering from a sense of revulsion in the last few minutes. I've had to reason with myself, to tell myself that all this is not of their seeking. I am a witness not so much of a statement as of a response. Out of the nearest row of seats a few familiar faces have already lifted themselves. Faces of men I have worked with, eaten with, drunk with. Warm-hearted men who have advised me, helped me, talked to me—about their homes, their wives, their children, their multitudinous little interests.

But I know quite positively that a few minutes ago they also were part of the beast that rose up and snarled at the man in the black raincoat. Bitter experience has taught them that they assemble here in defence of all that they have.

And this is it—the Federation. This first row of seasoned old-timers, sitting primly upright with creased faces sunk in the collars of Sunday overcoats, nursing their carefully dented hats, their polished black boots resting flatfooted on the dusty floor. This community of silent, staring men fading away through a haze of tobacco smoke to the gloomy rear of the hall. These tall windows, filled with grey daylight, which have looked down on so much of the real drama of a great city. This Secretary of little education, who, a few minutes ago as I stood before his table, entered something in a ledger in the laborious painstaking hand of a schoolboy. This burly President—

". . . that these men be admitted to membership of the Waterside Workers' Federation of Australia. . . ."

How good it is, the warm acclamation of one's fellowmen! We've been listening to it all the afternoon out in the lane, but there's something special about it this time. Perhaps they feel we need some reassuring after the incident of the black raincoat. The applause continues even as we file off the stage. Some of us can distinguish our first names being called out:

"Good on you, Bob!"

"You'll do us, Steve!"

The recruit immediately preceding me turns to give me a happy smile, and both of us spontaneously salute. We feel suddenly rich. And not because of bigger pay envelopes to come. We've got ourselves three thousand mates. We've come through. We're Federation men. We can wear the little blue button with the clasped hands on it. . . .

My palms tingle. How much more is it than the simple design of a badge!

Australia

Vivian Smith

FOR MY DAUGHTER

Made from nothing: bud and rose,
kisses, water, mystery;
you who grew inside our need
run, in your discovery,

out of the garden's folded light,
out of the green, the fountain's spray,
past the shrubs, the dew-lit ferns,
out to the noise, the street, the day:

and stand, in your astonishment,
beneath the hanging heavy limes
(O my child, O my darling daughter,
summer was full of wars and crimes)

to see the foal, the clown, the doll,
the circus and procession band
march up the street and march away . . .
And so you turn and take my hand.

❧❧❧❧❧❧❧❧❧❧❧❧❧❧❧❧

THE MAN WITH THE EVIL EYE

*T*HE bountiful paddy crop, which should have been ready for reaping in February, was rotting in the fields. The storms and flood of the north-east monsoon, particularly severe that year, had laid it waste. The farmers of Atchuvely were troubled, and the village was full of rumours.

"Raman said he thought the Monmari (August-February) crop should be good this year—and look what has happened." I heard Farmer Chellar tell the others. Being prosperous, he was a sort of village elder among them, and in fact older than most. His red eyes, flushed with toddy, were dangerous over his fillet-of-fish cheeks. Even his capacious belly, attached to fat legs like a child's, usually so comfortable-seeming in its nakedness, looked dangerous scored with vigorous black hair.

The other farmers who had gathered under the tamarind tree by the junction, their usual meeting place in the evenings, talked among themselves excitedly. The seller of sweet-meats under the tree was the only person who seemed unaffected, since trade was as usual.

"My child had the measles last year, and it was all due to him!" the young Farmer Kaspar shouted, as village people shout when they are talking, holding on with hands to his white shawl which hung toga-wise across his shoulder, revealing patches of nut-brown skin. He was a simple and straightforward man and much liked in the village. "Raman is dangerous," he said. "We shall have to make him leave. The place is not healthy with him here."

"Don't be crazy! He has as much right to live in Atchuvely as we have!" shouted the angry voice of Farmer Nesan, although he was not angry. When village voices were rhetorical they always sounded angry to me.

"Raman is coming. I'm going home," said Farmer Chellar, shuffling his sandals along the limestone road. He spat out some red betel-chew explosively.

When Raman, who was with the Evil Eye, arrived the farmers exchanged quick, veiled glances as they usually did when Raman praised something, or looked approvingly at anything that had caught his fancy. The poor man suffered from the Evil Tongue as well. If he praised a beautiful child it was bound to sicken, or if he looked approvingly at a crop it was bound to wither.

Whereas in the other villages the one with the evil eye was a woman (and every village had one) our village had been cursed with a male whose influence was correspondingly more powerful. So every farmer had put up a pole in the middle of his field and balanced a pot with white lime marks on top to counteract it. Since the betel vines were especially susceptible, being so feminine and delicate, those farmers who could lay their hands on one for a charm had hung an ox's skull near by.

"Aepuddi chukkam?" (Greetings; how's your health?) Farmer Nesan asked Raman loudly. He was being friendly toward Raman, who he realized was in a fix, although the man did not know it.

The crows in the tamarind tree cawed loudly and flew away as Farmer Kaspar threw a stone at them.

"What's one to do? All our crops are ruined," Raman replied.

"Whose fault is it?" shouted one of the farmers. Raman looked at him innocently.

At normal times the village folk were too kindly ever to let Raman know what he was afflicted with, but the unprecedented disaster was proving too much for them.

"Oh, ask the crows," Raman said.

Farmer Kaspar picked up another stone and threw it at the milk-hedge, which bled.

Although the farmers usually spent a long time chatting under the tamarind tree every evening, after their visit to the tavern, they began to disperse early today.

Nesan stayed on with Raman chatting in a friendly manner, and I returned homeward.

When I reached Stone House, where my older brother Rutnam and I were staying with grandfather, I asked him about Raman's evil eye.

"It's a lot of nonsense," grandfather told me. "They paint eyes on the houses to keep the evil eye away in Italy. Here they paint eyes on pots."

He was being wise and tolerant. He was a famous editor and poet, besides being a philanthropist, and what he said was better than the law itself in Atchuvely. So I didn't worry much about Raman.

Besides, I remembered that Raman believed in the Evil Eye. If he was afraid of it, how could he have it himself.

I remembered the evening three years back when my brother Rutnam and I were walking down the road where Raman lived. Raman was sitting on the nicely carved oblong stone opposite his house where he often sat in the evening, chewing his betel and tobacco, and drinking in the air that had been cooled by his wife sprinkling water on the heated road and compound. We averted our eyes and hurried on. But he called out our names, so we had to stop.

"Children, how is Grandfather of Stone House?" he asked, fixing us with his eyes which were too close to each other in a narrow face which was otherwise quite handsome. They looked somewhat unnatural and I think, may have been the chief cause of the villagers' superstition.

"He is well," Rutnam answered politely.

"He is having trouble with the Ford. A man from Jaffna is coming to have a look at it," I added.

"Oh, is he?" Raman asked. "It is pretty old, isn't it? I suppose he is using the Dodge now?"

"No." I replied. "He drove to Jaffna in his horse carriage this morning. He told us that never gave him any trouble."

Farmer Raman laughed, stretching his thin lips like india-rubber bands between his well-shaped long nose and his jutting jaw, which looked slightly out of place on so narrow a face. "He won't give up his horses. He is the old type of gentleman. How old are you now?" he asked.

"Five," I replied timidly.

"Come into the house," he said. "I will give you children some of my special ottu (grafted) mangoes."

I tugged at my brother's shirt-sleeve to warn him I would like to go on. But he said, "Oh! that is nice of you, Raman," and started across the road with him; so I followed helplessly.

We walked through his gate set in greying walls, and sat on a bench in a courtyard while he shouted to his wife to slice some ottu mangoes. I looked past his well on the left to his kitchen garden. In the middle of it stood a pole with an overturned clay pot painted with white lime marks.

I was surprised to see such an object in his house.

"Why do you have that?" I asked Farmer Raman.

"Don't you know?" he asked in a surprised voice. "That is to keep the evil eye away."

Eating the mangoes I had thought then: if Raman is afraid of the evil eye he surely can't have it himself.

When Rutnam and I woke up next morning, the ayah gave us our morning baths, and painted the black pottu or beauty-spot on the forehead with more than usual care. They were meant to avert the evil eye and all children were made to wear it whether they were Hindu or Christian.

"Now remember to slip back into the house if you see Raman," she warned. The mothers and ayahs ordered the children inside the house if Raman came up the road. But he never seemed to notice anything unusual.

"Nonsense," I replied. "The crops failing have nothing to do with Raman."

However, the childhood impression persisted in the back of my mind, that the evil tongue and the evil eye could bring harm. I had seen visitors refraining from praising children in case they had the evil eye unwittingly; and when strangers admired a child, the womenfolk had looked troubled. I had watched "lime cutting", ceremonies in which the exorcist sliced a hundred limes on the forehead of a person cursed with the evil eye, to drive it away with special incantations and the sprinkling of virgin water from a new spring dug secretly at night. All these things had left an impression on my unreasoning mind. So in spite of my retort to the ayah I felt vaguely troubled that morning.

More news of impending trouble arrived at Stone House when Farmer Nesan arrived around ten o'clock to speak with grandfather. It was not unusual for the farmers to bring their problems and their disputes to him.

"Well, Nesan, what is the trouble now?" asked grandfather looking up from the proof he was correcting. Innumerable proofs littered the floor and the printing presses rumbled in the adjoining outbuilding.

"It's about Raman," Nesan replied. "Chellar and Kaspar have persuaded the washer-man not to take in Raman's laundry. Raman beat the man up. And now the oil-man won't call at Raman's house since the farmers have threatened him with violence. What are we going to do?"

"Does Raman know what it's all about?" asked grandfather.

"He thinks someone is trying to harm him."

"Tell Chellar and Kaspar I would like to see them," said grandfather.

Chellar and Kaspar called after their lunch just as grandfather was thinking of his siesta. They looked embarrassed, hung their heads down and twiddled their fingers. They sat down on the floor in front of grandfather.

"Look here Chellar and Kaspar," grandfather said, "Raman has as much right to farm in Atchuvely as you have. He was born here and so was his father. Now be good men and don't create any trouble for him."

"We have lost our crops, sir, and that is a serious matter. As long as he is here we will have ill luck. What are we to do?"

"Put yourself in his place. What would you have done if the village thought the same about you both?"

Chellar and Kaspar didn't say anything but hung their heads; they murmured a sheepish poetu-vaaraan (*I will go and return*) and shuffled out clutching their shawls.

They did not seem convinced, but it seemed unlikely that they would go against grandfather's request.

I was impatient for the evening so that I could go to the junction and hear what the farmers were saying.

Before the sun touched the horizon Rutnam and I set out for the junction. The mangoes and neems rustled pleasantly and we stopped under the jujube tree to pick up some fruit. The homing

263

crows squawked across the sky. The white limestone road glowed a soft pink in the air that had suddenly become cool.

When we neared the junction we found that a large crowd had assembled. They were all excited and the vendor of sweet-meats under the tamarind tree was doing a brisk trade serving out portions of the roast gram, lentils, doughnuts with shrimps, boiled manioc and curry relish and other delicacies spread out on the trestle lit with a naked carbide flame.

Chellar and Kaspar eyed us as if we were spies. We felt bad about it but we couldn't help our itching curiosity. Nesan nodded to us. "This is a bad affair," he said.

"It is a bad affair," another added. "It is for the good of the village."

"You are all fools," growled Nesan who seemed to have thought it out deeply in the toddy tavern.

When Raman arrived, looking agitated, a silence fell on everybody. He went straight up to Chellar and Kaspar and asked in a furious voice, "What do you mean by the things you told the washer-man and the oilmonger?"

"What do you mean?" asked Kaspar drunkenly. He picked up a stone and threw it at the milk-hedge. He hit it accurately and it bled again.

"Look Raman, we all like you, but it is time you left the village," said Chellar ingratiatingly, looking rather ridiculous and fat, with a hanging sausage-fruit lower lip that showed his teeth.

"What do you mean?" shouted Raman as if he had lost all control of himself. His face was distorted and his fingers bunched. In another minute he would have knocked Chellar down.

"We can't help it, Raman, it's your evil eye that's the matter," replied Chellar almost sorrowfully, regarding him gravely with his red ones.

All the rage seemed to drain from Raman's face when he heard Chellar's words. He looked shocked and bewildered. He stared unbelievingly at Chellar and Kaspar and round at the crowd.

Then he turned on his heels and walked slowly away like a man in a daze, and the crowd gazed at him with pity.

264

Farmer Kaspar picked up another stone and hurled it at the tamarind, from which the crows darted squawking angrily.

Rutnam and I felt sorry for Raman. The villagers had behaved atrociously to him.

We saw nothing of him for several days. Raman did not come to the junction any more. He was not to be seen in his field or outside his house sitting on the carved stone, although the road in front of it had been sprinkled with water as usual. No one mentioned his name.

And then one morning he came to see us. His bullock cart stood outside laden with his belongings, with his wife sitting on the front plank, a patient, still figure. He told us he had come to wish us good-bye. He was going away to Mannar, a hundred miles away, to settle down with a cousin. He had rented out his farm to Nesan.

Grandfather stared at him in a strange way, and then he nodded his head. Even his wisdom could see no other way out for Raman.

Raman then went to his cart, beat the bulls with the stick, and bit their tails with his teeth, so that they raced.

Nick Joaquin

MAY DAY EVE

THE old people had ordered that the dancing should stop at ten o'clock but it was almost midnight before the carriages came filing up to the front door, the servants running to and fro with torches to light the departing guests, while the girls who were staying were promptly herded upstairs to the bedrooms, the young men gathering around to wish them a good night and lamenting their ascent with mock sighs and moanings, proclaiming themselves disconsolate but straightway going off to finish the punch and the brandy though they were quite drunk already and simply bursting with wild spirits, merriment, arrogance and audacity, for they were young bucks newly arrived from Europe; the ball had been in their honour; and they had waltzed and polka-ed and bragged and swaggered and flirted all night and were in no mood to sleep yet—no, caramba, not on this moist tropic eve! Not on this mystic May eve!—with the night still young and so seductive that it was madness not to go out, not to go forth—and serenade the neighbours! cried one; and swim in the Pasig! cried another; and gather fireflies! cried a third— whereupon there arose a great clamour for coats and capes, for hats and canes, and they were presently stumbling out among the medieval shadows of the foul street where a couple of street-lamps flickered and a last carriage rattled away upon the cobbles while the blind black houses muttered hush-hush, their tiled roofs looming like sinister chessboards against a wild sky murky with clouds, save where an evil young moon prowled about in a corner or where a murderous wind whirled, whistling and whining, smelling now of the sea and now of the summer orchards and wafting unbearable childhood fragrances of ripe guavas to the young men trooping so uproariously down the street that the girls who were disrobing upstairs in the bedrooms scattered screaming to the windows, crowded giggling at the windows, but were soon sighing amorously over those young men bawling below; over those wicked young men and their handsome apparel, their proud flashing eyes, and their elegant moustaches so black and vivid in the moonlight that the girls were quite ravished with love, and began crying to one another how carefree were men but how awful to be a girl and what a horrid, horrid world it was, till old Anastasia plucked them off by the ear or the pigtail and chased them off to bed—while from up the street came the clackety-clack of the watchman's boots on the cobbles, and the clang-clang of his lantern against his knee, and the mighty roll of his great voice booming through the night: "*Guardia sereno-o-o! A las doce han dado-o-o!*"

And it was May again, said the old Anastasia. It was the first day of May and witches were abroad in the night, she said—for it was a night of divination, a night of lovers, and those who cared might peer in a mirror and would there behold the face of whoever it was they were fated to marry, said the old Anastasia as she hobbled about picking up the piled crinolines and folding up shawls and raking slippers to a corner while the girls climbing into the four great poster-beds that overwhelmed the room began shrieking with terror, scrambling over each other and imploring the old woman not to frighten them.

"Enough, enough, Anastasia! We want to sleep!"

"Go scare the boys instead, you old witch!"

"She is not a witch, she is a maga. She was born on Christmas Eve!"

"St Anastasia, virgin and martyr."

"Huh? Impossible! She has conquered seven husbands! Are you a virgin, Anastasia?"

"No, but I am seven times a martyr because of you girls."

"Let her prophesy, let her prophesy! Whom will I marry, old gypsy? Come, tell me."

"You may learn in a mirror if you are not afraid."

"I am not afraid, I will go!" cried the young cousin Agueda, jumping up in bed.

"Girls, girls—we are making too much noise! My mother will hear and will come and pinch us all. Agueda, lie down! And you, Anastasia, I command you to shut your mouth and go away."

"Your mother told me to stay here all night, my grand lady!"

"And I will not lie down!" cried the rebellious Agueda, leaping to the floor. "Stay, old woman. Tell me what I have to do."

"Tell her! Tell her!" chimed the other girls.

The old woman dropped the clothes she had gathered and approached and fixed her eyes on the girl. "You must take a candle," she instructed, "and go into a room that is dark and that has a mirror in it and you must be alone in the room. Go up to the mirror and close your eyes and say:

> *Mirror, mirror,*
> *show to me*
> *him whose woman*
> *I will be.*

If all goes right, just above your left shoulder will appear the face of the man you will marry."

A silence. Then: "And what if all does not go right?" asked Agueda.

"Ah, then the Lord have mercy on you!"

"Why?"

"Because you may see—the devil!"

The girls screamed and clutched one another, shivering.

"But what nonsense!" cried Agueda. "This is the year 1847. There are no devils anymore!" Nevertheless she had turned pale. "But where could I go, huh? Yes, I know! Down to the sala. It has that big mirror and no one is there now."

"No Agueda, no! It is a mortal sin! You will see the devil!"

"I do not care! I am not afraid! I will go!"

"Oh, you wicked girl! Oh, you mad girl!"

"If you do not come to bed, Agueda, I will call my mother."

"And if you do I will tell her who came to visit you at the convent last March. Come, old woman—give me that candle. I go."

"Oh, girls—come and stop her! Take hold of her! Block the door!"

But Agueda had already slipped outside; was already tiptoeing across the hall; her feet bare and her dark hair falling down her shoulders and streaming in the wind as she fled down the stairs, the lighted candle sputtering in one hand while with the other she pulled up her white gown from her ankles.

She paused breathless in the doorway to the sala and her heart failed her. She tried to imagine the room filled again with lights, laughter, whirling couples, and the jolly jerky music of the fiddlers. But, oh, it was a dark den, a weird cavern, for the windows had been closed and the furniture stacked up against the walls. She crossed herself and stepped inside.

The mirror hung on the wall before her; a big antique mirror with a gold frame carved into leaves and flowers and mysterious curlicues. She saw herself approaching fearfully in it: a small white ghost that the darkness bodied forth—but not willingly, not completely, for her eyes and hair were so dark that the face approaching in the mirror seemed only a mask that floated forward; a bright mask with two holes gaping in it, blown forward by the white cloud of her gown. But when she stood before the mirror she lifted the candle level with her chin and the dead mask bloomed into her living face.

She closed her eyes and whispered the incantation. When she had finished such a terror took hold of her that she felt unable to move, unable to open her eyes, and thought she would stand there forever, enchanted. But she heard a step behind her, and a smothered giggle, and instantly opened her eyes.

"And what did you see, Mama? Oh, what was it?"

But Dona Agueda had forgotten the little girl on her lap: she was staring past the curly head nestling at her breast and seeing herself in the big mirror hanging in the room. It was the same room and the same mirror but the face she now saw in it was an old face—a hard, bitter, vengeful face, framed in greying hair, and so sadly altered, so sadly different from that other face like a white mask, that fresh young face like a pure mask that she had brought before this mirror one wild May Day midnight years and years ago . . .

"But what was it, Mama? Oh, please go on! What did you see?"

Dona Agueda looked down at her daughter but her face did not soften though her eyes filled with tears. "I saw the devil!" she said bitterly.

The child blanched. "The devil, Mama? Oh . . . OH!"

"Yes, my love. I opened my eyes and there in the mirror, smiling at me over my left shoulder, was the face of the devil."

"Oh, my poor little Mama! And were you very frightened?"

"You can imagine. And that is why good little girls do not look into mirrors except when their mothers tell them. You must stop this naughty habit, darling, of admiring yourself in every mirror you pass—or you may see something frightful some day."

"But the devil, Mama—what did he look like?"

"Well, let me see . . . He had curly hair and a scar on his cheek——"

"Like the scar of Papa?"

"Well, yes. But this of the devil was a scar of sin, while that of your Papa is a scar of honour. Or so he says."

"Go on about the devil."

"Well, he had moustaches."

"Like those of Papa?"

"Oh, no. Those of your Papa are dirty and greying and smell horribly of tobacco, while these of the devil were very black and elegant—oh, how elegant!"

"And did he have horns and a tail?"

The mother's lips curled. "Yes, he did! But, alas, I could not see them at that time. All I could see were his fine clothes, his flashing eyes, his curly hair and moustaches."

"And did he speak to you, Mama?"

"Yes . . . Yes, he spoke to me," said Dona Agueda. And bowing her greying head, she wept.

"Charms like yours have no need for a candle, fair one," he had said, smiling at her in the mirror and stepping back to give her a low mocking bow. She had whirled around and glared at him and he had burst into laughter.

"But I remember you!" he cried. "You are Agueda, whom I left a mere infant and came home to find a tremendous beauty, and I danced a waltz with you but you would not give me the polka."

"Let me pass," she muttered fiercely, for he was barring her way.

"But I want to dance the polka with you, fair one," he said.

So they stood before the mirror; their panting breath the only sound in the dark room; the candle shining between them and flinging their shadows to the wall. And young Badoy Montiya (who had crept home very drunk to pass out quietly in bed) suddenly found himself cold sober and very much awake and ready for anything. His eyes sparkled and the scar on his face gleamed scarlet.

"Let me pass!" she cried again, in a voice of fury, but he grasped her by the wrist.

"No," he smiled. "Not until we have danced."

"Go to the devil!"

"What a temper has my serrana!"

"I am not your serrana!"

"Whose, then? Someone I know? Someone I have offended grievously? Because you treat me, you treat all my friends like your mortal enemies."

"And why not?" she demanded, jerking her wrist away and flashing her teeth in his face. "Oh, how I detest you, you pompous young men! You go to Europe and you come back elegant lords and we poor girls are too tame to please you. We have no grace like the Parisiennes, we have no fire like the Sevillians, and we have no salt, no salt, no salt! Aie, how you weary me, how you bore me, you fastidious young men!"

"Come, come—how do you know about us?"

"I have heard you talking, I have heard you talking among yourselves, and I despise the pack of you!"

"But clearly you do not despise yourself, senorita. You come to admire your charms in the mirror even in the middle of the night!"

She turned livid and he had a moment of malicious satisfaction.

"I was not admiring myself, sir!"

"You were admiring the moon perhaps?"

"Oh!" she gasped, and burst into tears. The candle dropped from her hand and she covered her face and sobbed piteously. The candle had gone out and they stood in darkness, and young Badoy was conscience-stricken.

"Oh, do not cry, little one! Oh, please forgive me! Please do not cry! But what a brute I am! I was drunk, little one, I was drunk and knew not what I said."

T

He groped and found her hand and touched it to his lips. She shuddered in her white gown.

"Let me go," she moaned, and tugged feebly.

"No. Say you forgive me first. Say you forgive me, Agueda."

But instead she pulled his hand to her mouth and bit it—bit so sharply into the knuckles that he cried with pain and lashed out with his other hand—lashed out and hit the air, for she was gone, she had fled, and he heard the rustling of her skirts up the stairs as he furiously sucked his bleeding fingers.

Cruel thoughts raced through his head: he would go and tell his mother and make her turn the savage girl out of the house— or he would go himself to the girl's room and drag her out of bed and slap, slap, slap her silly face! But at the same time he was thinking that they were all going up to Antipolo in the morning and was already planning how he would manoeuvre himself into the same boat with her.

Oh, he would have his revenge, he would make her pay, that little harlot! She should suffer for this, he thought greedily, licking his bleeding knuckles. But—Judas!—what eyes she had! And what a pretty colour she turned when angry! He remembered her bare shoulders: gold in the candlelight and delicately furred. He saw the mobile insolence of her neck, and her taut breasts steady in the fluid gown. Son of a Turk, but she was quite enchanting! How could she think she had no fire or grace? and no salt? An arroba she had of it!

"*. . . No lack of salt in the chrism*
At the moment of thy baptism!"

he sang aloud in the dark room and suddenly realized that he had fallen madly in love with her. He ached intensely to see her again—at once!—to touch her hand and her hair; to hear her harsh voice. He ran to the window and flung open the casements and the beauty of the night struck him back like a blow. It was May, it was summer, and he was young—young!—and deliriously in love. Such a happiness welled up within him the tears spurted from his eyes.

But he did not forgive her—no! He would still make her pay. He would still have his revenge, he thought viciously, and kissed his wounded fingers. But what a night it had been! "I will never forget this night," he thought aloud in an awed voice, standing by the dark room, the tears in his eyes and the wind in his hair and his bleeding knuckles pressed to his mouth.

But, alas, the heart forgets; the heart is distracted; and May-time passes; summer ends; the storms break over the rot-ripe orchards and the heart grows old; while the hours, the days, the months, and the years pile up and pile up, till the mind becomes too crowded, too confused: dust gathers in it; cobwebs multiply; the walls darken and fall into ruin and decay; the memory perishes . . . and there came a time when Don Badoy Montiya walked home through a May Day midnight without remember-ing, without even caring to remember; being merely concerned in feeling his way across the street with his cane; his eyes having grown quite dim and his legs uncertain—for he was old; he was over sixty; he was a very stooped and shrivelled old man with white hair and moustaches, coming home from a secret meeting of conspirators; his mind still resounding with the speeches and his patriot heart still exultant as he picked his way up the steps to the front door and inside the slumbering darkness of the house; wholly unconscious of the May night, till on his way down the hall, chancing to glance into the sala, he shuddered, he stopped, his blood ran cold——for he had seen a face in the mirror there—a ghostly candlelit face with the eyes closed and the lips moving, a face that he suddenly felt he had seen there before though it was a full minute before the lost memory came flow-ing, came tiding back, so overflooding the actual moment and so swiftly washing away the piled hours and days and months and years that he was left suddenly young again: he was a gay young buck again, lately come from Europe: he had been dancing all night: he was very drunk: he stopped in the doorway: he saw a face in the dark: he cried out . . . and the lad standing before the mirror (for it was a lad in a nightgown) jumped with fright and almost dropped his candle, but looking around and seeing the old man, laughed out with relief and came running.

"Oh, Grandpa, how you frightened me!"

Don Badoy had turned very pale. "So it was you, you young bandit! And what is all this, hey? What are you doing down here at this hour?"

"Nothing, Grandpa. I was only . . . I am only . . ."

"Yes, you are the great Senor Only and how delighted I am to make your acquaintance, Senor Only! But if I break this cane on your head you may wish you were someone else, sir!"

"It was just foolishness, Grandpa. They told me I would see my wife."

"Wife? What wife?"

"Mine. The boys at school said I would see her if I looked in a mirror tonight and said:

> *Mirror, mirror,*
> *show to me*
> *her whose lover*
> *I will be."*

Don Badoy cackled ruefully. He took the boy by the hair, pulled him along into the room, sat down on a chair, and drew the boy between his knees. "Now, put your candle down on the floor, son, and let us talk this over. So you want your wife already, hey? You want to see her in advance, hey? But do you know that these are wicked games and that wicked boys who play them are in danger of seeing horrors."

"Well, the boys did warn me I might see a witch instead."

"Exactly! A witch so horrible you may die of fright. And she will bewitch you, she will torture you, she will eat your heart and drink your blood!"

"O, come now, Grandpa. This is 1890. There are no witches anymore."

"Oh-ho, my young Voltaire! And what if I tell you that I myself have seen a witch?"

"You? Where?"

"Right in this room and right in that mirror," said the old man, and his playful voice had turned savage.

"When, Grandpa?"

"Not so long ago. When I was a bit older than you. Oh I was a vain fellow and though I was feeling very sick that night and merely wanted to lie down somewhere and die I could not pass that doorway of course without stopping to see in the mirror what I looked like when dying. But when I poked my head in what should I see in the mirror but . . . but . . ."

274

"The witch?"

"Exactly!"

"And did she bewitch you, Grandpa?"

"She bewitched me and she tortured me. She ate my heart and drank my blood," said the old man bitterly.

"Oh, my poor little Grandpa! Why have you never told me! And was she very horrible?"

"Horrible? God, no—she was beautiful! She was the most beautiful creature I have ever seen! Her eyes were somewhat like yours but her hair was like black waters and her golden shoulders were bare. My God, she was enchanting! But I should have known—I should have known even then——the dark and fatal creature she was!"

A silence. Then: "What a horrid mirror this is, Grandpa," whispered the boy.

"What makes you say that, hey?"

"Well, you saw this witch in it. And Mama once told me that Grandma once told her that Grandma once saw the devil in this mirror. Was it of the scare that Grandma died?"

Don Badoy started. For a moment he had forgotten that she was dead, that she had perished—the poor Agueda; that they were at peace at last, the two of them, and her tired body at rest; her broken body set free at last from the brutal pranks of the earth—from the trap of a May night; from the snare of summer; from the terrible silver nets of the moon. She had been a mere heap of white hair and bones in the end: a whimpering withered consumptive, lashing out with her cruel tongue; her eyes like live coals; her face like ashes . . . Now, nothing—nothing save a name on a stone; save a stone in a graveyard—nothing! nothing at all! was left of the young girl who had flamed so vividly in a mirror one wild May Day midnight, long, long ago.

And remembering how she had sobbed so piteously; remembering how she had bitten his hand and fled and how he had sung aloud in the dark room and surprised his heart in the instant of falling in love; such a grief tore up his throat and eyes that he felt ashamed before the boy; pushed the boy away; stood up and fumbled his way to the window; threw open the casements and looked out—looked out upon the medieval shadows of the foul street where a couple of street-lamps flickered and a last carriage was rattling away upon the cobbles, while the blind black houses muttered hush-hush, their tiled roofs looming like sinister chessboards against a wild sky murky with clouds, save where an evil old moon prowled about in a corner or where a murderous wind whirled, whistling and whining, smelling now of the sea and now of the summer orchards and wafting unbearable Maytime memories of an old, old love to the old man shaking with sobs by the window; the bowed old man sobbing so bitterly at the window; the tears streaming down his cheeks and the wind in his hair and one hand pressed to his mouth—while from up the street came the clackety-clack of the watchman's boots on the cobbles, and the clang clang of his lantern against his knee, and the mighty roll of his great voice booming through the night: *"Guardia seren-o-o! A las doce han dado-o-o!"*

Philippines

Ricaredo Demetillo

THE AMBITIOUS FAILURE

HEARING the secret stammering in things,
The boy, emboldened by the sun-drenched hills,
Envied the lordly insolence of wings.

For Phaeton too had kinship with the god.
What else coaxed him out of a spanieled ease
And made him spurn the herd and cackling geese?

He sought to seize the chariot of the sun
That he might prove his sonship with the deed,
Apollo nodded. Importunate the need.

Neither too high nor low, the level flight
Is best between the earth and sky; but he
Forgot this counsel in the sudden daze of light.

Could the boy foresee the rampage of each horse,
The dark down plunge, the dazzling furious surge?
The tugging wrenched the sockets of a curse.

And as the reins lost the purpose of the will,
The hooves alarmed a stampede in his brain.
The corn on uplands scorched in a fiery rain.

The one erratic moment, his very sire
Feared for the sky. Mercy in a thunderbolt
Repaired the havoc with its fire.

Philippines

Bienvenido N. Santos

CAUTERY

My way of earning bread and nails
Is climbing up towers
Fondling blades of grass
And blowing into swollen entrails
Of caustic moments and velvety satire.
It is the only way for me
Whose hands are thus, whose eyes
Inhabit dark corners canopied with fire.

For golden moments the heart has sole keep
And while hands fumble in the green
And self seeks the turret heights
Living takes on beauty. But to weep
Is to remember wine, bells across the seas
Time out from blowing, holiday
From hardness, and finally
Peace softens earthward and all strivings cease.

Khwaja Ahmad Abbas

❧❦❧❦❧❦❧❦❧❦❧❦❧❦❧❦

MAHARAJA'S ELEPHANT

O NCE upon a time—and it seems it was very, very long ago—
when Maharajas were Maharajas and not amusing mascots for
airlines, the importance of a ruler was reckoned by the number
of guns to which he was entitled as a royal salute, the population
of his harem, and the number of elephants in his *feelkhanna*
(elephant house).

Judged from this standard, Raja Suryakumar Chandrakumar
Vijaysingh Shumsherjung of Chhamchhampur (only two crackers,
seven wives and one elephant) was not among the top ten or
even top two hundred of the rulers of princely states. Indeed,
his state (area: 1704 square miles, population: 274,589), nestling
insignificantly somewhere in the barren plateaus of Central
India, was no bigger than a big *zamindari* (landholding); nevertheless, its relations with the *Angrezi Sarkar* (English
Government) were governed by the terms of a treaty that the
great-grandfather of the present ruler, the redoubtable Raja
Narsingharao Bhimsingh Arjunsingh, had personally signed with
Lord Canning.

As a matter of historical record, let it be stated that Chhamchhampur was not always so small and insignificant a state. There
was a time when the writ of the Maharaja of Chhamchhampur
ran over a great part of Rajputana and what is now known as
Madhya Pradesh. But the successive Maharajas' overfondness
for wine (extracted from the *mahoba* flowers that grew wild all
over the state) and women (especially dancing girls, the *chham-
chham* sound of whose anklet bells was reputed to be the genesis
of the state's name, Chhamchhampur) had worked havoc with
the martial qualities of the ruling family, and one after another
various parts of the state had been swallowed up by the more
energetic and avaricious rulers of neighbouring states, not to

278

mention the big slice that had been *conceded* to the *firangees* (Englishmen) in return for the protection afforded by their troops against Chhamchhampur's marauding neighbours.

And thus it had come to pass that by the year 1945 the Maharaja of Chhamchhampur was left with only seven wives and one elephant; and when, under pressure of public opinion, the Viceroy ordered a further cut in the privy purse, the Maharaja found himself financially incapable of maintaining even such a depleted harem and *feelkhanna*.

A man of ample girth, nevertheless he decided to tighten his belt both literally and figuratively. He put all his wives (except the youngest, who was naturally his favourite) on short rations, ordered a cut in their allowances; and on the pretext that robbers were rampant in the state capital he divested them of their jewels, which were duly deposited in the royal treasury for safe keeping—so it was given out—though the fact was that the precious stones were taken out and sent to a firm of jewellers in Bombay, and the gold was melted and secretly sold to a bullion merchant in Delhi.

Looking about for further economies, the Maharaja spotted Lakshmi, the solitary old cow elephant in the huge *feelkhanna* that was originally designed to house a dozen elephants. According to the Comptroller of the Royal Household, the maintenance of the *feelkhanna*, including the rations for the elephant and salary for the *mahout* (driver), came to no less than Rs. 350/- per month—i.e., over four thousand per year! To the Maharaja's newly awakened sense of economy this seemed a waste of good money, for after all he never rode on the elephant even for state processions, and the very idea of doing so sitting cross-legged in an uncomfortable *howdah* struck him as ridiculous when he had a whole fleet of Daimlers and Packards for luxurious driving. So he decided to get rid of old Lakshmi. But he could not afford to lose face by making it public that he was closing down his *feelkhanna* because he could no longer afford it. It had to be done with diplomatic circumspection and royal finesse. He was debating the issue in his mind when the Resident, Sir John Rollingstone (pronounced Rawlington) was announced.

Sir John was an officer of the Political Department who had risen from the ranks, as it were. The son of a Manchester tailor, he had worked his way through college with the help of scholarships, crammed Latin and Ancient History to get into I.C.S., and had served for 20 years in various malarious *mofussil* (country) towns, first as Joint Magistrate and then as Collector, before he was drafted for the Political Department. A secret romanticist who spent all the leisure hours of his bachelor life reading Kipling and Churchill and Yeats-Brown, his original inferiority complex had been transformed into a fascination for what he regarded as the chivalry and old-world charm of India's princely courts. As such he was more interested in preserving the traditional pomp, pageantry and ceremonial of the princely courts to which he was accredited than in such prosaic matters as the administration of justice and the improvement of the irrigation system for the benefit of the impoverished *ryot* (peasantry). No wonder Sir John Rollingstone (pronounced Rawlington) was held in such affection and esteem by the princes he had served, but particularly by the Maharaja of Chhamchhampur.

And so it was natural that in recognition of his services, the Resident should receive a present from the Maharaja—and what present could be more appropriate for the romantic soul of Sir John Rollingstone (pronounced Rawlington) than a royal elephant, the symbol and epitome of all that pomp and pageantry, chivalry and gallantry that the Manchester tailor's son had always associated with his mission in the princely states of India. And so he was duly grateful for the royal present, and felt greatly moved when the elephant and *mahout* arrived to take their new quarters in the compound of his bungalow. It secmed to him the crowning moment of his career in India.

But he had not yet reckoned with the economic problem of maintaining an elephant. The few thousands he had been able to put by in his bank account were soon gone into the building of an over-sized stable for the elephant. The royal beast had a royal appetite, and soon a good bit of the Resident's far-from-ample salary was going into the purchase of sugar-cane and other costly rations. The Political Department flatly refused to finance this elephantine adventure, and made it clear that the Resident should consider himself lucky if he was not hauled up for so openly accepting a present from the Maharaja—which could easily be construed as illegal gratification.

All this was mortifying to the sensitive soul of one who regarded himself as the heir to the Kipling tradition. But with character-istic British tenacity Sir John Rollingstone (pronounced Raw-lington) stuck loyally to the elephant, even if it meant his resignation from the club (as he could no longer pay for his whisky-soda bills), giving up of the summer vacation in the hills, and other such self-imposed economies. Every evening he strolled over to the stable which he liked to call his *feelkhanna*. He derived immense consolation from the thought that soon, when he retired, he would take the elephant with him to England, where it would lend unparalleled distinction to his semi-detached cottage in Sunningdale or some such place. "That," he would be able to tell his envious neighbours, "is old Lakshmi, the royal ele-phant, that my friend the Maharaja of Chhamchhampur gave me as a present"—and it was a pleasant thrill to anticipate the look of envious wonder it would produce on the faces of those who had never ventured to the fabulous and exotic lands "east of Suez".

But when the time came for his retirement and impending departure for England, Sir John was dismayed to learn of the immense cost of transporting his royal elephant to England—the train to Bombay and the ship's freight to London amounting to more than the total gratuity to which the retiring civilian was entitled after 25 years in the service of the Empire. He could expect little help or understanding from the Political Depart-ment in New Delhi, for meanwhile, a bunch of Gandhi-capped ex-Seditionists had persuaded Whitehall to transfer the govern-ment of India to them; the Maharaja of Chhamchhampur along with many other rulers had agreed to the merger and integration of the state; and it seemed to Sir John Rollingstone (no longer pronounced Rawlington but even rudely spelt as Rolling Stone by the raw young Indian officials who had taken over the Secre-tariat) that the end of the world had come simultaneously with the loss of the brightest jewel in the British crown.

And so, with a heavy heart he bid good-bye to Lakshmi and, by a regular deed—the last document he would sign in India—gifted the elephant to Ganga Ram, the old hereditary *mahout*, who was no less bewildered by the new developments than "Raalingam Saab" as he called the Resident.

With seven salaams and many low bows of gratitude Ganga

281

Ram accepted the gift, but hardly had his old master's train steamed out of Chhamchhampur station than the poor *mahout* was obliged to revise his estimate of this good fortune that he thought had befallen him in acquiring the royal elephant as his personal property. For he was served with a notice to quit the stable, along with his elephant, as the Resident's bungalow and all its out-houses were being converted by the new administration into a school. With a petition drafted for him by a professional scribe for a fee of two rupees, he went the round of all the offices but found no sympathy from the new officials. So poor Ganga Ram, suddenly rendered not only homeless but friendless and unwanted in the strange and incomprehensible new world which had risen round him, sat on the neck of old Lakshmi and led her by gentle proddings of his *ankush* (prodding hook) to his village, where their arrival was heralded by much merriment by the village children.

It was his practical-minded wife, however, whose sharp tongue rudely made him aware of the economic crisis he had brought upon himself by accepting such a gift. Not only had they no place to accommodate the gigantic beast in their mud hut; the produce from their little piece of land (which an earlier Maharaja had given to Ganga Ram's father) was quite inadequate to feed their family, not to speak of the elephant which would eat more than a dozen human beings.

"Give it away to the temple on the hill—a gift to the gods," advised the Old Man of the village, and Ganga Ram, having exhausted his life's savings in feeding the animal just for three days, readily agreed.

With great ceremony, beating of drums and blowing of conches, prayers and intoning of holy *mantras* (hymns), the elephant was accepted by the *pujaris* (priests) and pandits of the temple who felt greatly exhilarated by the gift which proved—or so they thought—that faith was still very much alive, if a poor man like Ganga Ram could bring such a royal gift to the goddess.

To celebrate the occasion, the image of the goddess was placed on the back of the elephant and taken in procession round the surrounding villages, followed by a crowd mostly of children, drawn less by devotion or faith and more by impish curiosity about an elephant.

But soon the *pujaris* of the temple also learnt the disturbing facts and figures of the royal appetite of the Maharaja's elephant. Since the people in the villages began migrating to the city to work in mills, and schools began to lure the simple-minded peasants away from the path of faith (or so the *pujaris* thought), the income of the temple from offerings and donations had been steadily dwindling, with the result that now if the elephant had to be fed the *pujaris* had to starve.

"Then let the beast starve," cried a young hot-head among the *pujaris*, "if we keep her a little longer we will all die of hunger."

The Head Priest advised caution. "Don't forget the elephant is a gift to the goddess—so we cannot allow her to starve. Moreover, the elephant, too, is a god—the incarnation of our Lord Ganpati of the elephant's head. We will be earning the displeasure of the gods if we ill-treat this noble beast."

"Then you do want *us* to starve in order to feed this precious elephant?"

"No," the Head Priest calmly went on, "I only wish that this noble animal, this gift of the goddess, this incarnation of our Lord Ganpati, be gifted to the nation, to serve the people and to be served by them. Of course, that will also save us all from starvation but that is only incidental."

And so it came to be that on the auspicious day of August 15, old Lakshmi was decorated with sandal-wood paste and vermilion and taken in procession to the office of the local Community Project and offered as a gift in the service of the people. Now she can be seen in a certain obscure corner of the country, busy with such humble chores as carrying loads of stone or cement, or dragging a gigantic stone roller to level the road.

Which may appear to some like our old friend Sir John Rollingstone (pronounced Rawlington) as a sad come-down for a Maharaja's elephant; but there are others, and Mahout Ganga Ram (who has been engaged again to look after Lakshmi) is one of them, who say that the old Lakshmi has never looked happier in her whole life.

K. T. Krishnaswami

I PRAYED FOR POWER

I PRAYED for power.
I saw
A drop of rain—and
A child in tears.

I longed for the Himalayas.
I saw
A mound of grass—and
A lover's heart.

I yearned for beauty.
I saw
A dew drop in the sun—and
A pup and its mother at play.

I asked for philosophy.
I saw
A flower from a crannied rock—and
A cross with a crown of thorns.

I wept for God.
I saw
A universe in travail—and
A human face divine.

P. Lal

THE PROMISE

You will see in summer
A palm waving, and many
Cows on grass;
           monsoon pools
Where blue skies are polished,
And birds:
           a tintinnabulation in immaculate trees.

      I have nothing more to promise than the rain
      The beautiful but not without the pain.

And the grass drying in winter,
Pools still, and cows in cold comfort,
A slow fire,
           sky like steel;

My quiet arms when evening
tumbles into sunset and cawing and the night.

      O beautiful but not without the pain
      I have nothing more to promise than the rain.

David Forrest

THE KEEPER OF THE NIGHT

*E*VERY third night, after tea, Kinivan walked along the main street. He sauntered, resplendent in his uniform of tan casuals, jungle-green trousers bought from army disposals, wind-breaker embossed with the figure of a bikini-clad female; the whole uniform being set-off with a black and yellow beanie on the back of his head.

"Good grief," stuttered the conservative elements, and elderly tourists muttered darkly concerning the future of the nation.

Kinivan was a thin youth, sunburnt and laconic. His clothing was chosen for specific purposes. He never realized the effect that it had upon the stable element of the community.

His father died in one of the savage bayonet charges the dreadful day the Second Ninth Battalion went down to Cape Endaiadere. His mother managed a boarding-house, devoted her spare time to Legacy and the Red Cross.

When Kinivan had come to the end of the third block he disappeared into an office beside an open shed. In the night there were the faint outlines of cars in the shed. In the office, the occupant exchanged rude pleasantries with Kinivan, put on his cap, and went home to bed.

In Brisbane, Kinivan would very likely have enlisted in a surf life-saving club. In the rural sugar town of Kooloongana, he elected to camp every third night in the small dark room by the intersection.

As always when he entered the room, he paused for a moment to study the notice-board on the wall. There was only the one notice on the board and it caused him to grimace. The message was a warning, and read, "Mrs Alex Randall—D Day minus five."

Kinivan searched for a pencil and wrote another message on the paper, "You don't frighten me."

He tossed the pencil down, switched out the light and lay down on the bunk. He lay there, fully dressed, except for his casuals. Beside his pillow, on the table, was the telephone. During the day, he worked in Woolworths. Every third night, he camped in the room. Sometimes, the telephone called him. Many nights, it made no sound.

This night, Kinivan yawned and pulled the muffler off the telephone.

"Ring tonight," he promised the phone, "and I'll kick your guts in . . ."

For a moment he listened to the cars and the voices moving along the street towards the cinema, and then he was asleep. He went to sleep, knowing that the telephone would wake him instantly. It was curious, that. There was always a watchfulness in the room, an alertness. The mind stayed alert, even in sleep.

At two minutes past seven, when the true night had barely come, the telephone snapped him awake. His arm came out from under the blanket. His fingers scooped up the receiver in the blackness.

"Yeh," he said softly. A voice rasped and squeaked in his ear. "Yeh . . . yeh, O.K."

Then the voice startled him and he said a curt word through his teeth.

"Harrison went to the pictures. Dig him out quick. Yeh. If you go outside now you'll hear me comin'."

He sat up in a smooth swing so that the receiver went back on its cradle and his feet slid into the casuals in almost the same movement. He never wore shoes to the small dark room. Shoelaces wasted too many seconds.

No rush. No frenzy. Controlled haste.

He closed the side door with a practised flick of his fingers, opened the cabin of the big yellow car and slid in behind the wheel.

In the faint glow of the dashboard light, while he ran the motor in a brief burst, he appeared very slight and brown.

"The picture crowd," he thought absently, eyeing the passing traffic.

Then the shed was alive with noise and the big yellow car

287

came out with its great red light flashing and the siren opening up the night with its sickening rising wail.

The picture crowd parted like the Red Sea before Israel. To Kinivan, the cinema was only a brilliance of light in the night.

After the car had streaked past, they stood about and said soberly, "Wonder where he's goin'?" And, "That was Whittaker, wasn't it?" "No. Whittaker was on last night. Must be Kinivan." "Yair, must be Kinivan." "D'ya see him come inside that Holden?"

Then, when Harrison had run out of the theatre and driven away to the small dark room, then they forgot Kinivan and turned to a Hollywoodian epic.

Kinivan had left them behind. He slid the big car to a halt in front of the hospital gates and Doran snapped the door open and stepped precisely into the seat. The car surged forward with a power that pushed the doctor back into the upholstery.

Doran said, "Drive like hell."

The siren began to wail again, halting pedestrians, scattering traffic, bringing small boys at the run. An Austin Seven side-slipped into the kerb with a foot to spare. The ambulance howled through the level-crossing with a demanding frenzy that made men's blood chill on their skin.

"Missed," said Kinivan and began to wriggle into the shape of the upholstery. His wrists flung the big car screaming around the long bend out of town.

Doran said with a touch of anxiety, "Can you go faster than this?"

"Stick around," said Kinivan.

He wriggled again so that he was comfortably back against the upholstery.

"Had a sheila once who wanted speed, but only from the buggy . . . not from me. So I waxed the seat and took a bend about fifty. We stayed together quite a while . . ."

With a stab of his finger he extinguished the light in the dashboard.

"Duralen," said Kinivan, "here we come . . ."

Duralen was not so much a town as a collection of buildings, around a saw-mill. Stores, machinery, oil, barracks, cook-house.

In the cookhouse, the man on the ground had begun to move.

"Steady," said McIntosh and rested his hand on the other's shoulder.

"Why don't they come," sighed the man on the ground.

"They're coming," said McIntosh quietly, "Kinivan's coming. You know he never let anybody down yet . . ."

"Why don't they come," sighed the man on the ground.

McIntosh studied the bandages again and his expressionless face turned towards the several workmen about him.

"Where's the boss?"

"In town."

"Wonderful!" he said. "Where's Lacey?"

"In town."

He nodded without expression and folded the edge of a blanket around the man's shoulder.

"Sid, keep an eye on him for a moment."

He stood up and joined the other men at the end of the hut.

"Any of you blokes in the army ever?"

A few nodded; he said stolidly, "Remember your blood-groups?"

"A Two, I think."

"Think's not good enough. What about you?"

"O Four."

"Sure?"

"Yair . . . me and Bill here are the same. He give me a shot once."

"O.K. You two blokes be ready, just in case."

Armstrong, the tailer-out, said "That might have been all right for a war. The quacks are a bit more careful now."

"Not tonight they won't be," said McIntosh curtly and wrote some particulars on a table-top with a stump of lead pencil.

He walked the length of the hut, squatted down and re-set a bandage.

"Why don't they come," sighed the man on the ground.

"It's thirty-six miles," said McIntosh.

He walked along the hut once more and said, "Bill, fetch a couple more blankets."

A certain amount of warmth had accumulated in the closed hut and McIntosh began to unbutton his cardigan.

He was a very big man, hard and fit and rough.

He said with the hardness in his voice, "Which of you mugs decided to work right up ta dark?"

A pale youth at the rear said in a clipped voice, "I did."

The cold blue eyes glinted in the light . . . "Why?"

"The dough. I've gotta wife and kid to keep."

The big man had his fists on his hips . . . he said coldly, "Sonny, if you wasn't new ta this game, I'd make things so bloody willin' for you you'd be glad ta go back ta your cows. We drop enough fingers and arms in the normal course of events without goin' looking for trouble. There's been five accidents here in the last three years, sonny. Three of them were from blokes who thought they knew better—like the smart alec who took the guards off the bench so he could work faster. Fat lot of good it's done his widow."

Armstrong said, "Lay off him, Mac. He won't do it again."

McIntosh started to speak and changed his mind. He threw off his cardigan and rolled his sleeves up.

"From now on the riot act gets read to every mug before they're let near a saw . . . even if *I* have ta read it!"

He stumped outside and in the night his impotence boiled into naked anger.

"What's keeping that bloody ambulance?"

There was a quivering frenzy in the body of the ambulance which communicated itself to Doran and he braced his feet hard on the floor when he saw the signpost. The winking redness and the horrible wail keeled under momentum and the big car dragged its tyres whining around the Duralen turn-off.

"Put two wings on her," said Doran, "and we'll fly."

Kinivan fought the car straight again and said seriously. "Her aero-dynamics are a bit weak."

He added, "There was a Car Trial bloke rolled over there doing that. Only doin' forty-five he said."

Doran imagined that the car gathered fresh pace.

Kinivan said, "I might throw you about a bit now. This is the end of the bitumen."

Doran said helpfully, "You don't need the siren now, do you?"

"Leave it on," said Kinivan and his wrists and fingers drove the trembling steel with new concentration.

"I have a theory it makes the cows get off the road."

"Cows?" said Doran suspiciously.

"Cows," agreed Kinivan, "you know . . . four legs and four tits."

"Oh . . ."

"That's all they're good for, actually . . . giving milk. I come out of a bend on the Highway one night doin' seventy . . . and there's a great four-footed milk-factory standin' fair across me bows."

He fought a skid and drove furiously on the wrong side of the road.

"And what happened?" said Doran.

"I drove around her," said Kinivan explanatorily, "I heard after she gave separated milk for a week."

He slid the car expertly across the road to the left again so that Doran almost flinched as a level-crossing raced at them and was gone far behind.

"Heard of a bloke once in this game," said Kinivan, "doin' seventy-odd on the bitumen near Bundaberg. When he was fifty yards or so from a level-crossin' his lights went on him. Bashed his foot on the dimmer. Bashed it again. Presto! Lights! No crossin'. Way behind him."

In the lights of the car Doran saw a petrol-pump and a shed at the edge of the road. Beyond that he fancied the outline of a house.

"Mitchell's Crossing," said Kinivan, "we'll be climbing soon."

Doran grunted and picked up the radio-telephone.

"Base?" he said experimentally.

"Base. Who's that?"

"Doran."

"Where are you?"

"Just dive-bombed Mitchell's Crossing."

"Ah . . ." said Kinivan the connoisseur.

"I'll tell 'em you're comin'," said Base.

McIntosh heard the telephone ring in the mill-office. He sprang away from the cookhouse at the run. After a little while he

291

emerged again and walked into the group of waiting men. He saw them all look at him and the action told him that his face was not as impassive as he had thought.

He said, "Four minutes ago Kinivan came through Mitchell's Crossing."

After a moment, someone said, "He only left town a couple of minutes after seven."

One by one, they turned to study the clock in the cookhouse.

Armstrong said, "You know those silly buggers do it for nothin'."

The words seemed to bring McIntosh to life again. The thermometer, he noticed, had risen a trifle.

The man on the ground was very weak and he spoke no more. But when McIntosh squatted down, the eyes implored him . . . "Why don't they come?"

McIntosh's voice was soothing, "Kinivan's coming, Ern. He's comin' like a bat outa hell."

"It's cold," said the man on the ground, "God, it's getting cold."

After a moment, McIntosh said impassively, "It *is* cold, mate. Sid, get another blanket."

The restlessness was back in the big man. He paced along the hut and came to a stop in front of the pale youth.

"If you was as big as me, sonny, I'd take yer outside an' cut yer ta ribbons.

"Aah, hell!" he added and stared into the night.

In the night, the big car dipped across the river bridge and its tyres roared on the gravel in the cutting. Doran was silent while the guide-posts made staccato splats of whiteness.

The night was a fury of noise. The noise was the air whistling past the window, the heavy-duty tyres roaring on the gravel, the high-pitched whine of the engine, the siren howling to the star-lit sky.

The sound of the siren came wailing up the long ridge, through the high forest, through the night, right up to the mill. They heard it, thus, coming from afar off and it brought with it a sense of inevitability, as though all element of chance had been taken up ruthlessly and thrown to one side.

"He's mad," said McIntosh, in soft wonder. "The man's mad."

The sound came nearer, and now that it represented action, McIntosh was at once resolute and ready.

"Bill, grab a torch and flag him down. Dave . . . Blue . . . Sid . . . meself . . . stretcher. You two blood-group blokes stand over there. The rest of you get to hell out of it."

He saw the torch waving beside the road, saw the road light up in the head-lights of the car, heard the dying wail of the siren, heard the engine whine under the gear-change and for one brief second the heavy-duty tyres skidded on the gravel.

Doran was out of the car and gone before it was halted.

In the sudden silence of the car, Kinivan flexed his fingers and stepped down stiffly to the road. He walked around the car, tested the temperature of the heavy tyres with his hand, opened the van doors and pulled out the stretcher.

Someone in the darkness said, "Can I give you a hand?"

"Yair," said Kinivan, "take this stretcher in."

He leant into the cab and switched on the telephone.

"Kinivan, chum."

"Base."

"We're there."

After a moment, Base said, "You know, Johnny, I'll buy you a beer tomorrow."

"You're a jerk," said Kinivan rudely and switched off.

He turned from the car and plodded towards the rectangle of light in the darkness. As he walked, he mopped the film of perspiration from the palms of his hands onto his trousers and felt the onslaught of a weariness which he supposed was only reaction. He shrugged and walked into the hut.

And then he was looking at Doran and Doran was looking at him. The others were all looking at the ground.

Doran said impersonally, "Dead-heat, mate."

He searched for a cigarette.

There was a moment of complete stillness, until Kinivan broke it, with mechanical deliberation, pulling out a handkerchief and wiping his hands. When he had pushed the handkerchief away, he sat down, slowly, on a box and stared at the blanket bulged up on the stretcher.

"I never lost one before," said Kinivan.

293

Judith Wright

THE HAND

Put your hand out, and hold it still, and look.
Like something wild picked up and held too long
it loses truth; light fades on the stopped wing.
Infinite cleverness pivoted on a clever stalk,
it lives in time and space, and there is strong;
but draw it outside doing into being,
it pales and withers like a sea-star dying.

The hand is drawn from the flesh by its own uses.
Powers unchannelled, shapes unshaped await it;
and what has long since happened and been completed
lies in it and directs its bone and chooses
stress and muscle. Textures thrust to meet it,
for it is their answer; stuff that cannot move
moves under the hand that is all it knows of love.

Do not look at me, the hand says. I am not true
except as means. I am the road, the bridge,
not starting-point nor goal nor traveller.
I am not you, the doer, nor what you do.
I am extension; I am your farthest edge.
I am that which strokes the child's hair, tenderly—
    tenderly—
and drives the nail into the hand stretched on the tree.
My shape is action. Look away. Do not look at me.

F. Sionil José

THE ANCESTOR

*T*HEY reached Po-on in the late afternoon. The day still washed the squat, thatched houses, embossed them all, faint grey against the dark massive blue of the nearby foothills. The dirt road which was just wide enough to admit the car had broadened or disappeared, rather, into what seemed to be the village plaza, actually a wide yard in disarray, cluttered with half-naked urchins playing hole-in and ill-clothed women nursing babies and chatting beneath the grass marquee of the barrio store at the far end.

Antonio Samson breathed deeply. The earth smelled rich, its aroma compounded of the sun's rage upon the ripe November fields and the dung of work animals. The air was brilliant and a cool wind that came from the direction of the sea creaked in the small grove of bamboo that formed a natural arbor, a gateway to the village.

His wife, Carmen, had taken over the wheel since they passed the town because she didn't trust his judgment on the quality of the road. She had driven slowly and he hadn't been aware that she had already stopped. His eyes roamed about, to the huddle of houses, the children who paused in their raucous game and were now looking at them with awe.

So this is Po-on, he mused; so this is where my great-grand-father, the illustrious Eustaquio, lived. What did he look like? If he was a scholar as the old people said he was, what were the complexities which he had simplified and believed in? Could it be possible that he may have left here a few sprouts of his wisdom for me to glean?

Some of the women at the store approached them and so did two men who were spinning cotton with wooden spindles which they held at arm's length. The women were dark-skinned and the men, like most Ilocano males, were heavy-jowled.

They stepped out of the car and to the crowd he extended a greeting. They answered as one and without hesitation.

Carmen held on to his arm as if she was afraid she would melt away and become a part of the mass. She had told him at the start of the trip that there was no sense in it, in looking up members of a family three or five generations back because they couldn't matter any more or alter his attitudes. What is tradition anyway? A catchword, she had nagged at him; if one has none of it he can always fashion one and maybe, it will even be more sensible than the stamp which he seeks.

"This is Po-on?" he addressed the nearest woman smoking a black cigarette with the lighted end imprisoned in her mouth.

"Ay, it is so, Apo," the woman answered. "What can we do for you?"

"We came from a remote place." He spoke to no one in particular in their own tongue, which was also his. He turned briefly to his wife who was contemplating the crowd. "My wife and I . . ." he paused. "You see, it may surprise you but I have come here to seek my relatives. Our root—my grandfather by the knee—he was from here."

In the many peasant faces he could discern the bright, new kinship that he had established and, by their mien, he knew that they accepted him.

"Samson—that was his family name, and mine."

The crowd murmured and the woman with the cigarette spoke again. "But there's no Samson here, Apo. I don't remember a Samson here at all and I'm now thirty-five years old."

"I was thinking," he tried again, "if you can point to me the oldest man here. Maybe he knows."

The crowd started a discussion. "What are they talking about now?" Carmen nudged at him.

"They are deciding who the oldest man is," he explained, catching on to their every word.

The woman with the cigarette stepped forward. "My grandfather, Apo," she said brightly, "he can help you find your root."

The man they sought was not in the village but in a sitio across the fields. "It's not a long walk," the woman explained. "And besides, the sun can't hurt you now."

He was glad that his wife had worn comfortable pumps

instead of high heels. Once, in Washington, during a humid and burning summer, they took a long walk. They had met barely a week before. Looking at it now with the objectivity that marriage makes a mockery of, he knew that she had been interested in him. He was doing research in the Library of Congress for his thesis and she had gone there that afternoon to have him show her the cold efficiency with which the library operated. It was five when they went out and the sun hung over the gleaming city in a grey haze, glinting in the elms and on the ebony pavement, empty now of buses and streetcars because the city's whole transportation system was on strike. He had told her earlier that they would walk home to Dupont Circle across the city where she lived and she had acceded. They hadn't gone through ten blocks when she decided to rest in one of the city's many parks. And there, while she watched the squirrels nibble at the crumbs that an old lady tossed, he realized that he had been insensate to her suffering: she wore high heels and there lay before them a long stretch of pavement yet. He was on a scholarship and he was making every penny count, knowing as he did the bitterness of a niggardly winter the year past and he desisted from calling a cab. It was she, when they started out again, who hailed one and within, while his cheeks burned, he confessed that he didn't have enough money for the fare. "It's all right, Tony," she had said, "I can pay the cab and, if you care, may I treat you to dinner, too?" He refused, of course, but he had never been able to live the incident down and afterwards, even when they were already married, his inner self would cringe in embarrassment every time he thought of her, so calm and poised, listening to his stammered apology.

But she was walking beside him now, doggedly as a wife should. He wondered if she recalled Washington still and he took her hand. "Remember our first hike," he asked.

There was no humour in her answer: "Of course," she said, "I just wish our being here is well worth all the trouble."

He did not reply for he, himself, wasn't yet sure. Why was he here among the new hay and what force was it that propelled him beyond the comfortable confines of his office and made him break out of the full life into this past that is anonymous and dead? He could not recall when it all started; it could be when he was young and there was an old man he called Grandfather, who told him of barren hills and wicked fields and the charging sea, who carried him on his shoulders and told him in pious whispers of still another man, his father, who led them away from the wasteland to the plains; a learned man who could read Latin and speak it like a monastic scholar, who wrote about death and life and the suffering in between. Istak, that was what he was called, and Eustaquio was his Christian name.

Mark him, his grandfather had said, for you are descended from a big root.

And much later, when his billfold was empty, he still felt benign. He had married Carmen and was living in her comfortable precinct and yet he knew something was slipping away and that he had become, in essence, poverty-stricken. "Honey," she said, holding his hand as they trudged down the fringe of the village with their guide ahead of them. "Will we really get something from this? I doubt if this old man has the attitude of an historian, or even a chronicler."

He smiled inwardly at her prognostication. "It's a quality of the rich," he said evenly, "to be sceptical, but not of us, Baby, us who were made to choose between the sea or the bald hills——" With his hand, he made a sweep of the hills at their left, barren indeed and dying. "We always expect the worst and still are able to laugh."

"You are talking in poetry again," she said sourly. "Can't you stop being so pretty about your tribe?"

The path dipped down a newly-harvested field with the bundled grain still spread out in the sun. It curved through the field and disappeared into a cluster of marunggay trees. Within the cluster stood a house.

The man they sought was perched on one of the rungs of the bamboo ladder. He, too, like many of the men they had seen in the region, was spinning cotton. He was barefooted and his trousers which were of blue Ilocano cloth were frayed at the knees. His toes, unused to wearing shoes, were spread out. He was probably seventy but his short white hair made him appear too venerable to have something as trivial as age. He stopped spinning and peered at the faces of his three visitors.

"It's I, Simang, Grandfather," the woman who accompanied

them spoke. She took the patriarch's wrinkled hand and pressed it to her lips. "We have visitors from Manila and they would like to talk to you because you are the oldest here and you know so many things. . . ."

Tony greeted the old man amiably but the eyes that regarded him were beady and cold.

"Yes, I know many things," the old fellow coughed. "And everything is here, stored in my mind." He brought his forefinger to his temple and gestured twice. "Everything there is to know, I know." His beady eyes closed, the old man turned and climbed to the house.

Their guide mumbled an apology, then went up to the house. In a while, she returned and behind her hobbled the old man, looking at them dourly still.

"They were from this place once, Grandfather, and they want to know if some of their relatives are still in our midst."

The angry countenance vanished. "Who were they, my children?" he bent forward, eager to know. The arrogant chin had dropped and the cracked voice was warm.

"They left about a hundred years ago," Tony Samson said simply.

The old man picked up the talk. "A hundred years! I'm not that old but I know there were many who left in search of better land. I was but one of the few who stayed, and now I'm alone. I could have gone too, but my place was destined to be here."

Tony groped for the proper words. "He was a learned man, Apo," he said, searching the old face for a sign of recognition. "The family name is Samson. My grandfather by the knee—he travelled to Rosales; that's in Pangasinan. He wanted to go to Cagayan Valley but the land in Pangasinan tempted him. He couldn't resist. . . ."

"Yes, Pangasinan," the old man threw his back against the rung of the ladder. "All of them wanted to go there where they said rice grows taller than a man. Fate shackled me to this land. Maybe I was not strong enough to cut the umbilical cord which tied me to it. But there's no cause for regrets. God willing, this land still produces and its kindness still suffices . . ."

The talk was drifting away and Tony Samson quickly salvaged

299

it. "The family name is Samson, Apo. Surely you know of some people who bear it."

The old man faced him again. "Samson?" His brow crinkled. "There's not one Samson in all Cabugao whom I know. So your grandfather by the knee went to Pangasinan, eh? The first trips were difficult, so I was told, and some were killed by the Igorots. A few drowned crossing the bloated rivers. I know their problems in the new land. I would have joined them, too, but I didn't feel the need. It's only now when my days are numbered that I do . . ."

"You didn't know of a Samson among them? Or isn't there a Samson left behind?"

The venerable head shook.

"I suppose we should have gone to the church first when we passed through the town," Carmen said as they drove out of the village. He nodded and fondled the scene once more, the yellow fields, the catuday trees with their white cascade of flowers and Po-on itself, unchanged and immemorial.

Dusk slowly fell as if it had reserved the day for him to sum up all: the quiet trees, the blurred shapes of houses. I must find him, press my feet upon his footprints and feel the solid, permanent things which his hands shaped. What am I he once asked Carmen in a moment of self-scrutiny. Impossible, that's what you are, she had told him bluntly but without rancour or malice. She had gone to America ostensibly to finish college, but actually she admitted to him sheepishly later, "to hook a man, since the best hunting ground is no longer Manila or Hong Kong —but America." He was in the last year of a scholarship in history and they struck it off wonderfully because she was so determined and he was so lonely.

She swung the car out of the gravel road as it climbed the stone highway and now the engine purred steadily. The landscape was even again and to his right, in the direction of the sea, the sky was a deep purple ribbon stretched along the far horizon.

"Just hope now," she said above the steady thrum of the car, "that there's a priest who knows what you are looking for. Records. They keep all sorts of papers there."

He grunted in reply. The dark covered the land completely and the yellow blob of the headlights showed the white road, the edges of the fields and some farmers trudging home with neat bundles of grain balanced with poles on their shoulders.

The town, like most Ilocano towns, was shabby and it did not have the bold pretensions to progress, the profusion of soft drink signs and the brash architecture that the municipalities of Central Luzon always have. The church was not difficult to locate; they had passed it earlier in the afternoon, a huge stone building with a tin roof, set on a green, scraggly yard. In the darkness it loomed dark and secret, with pale squares of yellow light framed in the windows of the adjoining convent.

She drove into the yard. Together they went to the door—an unwieldy mass of wood that towered above them, solid like the stone walls of the convent itself. He picked up the iron knocker and rapped twice.

"You better finish the interview as quickly as possible," she said. "Remember, we still have a long drive to Vigan."

He grunted again, more in displeasure than in assent. Footsteps echoed within the convent and dispelled from his mind what he wanted to tell her. In a while, the low, second door opened and a beefy man in a white soutane stood before them, a candle in his hand.

"Good evening. We would like to see the parish priest," he said. "My name is Samson."

The priest peered at the darkness behind them to see the car perhaps. "Yes, yes," he said. "I'm the parish priest. Come in and sit down." He was past middle age. The candle flickered but it was bright enough to show his features, his rimless glasses, the smudges on his soutane, and its frayed cuffs. He smelled faintly of tobacco.

"This is my wife, Padre," Tony Samson said, taking Carmen forward.

The priest raised the candle higher to get a better look at her. "Yes, yes," he repeated. "Do come in and sit down."

They entered what seemed like a medieval cavern, a high-ceilinged room with well-scuffed tile floor. The priest stood the candle on a circular table in the middle of the room and bade his guests sit on the wooden bench before it.

301

"I came here," Tony Samson apologized, "because I may not find another convenient time again."

"Yes, yes?" the priest clasped his hands and nodded as if wanting to prod his visitors into talking more.

"I was a teacher, Padre," he said as if he was nettled into admitting it. "I taught history in college and did some writing. But I'm now in the real estate business . . ."

"Where there's definitely a lot more money," Carmen hastily added.

"Ah, yes, yes," the priest agreed in his toneless manner. "But have you eaten supper?" He called out a name and a boy emerged from the shadows. "Do prepare two more plates," he shouted and the boy disappeared beyond the door. To his guests, the priest returned: "Yes, yes, history. Could it be history that brought you here?"

"It may seem foolish to you, Padre," Tony Samson said self-consciously. To his wife he turned for encouragement but she was not looking at him. She had turned away, her eyes on the walls and the narrow grilled windows.

"Why, why?" the priest asked, throwing his head back.

"I'm Ilocano, Padre," he said, the naturalness settling back in his voice. "And my grandfather by the knee came from here. I've come to see if I've relatives left."

The priest rose. What he heard obviously impressed him.

"I've never seen one like you returning to where his ancestors were born, as a sort of pilgrimage." He spoke with enthusiasm. "Of course, I know that Ilocanos . . ."

"They are all over the country, Padre," Carmen joined him. "The country is crawling with Ilocanos."

"Ah, yes, yes," the priest went on after a short, brittle laugh. He cracked his knuckles and peered at the woman. "Indeed, you'll find them saying our root is in this or that town, but do they know what the Ilocos looks like? I've been here all my life and I know it hasn't changed much. The houses are still small, the rice is still the same—the hardy variety. They are planting Virginia tobacco now—too much of it, but that's the only difference. And, of course, a few new houses with galvanized iron roofs . . ."

The boy who set the table returned and told them that supper was ready. They padded through a dark corridor into another wide room as shabby as the first.

The boy hovered by a table, a paper wand in his hands. As Tony had expected, the convent larder was well stocked. They had fried rice, broiled pork, chicken broth and omelet.

"Eat, eat," the priest said amiably.

Tony did not want to waste time. They had barely started with the soup when he spoke again: "You could have heard of him. You see, about a hundred years ago, he used to be in this very church, serving as an acolyte."

The priest dropped his spoon. "No, no," he said. "I cannot really say. A hundred years ago. But I wasn't even born. And Samson? None of your relatives have I met. There's not one Samson in the whole town—that's what I know."

"Surely, Padre," Tony didn't want to give up, "there must be something here that will be conclusive." His appetite had dwindled. "Church records, baptismal notices. They could hold his name. You see, he migrated to Pangasinan. With his whole clan. But this may not be true. And he was a scholar—I remember now. He wrote in Latin, yes." He felt very proud. "He was a learned man!"

When they finished a dessert of preserved nangka, the priest took them down, explaining that they may find something among the records. They walked silently along corridors. The taper threw their shadows against the crumbling masonry and etched the thick, rotting posts, the red brick. They stopped before an appallingly large wooden cabinet which seemed to sag into the very floor, an elaborately carved relic with iron handles.

"We might be able to see something here," the priest said. "Most of the old records are here, from 1800 and up."

He gripped the rusty bar and with a violent tug, opened the cabinet.

The priest picked at random one of the ledgers. Its cover was clearly marked, "Registro de Defunciones, 1840". He leafed perfunctorily through the pages. The line marks which may have been straight and black once were all smudged and the pages themselves seemed to break apart, like flakes, if they were flipped. In the shallow light, however, Tony Samson could trace the fine scrawl, the elaborate crosses of the t's and the flourishes

303

v

at the start of all the capital letters. The priest read aloud some of the names and, after two pages, stopped.

The boy who had served them at the table joined them with a Coleman lamp and the shimmering light identified everything in the giant room, the thick wooden floor, the battered chairs. The priest reached for the top shelf and, at random again, got two ledgers. Tony Samson read the inscriptions, on the covers. One was marked, "Registro de Casamientos, 1860-1865". The other bore the equally elaborately written title, "Registro de Nacimientos, 1865-1867".

"I once saw a manuscript in Latin—a philosophical one—written by an Eustaquio. It should be somewhere here." His fat pudgy fingers went through the ledgers, then he brought it out—a black, tattered book, and on its cover the priest read aloud: "Eustaquio Salvador."

"Eustaquio Salvador?"

Tony knew the name vaguely. Salvador, Salvatero, Sabado—many family names in Cabugao used to start with the letter S, a convenient arrangement initiated by the friars. By knowing a man's family name, it would be easy to deduce what town he came from.

Salvador!

Then it struck him with its full and magic force and he remembered how once his grandfather had told him that their name wasn't really Samson. Clasping the battered thing, his heart now a wildly pounding valve, Tony Samson turned to his wife and cried, "This is it, Baby. Written in his own hand."

Carmen hedged closer. "It's Salvador, Honey. Not Samson."

"But haven't I told you once his real name was Salvador? That he had to change it because of a quarrel with the Spaniards?"

She laughed: "It's an alias then. I wonder what the Spaniards did when they found out."

"I wouldn't know," the priest said, handing the manuscript to her husband.

Tony Samson read the title again. It was legibly written in block letters: *Philosophia Vitae, Ab Eustaquio Salvatera.* "A Philosophy of Life," he translated it aloud and turned questioningly to the priest for confirmation.

He nodded. "You know Latin well?"

"I had a year of it in college, Padre," Tony said, "but that wasn't enough." He handed the book back to the priest. "Please read to me some lines."

The priest moved to the light and opened the book to its first page. He mumbled the phrases, then recited haltingly their translation in English: "Cum magna pretentione—It is with great pretention that I start this book for I'm but eighteen and when one is that old," he paused to flick a glance at the great-grandson, "he seldom has enough strength to resist temptation just as I have surrendered now to the temptation of recording the dreams to which I aspire."

The priest paused once more.

"Dreams," Tony Samson mused aloud, and quoted the Spanish poet, *"All of life is a dream, and all those dreams are dreams . . ."*

"Yes, yes," the priest intoned dully, "but you see, he apologizes for that. He was but eighteen."

"Please, Padre," Tony repeated. "Do go on—one paragraph more . . ."

The priest opened the book to the page which he had left and as he continued, his face brightened up. "Listen to this now," he enthused: "Mundus viro no spcrat. Eo tempus non habet—The world does not wait for a man. It has no time for him." He returned the book to Tony and his voice was warm: "He had the sensibility of a poet, and humility, too. This is the virtue of all those who create and who are great, no matter how obscure they may have been. Why, I believe that God, even in His greatness, was most humble. He—your forefather, had this quality and more. He was restless, too, and now I know why he left Cabugao."

Tony flipped the pages of the book while his whole being flamed and the vacuity within him seemed suddenly filled with something that burbled and glowed and lifted him beyond the common touch. "Now I leave you to your discovery." The priest sounded remote behind him. "And, of course, you have to sleep here. I'll have the cots prepared upstairs. Come up when you are sleepy."

"Thank you, Padre," he said happily without lifting his eyes from the engulfing maze, the fancy script and the words he couldn't read and understand. And holding on to the ledger, he felt kinship at last, tangible and alive, with this obstruction called the past. Maybe there is wisdom buried in this, or romance, or just a diurnal account of a young man's fancy, his pride and his hurt. The transcription will not be important, he decided quickly; it was this solid memento that mattered most because it was the root on which he stood.

"You can ask him to give it to you. It is but a scrap of paper which he has no use for anyway," Carmen said.

He lifted the Coleman lamp which was left atop the wooden pedestal beside the cabinet. At the door, the boy waited for them, his eyes droopy with sleep, and showed them to their room.

In the dark, as they lay in two cots that were brought together, they held hands—a soothing domestic habit—and were motionless now but for their measured breathing. Beyond the heavy sill and sash shutters which were flung to the remotest edge, the stars shone clear and tremulous in the cloudless sky. A silky breeze breathed in, laden with the scent of the warm earth. A dog barked in the unknown recesses of the dark and in the rotting eaves he heard the soft scurrying of mice and the snap of house lizards.

"It's just like Washington, Honey," she said after some time.

"Why Washington?" he asked, pressing her hand.

"The Library of Congress," she said. "The first printed Bible. The American Constitution. They were all nicely framed and lighted, in special containers, heated to keep out the frost and the humidity. It must have cost some money to install those devices . . ."

He recalled again her visit to him at the library, how she had gone there because "when you are in Washington, you just can't miss the biggest library in the world", and how valiantly she had tried deciphering the scrawl in the documents.

"You are way off the track," he said, divining her thoughts.

She turned on her cot and tweaked his nose. She smelled clean and even in the soft dark, he could make out her young, beautiful face. "Oh, now, I'm not saying that we will have to go to so much expense, trying to preserve your great-grand-father's manuscript."

"What then . . . ?"

"But you can do it, maybe have an Augustinian friar in Manila transcribe it and then, who knows, it may be some important document in literature. Or ecclesiastical history."

"That's not funny," he chided her.

"But I'm not trying to be funny," Carmen said. "I'm merely carrying to a logical end what you have started. If you won't have it translated then, at least, we can bring it back with us. Not just the book, mind you, but all the other papers that are written in his hand. Think what wonderful conversation pieces they will make."

The situation had suddenly become ridiculous and he didn't know whether to laugh or stand up and curse everything. There was something pathetic in his encumbrances, in his attitudes compared with the crass measurements of the aristocracy into which he had migrated.

He brought to mind once more the American lady, in her sixties, on the boat crossing the Atlantic for England. She was on an almost religious mission to a Sussex hamlet to seek the well-spring of her ancestry that was, she was told, still intact. A genealogical research agency had promised to do the job for a few dollars, "dirt cheap it is", she regarded the deal with the patent exuberance of the American who had accidentally stumbled upon a bargain. He recalled, too, the rapt crowds at the National Art Gallery in Washington, at the Louvre and the Prade, the horde of Americans gaping at the old pictures, searching for beginnings in the cemeteries of art, as if they were afraid to drift into the limbo of their own making, and these frames were the anchors that would make them and the future secure. Their faces were all indistinct, yet vaguely familiar, exuding as they did an enthusiasm and a dedication. He had now struck an infallible identity with them because he, too, had come to great lengths to find but a book and a vanished name in a small Ilocos town.

She turned to him and laid a hand across his chest. "What is it you want? We can always ask Papa."

To her it all seemed so simple; *we can always ask Papa*, omnipresent, omnipotent. But one couldn't reshape a woman, much less a perspective as chronic and as acute as hers.

"One thing," he told her, kissing her on the chin. "And that's to be myself."

"The past is past. None can alter it," she said, returning his kiss.

But the past still mattered, he knew that keenly now as he had never known it before. And this wasn't all; there was the continuity, too, the belonging to a huge and primeval wave, and with the knowing came that transcendental joy since he was, after all, not a drifter upon the vast oceans of want. What could he show? An old book from an old church. If he could only return to his teaching and, once in a while, write maybe about the urgencies he believed in; if he could only forsake the drudgery, maybe he could do more for some future searcher to covet.

There flashed again, vivid and taunting, the face of the old man he had talked with in Po-on earlier in the day and, finally, the faceless vision of the gentleman, the forbear who, perhaps lived in this very room, a pen in his hand. How did they, in their listless youth, react to the whirl, to the chasms between fancy and the fact? One refused to pioneer, to forsake the barren land, and the other wrote a book, then with his puny legs led a whole clan in a journey to a strange new land.

"Baby?" he spoke softly, tentatively.

"I know what you are going to tell me," she said without remorse. "But it all seems such a waste. We can buy the book, if the priest won't give it for free . . ."

"Yes," he said tonelessly, as if in abject surrender. "You can buy it. Your money, it can buy everything."

Edith L. Tiempo

ROWENA, PLAYING IN THE SUN

GOD, who stirred the void and in Motion's birth
Revealed yourself; the warm limbs wake
Along the dark stairways, the far eyes lift to take
The fixed commotion of the stars, their dim furious
    speed
Predictive in the blood; the cupped hands hold the
    spinning sun,
Till all this reaching tips the rim of heaven to the
    earth,
Spilling the primal colours from the splitting of a
    seed,
Waving the tall green like a great sea waking;
And in the golden light, tiny hands lifting, falling,
Turning in God's own orbit, my golden one.

Bhabani Bhattacharya

THE CARTMAN AND THE
STEEL HAWK

THE news came at sunrise and charged the air with echoes, like the beat of a drum. Men sped up from the fields, wiping earth-stained hands on their loincloths. Women shouted for their children as they hurried, their voices swift and shrill. And the children danced with joy, clapped each other on the back and yelled:

"It's the flying wonder, you hear? We'll go a-riding in the sky."

"We'll touch cloud, we'll squeeze cloud in our fists to make rain."

For, in the large meadow on the western edge of the Indian village stood the flying wonder, the sun sharpening on its wings, the crowd around swelling fast every minute.

Bishan, the carter, had yoked his pair of bullocks and was coming along in hot haste. He cajoled the pair. He prodded them with a short thick rod. Once or twice he pulled each one by the tail. "Tchuk! Tchuk! Run. Do not fall asleep, dear brother." There was not an eye-flick of time to lose. The flying wonder would be gone any moment. Who would expect such an opportunity to cross a man's life twice? They had seen those wonders on the skyways, looking like great strange birds in the far blue, or, at night time, like pilgrim stars, but to see one lie afield, a mere wagon tied to earth! To touch the winged body! And there was the mystery to solve. Why had it come? Only to rest for a bit on solid earth? Or could there be a hidden reason, as folks hinted?

The wheels of wood thwacked the deep dust of the road. The bullocks raced, their heavy flanks quaking, and grew dizzy with speed. "Tchuk . . . tchuk! Run hard, gentlemen, run till you lose your breath."

As the cart passed the Balcony of Knowledge where the village school teacher lived, Kamini, the teacher's young wife, hailed from the doorway:

"Ox-cart, will you take me to the Meadow of the Man-Lion on which has descended the wonder of wonders?"

Red dust clung to her bare feet. One hand held a half-drawn veil, the other clutched the arm of Bablu, her six-year-old daughter.

"What fare, Ox-cart?" she asked as the cartman pulled up.

"Why, mother, I am going there to please my own eyes. How could I charge you a fare?" But suddenly, his glance rose to the thatched kitchen roof and his face beamed. "A-ha, what a pumpkin vine you have raised, what tendrils strong and lithe, what leaves!"

"The first fruit of that plant will be yours." And so, when the bargain was settled, Kamini climbed in at the cart's back with her daughter.

The cowbells jingled and the cart trekked down the pathway to the meadow, skirting a shadowed mango grove, and turned to a lane between fields of paddy, a red tape zigzagging through sweeps of bright yellow. The tall paddy with full-kernelled grain drooped under the wind's weight.

"Never will she set eye on *this* wonder," the cartman spoke softly as if to himself, shaking his close-cropped head with sadness. "What evil fate that gout should strike her bones on this day, of all days, so she cannot even stand on her feet. The whole village sees the wonder and she alone is denied."

"Who, Ox-cart?"

"Old Grandma, poor soul. Mad about tricky machines, right mad. Same today as in her long-ago days when the railroad first came this way."

"Railroad?" said Kamini in surprise. "The railroad came this way countless years ago."

The cartman smiled. "And is not Grandma countless years old? It happened when she was 14-15 . . ."

"What happened?" cried Kamini. "Tell me, cartman," the voice pleaded.

"A railway station was built at Choorni, an hour's walk from our Sonamati."

"Yes. What then?"

"Grandma was 14-15. Wed a short while."

"I am listening," said Kamini, for the cartman had paused again.

"Grandma had seen fire-engines and trains thunder past, belching thick sooty smoke, but now at last she could see one standing by, quiet as an elephant, and she could reach out her hand and feel the iron skin, for Grandpa read the urge in her mind and he took her to Choorni one day in his cart."

And now Bishan warmed to his story. He neglected his oxen, turned his face toward his listener and let his voice go faster.

"Grandpa took her to Choorni station one day. They heard the rumble like twenty-one thunders. The fire-engine came hot-foot, a monster, trailing coach after coach of metal and wood, all ashine with paint, with glass. For full five breaths Grandma was quite still, like a picture, and she simply gaped, her eyes big, mouth open. But the train would not wait long, so Grandpa warned her, and Grandma came back to life. She, first of all, bent low to look at the hundred wheels. Then she walked to the engine, black-bodied, all greasy with the sweat of toil, and she took a good long look at it and also at the man who drove the monster. She turned back, peered in here and there to see the lights that burned without oil, the fans that made a breeze, and she turned her eyes this way and that way, at this and that passenger, man, woman and child.

"At last, when the fire-engine gave a long-drawn coo-ooh and moved off, whoosh-whoosh-whoosh, coach after coach going smoothly as if gliding on a road of glass, Grandma was quite still again. It was a little time before she could find her tongue. She turned round to Grandpa and said, 'Truly, truly, such an image of power and majesty exists! To see this I must have earned merit, great merit, by a hundred-and-one good deeds!' And she joined her palms to her forehead saluting the image of majesty. Grandpa burst out laughing, but his eyes were wet at the corners. Two, three days later they came again to Choorni station. This time they bought tickets and rode on the train. They got down at the next stop, folded their hands again to salute the fire-engine, and walked back home all the way."

Bishan paused for a while, returning from his mind-picture of the past. His voice grew soft. "Old she is, and crazy still about tricky machines, no less crazy than in her long-ago days."

"What sadness that she cannot see the flying wonder," said Kamini. "She would have been athrill as before, athrill to the marrow."

"What sadness, truly. But she bade me rush and see the wonder machine. I said to her, 'Grandma, I don't want to go. Without you it will be no fun.' And she said, 'Bishan, don't talk so. You must rush off and see this wonder. I shall see it later through your eyes.' She will want to know everything, be sure. How it looks, how it smells——"

There was a silence. The cartman prodded his bullocks. "Hey, brothers of an ass, run hard till you lose your breath. Faster, gentlemen, faster!"

Little Bablu, bored by such useless talk, now flung her voice. "Fast! Faster!" she urged on both man and beast. "Are we to get there when the winged one is gone?"

The crowd came in sight. Presently the cart stopped. Bishan unyoked his animals.

"Make way for the mother from the Balcony of Knowledge," he pushed his way gently through the press of people.

Beside the pilot bustled the fat figure of Roghunath, the village constable, deporting himself, as the women said with cool satire, like the *Lat*, Governor of Bengal. What a row he made, shouting, "Move back, good folks, move well back on all sides lest you get blown away by the wings like chaff." For the machine was about to take off. And no one could yet tell why it had made a landing. The constable feigned as if his belly was full with the great secret, but the dim bewilderment in his face belied his pretence.

The heart of every man, woman and child stopped beating when the long blades at the snout flashed into motion. The crowd gasped when the machine darted forward like an enraged ram, turned, leaped and was in the air. Rapidly it gathered speed and climbed the stairs of the sky with a groaning of its wings.

"Ma," cried Bablu, tugging at the hem of her mother's sari, "what will happen if birds fight the winged one when it touches the sky roof?"

"Birds have no malice, darling. They have clean hearts, all save the crows. And crows can't fly so high."

"What if a pack of robber crows rise as high, Ma?"

"Then the flying wonder will pour out a tail of poison fume and the crows will drop down dead, a heap of black feather and beak."

The cartman walked out of the crowd, with downcast eyes. Coming to his bullocks who had been feeding on grass he yoked them back and stood by, stooping over the hump of one animal, remote in thought. The flying wonder was handy and neat, he had to admit to himself. Went much faster than a fire-engine, faster even than a winged creature. Had great speed, that steel hawk. But why must speed greedily eat up the farness? Why fret to reach your journey's end in an hour or two hours? That he could not make out. Was it not more easeful to rattle along in a good sound ox-cart with well oiled axles? You could talk to the folk on the road (and no folk to talk to on the sky path!), pluck a bloom from the fields if it took your fancy, do a hundred other things.

Why must speed greedily eat up the farness? Grandma would know the answer, she, mad about tricky machines, right mad. Grandma could look at the flying wonder and go a-riding it in her fancy, zooming away mightily and shooting from sky to sky like a crazy star. Grandma had *that* sort of mind. She had it when she was young, and she still had it when her hair was without one black strand, all teeth gone, and sadness and pain written on her brow in each one of a hundred wrinkles, graven deep.

Bishan twisted his face, feeling a tenderness in him and yet a superiority, a knowingness. He bent over, whispering to one of his bullocks: "Be easy, dear brother. We are all right for speed. No cart like ours seven days' trek from Sonamati, north-south, west-east."

But even as he spoke the words they made a hollow ring in his ears. It was as though Grandma's spirit was catching up with him! She who was of Yesterday was possessed by Today. Then how could one who was of Today be otherwise? Could one belong in his mind to whatever time he liked? Could one person ever exchange roots with another, exchange the breath in his nostrils?

Bishan lifted his face skyward, his eyes hard with a kind of challenge.

What if *she* could be there, the aged Grandma, riding the steel hawk? And Bishan felt his heart swell. Would she not be even more athrill than when she saw the fire-engine for the first time, or when, two-three days later, she rode in one of the rumbling, rocking coaches?

Truly, truly, such a thing exists! Why, to see such a thing I must have earned merit, great merit, by a hundred-and-one good deeds.

And Bishan, his eyes on the sky, yielded to his fancy. . . . There she was, the aged Grandma with her modern dream, riding the steel hawk, soaring atop!

"*Ho*, pilot brother, take heed lest you lose your bearings. Take heed lest you brush against a shooting star; or move too close to the sun-god and get the wings of the hawk burned, dissolving like ice in summer. Take heed lest you be drawn into the dark realm of baleful Saturn. Take heed lest you be doomed to wander forlorn on the skyways, never to return to earth. Take all heed, *ho*, pilot brother."

Impatient cowbells tinkled into his reverie while he leaned against the fat white flanks of his ox, but his neck remained craned, his mind remote. For Bishan, the cartman of Sonamati, had yielded to the impulse of the age and was riding the steel hawk with his Grandma, zooming away mightily.

P. K. Saha

PICNIC

SLOWLY the afternoon grew rich
Like white skin tanned honey-brown in the tropics,
And the sun, tired of watching us
Through the split in the leaves overhead, grew sleepy
And leant back in the immaculate blue.
Dry leaves being blown along
(the drowsy murmur of reclining shadows)
And whispered words
Tumbling into laughter
Like naked boys into a river,
Splashing the sunlit joy about with candid insinuations;
And in the wind the trees around
Sighing with deep contentment.
Let us rise and shake the grass from our clothes.

Manas Chanyong

SHOOT TO KILL

A HUNDRED and forty men lived on the ridge of the hill in tiny huts roofed with rattan leaves. They all kept on with their task; they went on determinedly, felling big trees and small trees. Some of the trees were so huge that when they were chopped down they fell like thunder. Of the one hundred and forty men, only fifty or sixty could go out to work at a time. The rest were in bed shivering with malaria.

Every one of them was a great criminal. They had been sentenced to over ten years' imprisonment. They were serious, not given to much talking. They were men of deeds, not of words. When they were not working, they were thinking. Their thoughts—and their words, whenever they spoke—turned to their homes, their bits of land, their fathers and mothers, their wives and children. For them, at such moments, their wives were more beautiful than all the stars in the sky, more beautiful than all the flowers in the world and rarer than the most valuable pearl at the bottom of the sea. When would they see their beloved wives again? For one it would be in another seven years; for another, twelve. That was a long time to wait.

They were sent out from "Ayukadong", the headquarters of the convict settlement, a government office in the jungle area which was about 90 kilometres from the town of Yala, and the place where they were clearing the jungle was about 20 kilometres from headquarters. They had to chop down trees so that the Highways Department could press on with the Yala-Betong road. When they first arrived, they found it was quite a good spot. There was a small plateau there, the size of a football field, overgrown with spiky cogon grass. So they took it to be their home and called their little village, "Cogon-grass Hill".

317

They got rice from the office and were allowed eight satangs a day to buy food. A small co-operative shop there—only the size of a tiny grocer's shop in the capital—sold cooked food. Supplies were brought up to the shop by elephants. In the evening when they finished their work, they all helped themselves to cooked rice in small pots. Some got out salted meat to broil, and those who were rich from gambling ate tinned fish. They had never tasted fresh fish. If they made curry they would use tinned fish for that too. In fact, it was quite a treat to eat tinned fish curry deep in the jungles of the South. Some had for roasting birds called gawas or white peacocks, trapped at the top of one of the high hills. They used red chillies as baits. The white peacocks, with their tails spread out, would strut gaily up to the chillies and then get trapped. Sometimes they caught wild frogs as big as newborn babies. It rained there all the time so there were small yellow frogs and tree frogs as well which they also ate.

When the stock of food was very low, they borrowed my shotgun to shoot langurs, or leaping deer, as they were known locally, but they were really monkeys. Then they would make delicious langur curry. Real deer they used to get quite often. They got quite a number of tapirs too, and sometimes even bears. They shared the game out equally among themselves. Sometimes they fried grubs, insects and crickets and enjoyed these as delicacies. When they finished their meal they sat in groups and chatted, those with a bout of fever lying down and those who were just getting over one, sitting up. Who would envy them such a life?

I can still remember Porn, a man from Machongsorn, quite well. He was a good cook. He knew his way about in the jungle. Porn was not at all big, but he was extremely strong. Besides being industrious and loyal, he was a good musician. He took great pleasure in playing the seung in the dead of night, singing in such a piercing voice that your hair would stand on end. This seung which was a sort of mandolin shape, he sometimes played like a Spanish guitar, strumming his own accompaniment, and sometimes when he fancied a "gniew" tune from the North, he would slide his finger up or down the string, producing quite a Hawaiian guitar effect. His face was always smiling in spite of my ticking him off sometimes, but his eyes always looked sad.

I could not figure out why this sadness was lurking there. It could not have been anything else but his longing for home. No word is so sweet as the word "home". At times, I found myself pining for it too.

Whenever I was free, I would ask for two elephants from the Elephant Section and load them up with provisions and guns. I usually invited my colleagues to join me on my expedition. Prasit, a close friend of mine, often accompanied me. He was the youngest of us all. He was only 24 years old and a good singer as well as a good talker. Whenever he talked no one could help laughing. Ever since his school days he had always been keen on sports. But he was a bit hot-headed: he often boasted he had been awarded a cup for boxing and a gold medal for marathon running. Also, his friends sometimes found it hard to swallow his habit of contradicting and mimicking people. He could take off the voice and gestures of the person whom he had chosen as his victim with cruel accuracy. But by and large, most of the convicts loved him. He could not drink much, but whenever he did, he drank until we had to carry him to bed. He was a young man who craved for adventure, and that was why he had come out to work with me in the jungle.

Prasit had little weaknesses. He had been brought up in a missionary school and his curt manners and pettish irritability often caused misunderstandings. I knew him well and often gave him a long lecture on these points. However, his bad moods lasted only a short time. At heart, he was good.

One day we rode the elephants out into the jungle. It was a dense, pathless jungle. There were leeches everywhere underfoot. Except for the stream bed, there was no open ground, as the jungle was choked with thorny rattans. The elephants had to wade through the stream. Once they had climbed out and left the stream bed, they had to start climbing the hill, grasping the trees firmly with their trunks and at each step making sure whether the rocks could bear their weight. This they did by cautiously stepping on them and over some considerable time slowly letting their full weight down. When they were certain, they moved on. We passed the villages of foresters which had rarely been visited. We went to Banmaeward and pushed on to Wanghin, Puloa and Wangsai.

319

w

These were villages of real foresters who had never been anywhere, not even to Yala. Each village consisted of about twenty to thirty huts. These foresters used long bamboo stems to keep drinking water. They often had several of them in each hut. We bought some chickens and coconuts from them. They had fruit in plenty: durians, rambutans, lansas, and many other kinds, but we were tired of them all as we had been seeing such a lot of them on our way up. At night, the foresters took us shooting. My flashlight picked out a deer, and I shot it. The unfortunate animal was a large-sized deer. Its blood-red eyes were staring at the light. I shared the meat with them all.

At Wangsai we met a very pretty girl. I found out that her father was a Chinese who had come there to trade with the natives, so his daughter had a beautiful complexion. She would have looked very attractive if she had had better clothes to set off her figure. Porn had fallen madly in love with this girl some time ago. He loved her truly. Once he told me that when he had served his term he would stay on with me and marry Wan.

"Well, sir," he said, "Wan is pretty and a hard worker. At first, I was thinking of taking her to Maehongsorn but I don't think she'll go."

"Has she become your wife?" I asked.

"No, sir, but I can bet you a hundred to one she will be mine. Her mother likes me. Every time I get my money I buy her things."

I very much doubted whether the girl's parents would give their daughter to a convict. But it was possible they did not know the truth. I believed Porn had lied to them that he was a labourer, not a convict, because when he went out into the jungle he was well-dressed. He wore brown shorts, a good shirt and the sun hat that I had given him together with some canvas shoes. The girl's family might well have thought that he was an ordinary decent man.

One night, when I did not go shooting, I heard voices under the coconut palm. I went out stealthily on to the veranda and saw a man and a girl talking. I had to turn my face away from this loving couple. I thought of loneliness, of love which could not be found anywhere. I could hear crickets singing. Now and then a tiger roared angrily or a deer started barking. When the wind blew against the leaves of the wild bananas and elephant-canes at the foot of the hill it set up a drumming noise like the yells and cries of a huge army that echoed from flank to flank. And yet, between times, I could even hear the lovers' breathing, and it was then I felt that their lives were so sweet—so sweet and so blissful.

I heard footsteps coming up the stairs and turned my head to look. I could hardly believe my eyes when I saw that it was Porn. Who was it then, that was talking to the girl under the coconut palm? I went up to Porn and whispered: "So it isn't you down there then, Porn?"

He shook his head listlessly. Although it was dark, the light of the stars made it possible to see faintly. He looked dejected. His hair was falling over his forehead. He had the look of a criminal who was hearing his death sentence pronounced.

"Who was it then?" I asked.

"It's Nai Prasit," he answered in a voice so hoarse and faint that it was almost inaudible.

"Oh, Prasit," I moaned wearily. It was Prasit then who was plucking his wild jasmine. Prasit must have met this jungle girl and fallen for her. But Prasit did not realise that he had taken Porn's life.

"Doesn't she love you, Porn?"

Porn heaved out a deep sigh, he tried with great difficulty to swallow his sorrow.

"I will win, sir. I have never lost yet."

"Don't speak like that Porn," I told him, "you ought to know that 'one bad deed brings many sorrows in its wake'. Winning or losing, a man must take it as a man. If we don't win, we must put up with losing. If all men wanted to be the winners who would be the losers then?"

He only sighed. I did not know how much he understood my words.

"I believe in you—but I have never lost. I'd rather die," he said. "But you know, sir, when you come to think there are plenty of other fish in the sea. I think I'll survive this."

I patted him on the back. A little while later, Prasit took that innocent jasmine for a walk along a narrow path bathed in the dim starlight. They stopped at a rickety old fence. How happy

321

they were! But my own thoughts and feelings were running rather strangely along other paths. What about Porn—wouldn't he feel like a fish that had had its head bashed?

It was probably my words that had got him to lie down to sleep. But I knew he was not sleeping. How could he sleep when all his nerves were taut and fully awake? Nothing in this world could soothe and take away the burning sensation, except that wild jasmine, but she was not coming back to him. Prasit was thirty-eight and quite a tough customer. Compared with my young friend he was just like an oak to a sapling.

One morning Porn came to me and asked for a day off. He smiled a very dreary smile.

"Are you going to see her, Porn?" I asked.

"Yes, sir—today we'll know," he answered. "I have bought her some sugar and a few sweets that she likes."

I let him go. He had done his work well. It was a fine morning. Gibbons and langurs filled the jungle with their cries. Those who had not got fever went into the jungle to find food. Some sat cutting rattan stems to make walking sticks. Some sewed rattan leaves for roofing. I was writing a letter to my mother. After Porn had been gone for a little while I heard an elephant making its way through the grass. I turned my head and there was Prasit, with beaming face, astride the elephant's neck, one hand holding a rifle, the other hand holding the elephant's ear. He called out to me boisterously.

"Sakon—aren't you coming?"

"Where to?"

"Wangsai," he shouted, "I have fallen for that girl. Isn't that just too funny!"

I was frightened. I did not want Prasit to go. I had a premonition. But Prasit was a generous, good soul; the convicts loved him. I did not think Prasit would dare cause any trouble. Nevertheless, I could not help being worried. Porn's words about losing and winning were still fresh in my mind. However, I left things to take their course and went on writing my letter.

In the evening, I heard the bad news I had half expected.

Porn had grabbed the gun from Prasit and what was more, he had hit him in the face with the butt. Then he had fled into the jungle. He left me a note which read:

DEAR SIR,

I have to leave you sir, I have always believed in you, but I told you that I have never been beaten. He hurt me first. He did it in front of Wan. So I hit him back. For your sake, sir, I didn't kill him. I have to take the gun. They will probably issue a death warrant but I won't let them get me. I will escape through Saiburi. I beg you, sir, not to come after me. Let Nai Prasit do it.

PORN

P.S. Sir, will you be kind enough to write to my wife up North that Porn the Tiger has gone into the jungle again. Let her warn Teng to be prepared to answer for it if he steals my wife. If Porn dies in the jungle like a tiger then he will vow to have his revenge in the next life.

I folded the letter and put it away. That evening Prasit came back and I learnt more details. Prasit went on the elephant so it took him a long time. He arrived after Porn. On his arrival he saw Porn with the girl. Prasit tried to get rid of Porn by ordering him to go and buy drinks and chickens. Porn would not go and he talked provokingly, so Prasit slapped him in the face. Porn flew into a rage. He snatched the gun from Prasit and hit him with the butt. Prasit's face was swollen.

The head-warden was terribly angry. He came from Ayerka-dong himself the morning after he had received my report.

"Well, Sakon," he said, "is this Porn such a terror?"

"Quite a terror, sir," I answered.

"Get him dead then. Is that clear? We can't let him live. Here are the bullets; I have brought you some rifles as well. You've only got shotguns here, haven't you? They're always jamming, these Browning bird-guns! Get moving now. He can't have gone very far. We've told all the local villagers not to give food or shelter to any runaway."

I took the order, but in my heart of hearts I did not want to go at all. I was not afraid of Porn but I did not want to shoot him. I could recall the scene when I shot Yab the Tiger. Before he died he fixed his bright, clear eyes on me and his eyes stayed bright right up to his last moment. However I had to go. It was my duty to shoot anyone who violated the prison regulations. I dressed myself neatly and put leggings on to protect myself from

323

leeches. I had a rucksack in which I stuffed some preserved food. The convict carried rice and other heavy things. I would have been much happier if I were going hunting a tiger, but I was going after a "man" tiger, a tiger that had been as good to me as a kitten.

I went off in the direction of Wangsai. No matter what happened, Porn could not leave his sweetheart's place. The idea of escaping by way of Saiburi was just a trick, as every convict that had gone out that way had been sent back to us. He must have hidden himself in that neighbourhood. Furthermore, Porn had only five bullets. I had to get him back alive. I did not want to shoot him unless in self defence.

I split up our party into small groups and sent them along the main streams. He could not very well keep away from the streams, the highways of the jungle. Four days passed and still we did not hear anything. On the fifth day, we heard that a local villager had been ordered by Porn to boil rice for him. He did not take away anything, not even one satang. When he had had his fill, he had gone away and left the man some money. Whenever there was news of plunder, we followed it up but Porn was so quick that he managed to escape us every time.

One evening, a villager came up panting, and informed us that Porn was hiding in a deserted hut in the rubber plantation of a local man who had moved to Tarnto. It was certain that he was starving and in the grip of a deadly fever. I had my gun and my men ready. We set off without delay. I ordered my men to take separate routes and surround the hut at a distance. We all believed that this time we would get him.

Because of our old friendship and trust, I firmly believed that Porn would not shoot me. I walked towards the hut alone, carrying a Mauser rifle. As I got nearer and nearer my heart began beating faster and faster. I told myself he wouldn't shoot me. But his own character had such strong power over me that when I was at the door, I did not dare push it open.

"Porn, come out and let's have a talk."

My heart was thumping when the rickety door opened. I expected to see Porn emaciated by fever and hunger. But I was taken aback as if I had seen a ghost. It was not Porn but a girl, the lovely jasmine.

"Wan," I called. "Tell Porn to come out."

"He isn't here, sir," she answered in her southern Thai accent.

I flung myself through the door. It was true, Porn was not in the hut. I looked hard at her. I must have looked so fierce and brutal that the girl was frightened.

"He is very ill, sir. He went out a moment ago," she said. "He told me to ask you for quinine and cigarettes."

I turned away. I had never been so sad and depressed as I was then. I could not look at the lips of the innocent girl, lips that were delicate and soft as petals, trembling like her body. I pitied her love. I pitied Porn who had to fight danger from so many sides—from me as an official, from malaria, from hunger and from the bitterness of his love. How could he overcome all these? He was bound to lose. And yet, in a way, he hadn't really lost. Hadn't he got the jasmine of the jungle?

I had to go back, overwhelmed and tired. He had not shot me, but he wanted medicine from me. This made me think of various medicines that I had with me, quinine, atabrine, guinoplas, moquin. How delighted I would have been if I could have given them to him. But hadn't I been ordered to shoot him?

We all slept in mosquito nets and still every one of us had fever; we were all moaning and groaning. What about Porn? Where could he get a mosquito net? Soon he would have to give in.

I sent my men to shadow this wildflower. Now we knew she met Porn from time to time and sometimes by appointment but she was as quick as a wildfowl. I knew full well that she was a friend of the Negritoes. They did not walk, just vanished. They jumped from one bush to another. We could never see them. This wild jasmine of ours travelled like a Negrito, so we all shook our heads in despair. If we followed her, we were bound to lose our way.

Fifteen days passed, I still had nothing to report to headquarters. Whenever we heard that Porn had appeared at various places to grab food, we dashed over, but had to come back disappointed. I thought of the hot-headed Prasit with anger. He should have known that he was not living with ordinary human beings. He was living with creatures that we all called "giant's children". How could he range himself alongside a man who had really lived according to "the luck of the game"—a real sportsman.

In my last attempt to get Porn I went to the rubber plantation of a Chinese near Tarnto. Here Porn had snatched food again and this time he had also taken 3 bahts weight of gold. I knew well that the gold was for Wan; but he had disappeared in spite of our blocking every possible way of escape.

That night I left Tarnto, thinking of going back to Wangsai again. I had been away from "Cogon-grass Hill" nearly one whole month now, hidden away in the villages of the jungle people. On the way, our guide who was picking out the path by flashlight, stopped short.

"Sir," he whispered.

My men and I stood still, looking straight ahead. We saw two eyes as red as fire, so different from the eyes of all the usual wild animals.

"It's a tiger," he said.

"No, it can't be," said one of the men, "it's a tapir or a bear."

"Well," I thought, "whatever it is I'll shoot." I aimed between the two eyes. When the trigger was pulled, we heard it running off as fast as it could. It looked like a huge black bear. We flashed the light after it and saw the dark and bulky form stumbling away. With our light we examined the small plants on the ground that were wet with rain and found a trail of blood. We were not going to follow him. We would come back the following day. I ordered my men to move on immediately.

When I arrived at Wangsai, I caught the fever. After seven days in bed, I felt just about up to going after Porn again. On the eighth day, I began my work by coaxing the girl to give us information. It was no use: she did not give us any help, at all. I went out inspecting deserted huts and barns at night. I did not think he would have the nerve to sleep alone in the jungle. Besides, it was the beginning of the rainy season; how could he sleep in the rain?

A little while later, two of my men came running in out of breath to tell me the news.

"Sir," said one of them, between gasps, "I smelt a very nasty smell. I believe the big thing that you shot the other night is now stinking."

"That bear? How could it come and die this far away?"

"It's quite near the spot where you shot him that night, sir," he reported.

"Well, let's go then—I want its skin and gall-bladder."

We went over the hill following the smell. At the foot of the hill there were wild bananas and giant plantains. The stream was overhung with rocks. There were ferns of strange species and orchids hanging in long clusters. We saw an overgrown bush ahead of us. This must be the place? The bear that I had shot, the one which had spilled blood on the leaves, must have come to hide here and died. I quickened my pace and reached the bush. We pushed aside the branches. "Porn!" we all cried out together.

I felt stunned. His body was decaying all right. He must have been dead for several days—of malaria and hunger. My eyes filled with tears thinking back on how he had told the girl to ask me for medicine.

I could not be callous to him. I had really liked him. I told my men to dig a grave at once and we buried him. We stuck up a sign on the grave and stood still for a minute.

"I *have* given you medicine, Porn." I said in a subdued voice. "I dropped it on purpose at your Wan's house."

Roland Robinson

❧❦❧❦❧❦❧❦❧❦❧❦❧❦❧❦❧❦

THE OLD-MAN AND MARRGON THE LIGHTNING

Related by Rinjerira of the Djauan tribe

Illustrating the power of the lightning as an avenging and punishing agent.

A MAN had run away with a lubra belonging to an old-man. The man and the woman had run away together. The old-man looked about for their tracks. He could find nothing. The man and the woman had travelled over the rocks. The old-man looked about, looked about for their tracks. The old-man cried, cried, cried. He looked all about the rocks, he looked along the river, all round the spring, he could find no tracks. The old-man went back to his camp.

The old-man gathered grass. He made string. He began to bind and tie up that grass until he had made the figure of a man. As the old-man made this grass figure he sang the man and the woman who had run away from him. As he sang he fixed a stone-axe on the shoulder of the grass figure. He fixed another stone-axe on the other shoulder. A stone-axe he put at one elbow and a stone-axe he put at the other elbow. After that, a stone-axe he put at one knee and a stone-axe he put at the other knee. Like that the old-man made Marrgon the lightning.

The old-man sang the lightning. He sent the song Yarrada after those two who had run away. The old-man sang the lightning and sent the lightning after the man and the woman who had run away. Bye and bye that old-man sat down. He slept. He dreamed. He dreamed of those two who had run away.

The lightning followed up the man and the woman. The lightning followed them, followed them, followed them. Half way the lightning camped. He got up and went on again. He followed them, followed them.

The man and the woman had been out hunting. The man had killed a kangaroo. He had roasted the kangaroo. The lightning sneaked up, sneaked up, sneaked up. From a long way off the lightning smelled the grass where the man and the woman were cooking the kangaroo. Quick fellow, quick fellow, he sneaked up. He looked out for that man and woman. One way he went round. He found that man and woman.

The man looked back from where he was cooking the kangaroo. He looked. He saw an old-man with white hair. "O," the man said to the woman, "an old-man has come up."

The lightning had made talk-talk all the way: "Boi, boi, boi, boi!" The lightning came up tall, all the same like this one tree. "Spssh, spssh! Rai, rai, rai-dee-dee. Siss-siss-siss-siss!" He bled them. He split them up, finished them up. He went up along the sky.

That old-man was asleep. He dreamed about the man and the woman. The lightning came back. The lightning had brought back to the old-man the livers and hearts of the man and the woman. The lightning showed them to the old-man. Bye and bye the old-man talked. "O, you who have killed them." That old-man was dreaming you know.

Bye and bye the old-man went away to another place. The old-man travelled, travelled, travelled. The old-man found the place where Marrgon the lightning had cut up his lubra and the man who ran away with her.

No matter if it is a long way off that anyone sits down, that lightning will find them. Lightning, he is all bone. He has stone-axe along shoulder, knee, elbow. "Rai, rai, dee-dee. Siss-siss," he talks as he strikes, as he cuts anyone up.

Ngamul, he is different. He has stone-spear, long one. He goes like fire, like star when he runs, not little bit star, more big. He has white body, white painted body.

T. Inglis Moore

ALIGN YOUR ACT

CHESSMEN, dreams, and peacock feathers
    Delight in an ivory tower;
With no Ariadne, we voyagers wander
Threadless the maze of time's agenda,
    Yet strive to arrive at the ease of a flower.

These pilgrims here, the portulacas,
    Soon reach their Meccas in form
Of the sun's gold, but where is our guiding
Faith to hold, with the light fading
    And thunder leading black squadrons of storm?

Take a focus on yellow Arcturus
    Who heard Job cry in the night.
Turn from the tower, the solved equation
Of petals, the rancours of revolution,
    To the clear flame of the spirit's light.

In our birth, in desire, in the grave's ending
    We are one in the brotherhood
Of human bonding—shall hope not summon
The peoples' yearning for peace in common
    To morning unfearing, the way understood?

Align your act with the sun and Arcturus.
    Ascend with the iris to span
Self and the world, earth and heaven.
Explore the heart till we find the haven,
    Core of the maze, the integral man.

Mary Gilmore

NATIONALITY

I HAVE grown past hate and bitterness,
I see the world as one;
But though I can no longer hate,
My son is still my son.

All men at God's round table sit,
And all men must be fed;
But this loaf in my hand,
This loaf is my son's bread.

Oentoeng Soebroto

THE WISH

*T*HE mountain was a challenging dark silhouette against the red dusk. It was a perfect volcano, the slopes of the cone gracefully levelling off on either side in faultless symmetry. Parts of the town and sea, to the right below us, still managed to catch the rays of the setting sun, and they lay there, basking with obvious delight in a seemingly unreal world. Soon, though, the dark would triumph. Dusk is but a short-lived beauty in the tropics. Where we were it was already chilly, yet we sweated as we panted in single file up the track on the hill which guarded Mount Slamet from the sea and the hard, ever-encroaching town.

I remembered how my teacher once said that our island was travelling northwards, for the cliffs of the south coast were crumbling before the raging southern sea, while the rivers, all running north, deposited silt among the mangroves that fringe the flat coastal plains along the Java Sea. But this town had instead of moving north already begun to spread its tentacles southwards to spoil the tranquillity of the mountain and its guard. At that hour, however, I was less concerned about the injustice of the town, which was as hard and cold as the white concrete and the bricks that made it, than with myself.

As I tried to keep pace with the others in the silent sombre procession along the track that zigzagged upward, I had begun to wonder why I had asked to be taken with them at all. Santosa, my eldest brother, was in the lead. Then followed Bakri, the man responsible for our pilgrimage. Behind me there was another man, a stranger, but neither my brother nor Bakri had bothered about introducing him to me. Yet the aquiline nose between rather deep-set and dark eyes on a narrow face betrayed that a long time ago his forefathers must have come from the land of the Prophet.

The Eastern Star had already made its appearance, glimmering solitary in the unusually clear sky. It was a warning that dusk would soon give way to the night, and we had little time left.

Two hundred yards below the hilltop we arrived at the shack. In its one room there was a charcoal stove. A couple of big nails stuck out from the central log pillar that supported the *attap* roof. We threw the matting we carried on the earthen floor; the food bags went in the corner near the stove and the kerosene lamp was carefully hung on the upper nail. My brother broke the silence without waiting to rest. "It's close to six," he said. "We'd better go to the place now. All we need to take is the rope."

So we started the hard climb up the last few hundred yards to the top. The place my brother had referred to was the neglected grave of an Arab merchant missionary. For all I knew the grave had always been there. It was there when the East India Company came.

Bakri had always seemed a strange character to me. He and my brother were very much older than myself, and this made it hard for me to understand him. I was still at school. They were already earning their own living, as far as I could gather. There was a time when we had belonged to the same carefree world, but now they had already stepped out of it into another which I was yet to know. But the outward signs were enough to convince me that Bakri stood and lived on a different plane from my brother and his like. He never went fishing to the tip of Tegal Harbour pier, which pushed out for a distance that seemed to me about half a kilometre into the choppy Java Sea, a sea famous for its *kakap* fish. With a six-hooker and a fat prawn on each hook you seldom missed. You swung the waxed line round and round until it had gathered the right speed and then you let it go. It took some practice, but once you got the knack the lead-weight would fly fifty to a hundred metres before it would lose momentum and plunge into the sea. Then all you had to do was just pull and play the line. And you could never miss.

In our town, fishing from the pier was a popular pastime. Like the weather, it was a subject that always invited some sort of conversational response. Yes, fishing from the pier was a leveller of classes, and for high and low it was a mark of fellowship.

Bakri never went fishing. Nor even watched cock-fights for that matter. He never flew kites or made them fight with other kites and bet on them. There were other things, too, in which Bakri showed no interest, and this convinced me that somehow or other he belonged to another world; but in many ways he was like the rest of us. He would go to the puppet show, staying there cross-legged all night till the break of dawn, listening to the monologue of the *dalang*, and getting completely absorbed by the all too familiar loves and battles of the knights from the *Ramayana*.

I remembered how my brother once told me that Bakri was a mystic, but it did not reach my comprehension. Santosa ought to know, though. He was the only one of all the people I knew who could make Bakri talk and laugh like other people did. That is to say, next to Bakri's wife.

It was also from my brother that I first knew about Bakri's unhappy marriage. I wasn't quite old enough to be told about it. But I had insisted on being taken along when I heard about the planned pilgrimage to the grave on the hill. In my wanderings around the countryside with other boys from our *kampong*, we had always avoided the mysterious summit of the hill. Unintelligible taboos and fear of the supernatural were stronger than even our explorative curiosities. Thus when the opportunity arose to climb the hill under the escort of the three men, I took it eagerly. In my excitement I had not worried about the fact that the trip would not be for pleasure. It was to be a pilgrimage, and we would stay on the hill overnight. The reason behind the pilgrimage, my brother confided, was Bakri's childless marriage. Apparently, when people got married they wanted children.

We had heard about the grave on top of the hill that guarded Mount Slamet. People regarded it as a last resort for the fulfilment of their wishes. If God and prayers failed to help, you should go there on a Friday night and meditate and think and wish till the sun rose from the sea. You wouldn't be alone all night, for at midnight the spirit of the saint would arise to cross-examine you on your merits. To get your wish granted, if it was to be granted at all, you had to stay there the whole night. But few could stand even the strain of waiting till the stroke of twelve. They would run away, except those with the strongest souls.

I had never met anybody with so strong a soul. There was a money-lender who, it was said, had won riches after communion at the grave. But ever since I had known him he had been wealthy. Anyhow, the test was to remain on the hilltop the whole night through. And Bakri, who wished for the blessing of children, had decided to go to the saint.

When we reached the top we found a clearing in the bush. In the middle of this was the grave. Some withered flowers and scattered ashes with bits of charcoal told the tale of previous offerings. The grave was no more than a mound of earth, with a rectangular concrete border one foot high around it, green with moss and cracked and disintegrating in places. The marble tombstone, however, was still intact, and it was set, as in most Moslem graves, in the loose earth at the northern end—the seaward end—of the mound.

My brother looked at Bakri as if to assure himself that he had not changed his mind. The sun was completely down now, and darkness had fallen over the town and the sea, although dusk still lingered reluctantly here. Lights began to flicker down below. Bakri gave a nod and walked to the tomb. He spread his prayer rug near the foot and sat on it facing the sea, with his back pressing against the stone.

With the long hemp rope, the type used in mountain climbing, we tied him to the tombstone, winding the rope around crosswise and tying the knot behind the stone so that he could not reach it. That was to make sure that he would not run away out of sheer fright. It was Bakri's own idea. And after a last look we hurried back to the shack two hundred yards below. Bakri had already begun his meditation.

After supper, when we had stoked up the fire for warmth, we laid down our dead-tired bodies on the mats. The flickering oil lamp threw sinister shadows around us. I moved closer to my brother.

"Did his wife agree to this?" asked the stranger.

"I don't know," my brother replied. "Anyhow, what could she do to stop him? You know the way Bakri is."

Inside the shack soon settled a silence, broken only by the chirping of the crickets and the incessant singing of cicadas. The

335

x

wind rustled through the leaves of the *sono* trees, and the night seemed to drag on very slowly, leaving us to our thoughts.

"Brother San!" I murmured. I always addressed him as "Brother San", for he was much older than I.

"Yes."

"Do you really believe there is a spirit there?"

"Spirits are everywhere, really."

"Imagine being tied to that stone on a night like this."

"Well, he didn't have to do it."

A gust of wind rushed through the door. I shivered. The flame of the lamp danced wildly. The stranger stood silently and closed the flimsy bamboo pleat door and bolted it with a piece of wire.

"I wish Bakri had a child," I said.

"There are too many people having too many little bastards on this bloody island," said my brother, who never swore when Bakri was about. I listened to the wind and the flapping of the *attap* roof. It was very quiet now. Even the cicadas and crickets had become quiet. I hope the oil will last the night, I thought. I could never sleep in the dark. I never dared to. My soul could so easily go unnoticed out of my body in the dark.

"Half past eleven," my brother muttered. "We had better get some sleep while there is still time." He stood up and walked to the lamp that was hanging on the central pillar.

"Brother San," I pleaded, "please don't."

He watched me for a while as I lay there on the floor. The stranger was already snoring.

"All right," he said, looking serious. "I just forgot."

It was not very long after that when we heard faint shrieks from somewhere above. They grew louder and louder into blood-curdling cries. There was something inhuman about them that made my flesh creep. My brother stood tense. Then we heard the heavy sound of steps running on the damp earth outside. Closer they came, and closer. And with a final demoniacal yell someone crashed through the thin bamboo door, staggered for a moment and, gurgling something incoherent, collapsed on the earthen floor. A ragged dishevelled bundle. Still tied to Bakri's back was the tombstone.

Unknown

BECAUSE OF YOU

SWEET-SMELLING flowers are in my heart
For every bud that bursts alive
Has filled my heart with flowers of love.
My life, my love, I give to you.

My life is lived in a dance and dream,
A shadow moving on the screen;
Mine is the story of the shadow-play;
I dream and wake and dream again.

And so the shadow-play proceeds—
Telling of a puppet with a mourning heart
And how his heart is healed and filled with joy
When two souls meet again that had been parted.

For we are puppets, both of us,
To entertain the dalang in his song,
And on the screen our situations change
But the tune they sing is still the same.

Now we, the puppets, put aside,
Are coffined in an attic room,
A puppet—and so my love are you—
To entertain the dalang in his poem.

Chairil Anwar

STORY FOR A GIRL, DIEN TAMAELA

I AM Pattiradjawane
Guarded by the gods,
I alone.

I am Pattiradjawane,
Foam of the sea,
The bleeding of the blue.

I am Pattiradjawane;
When I was born
The gods sent a boat with me.

I am Pattiradjawane, guarded by the nut-
    meg forest,
Fire on the beach. Whoever approaches
Three times must call my name.

In the silence of the night the weeds
Dance to the sound of my drum;
The nutmeg trees become maidens and live
    until the dawn.

Come and dance
Play
And forget.

Make me not angry, beware!
For I will strike the nutmeg, the maids will
    stiffen and I
Will send the gods to you.

Throughout the nights, throughout the days
I am the rhythm of the weeds,
The fire that burns the isle.

I am Pattiradjawane,
Guarded by the gods,
I alone.

Sri Thandaveswara

❧❦❧❦❧❦❧❦❧❦❧❦❧❦❧❦

"ACHHA DOOD"

ALTHOUGH he earned his living by selling milk he called himself an honest man. True, all milkmen added water to the milk. But unlike the rest of them he made no secret of it.

When you paid him well enough he gave you milk straight and fresh from the cow, and he called it milk. But when you did not pay him well enough he gave you watered milk, but he would never call it merely milk. He would sell it only as "Achha Dood" or "nice milk".

The eager milkman pattered all this to the young couple, including that sly little joke against himself. But he saw from their look that Vasant and Jayanti were only amused, not coaxed into buying milk from him.

His pride in salesmanship was hurt and he vowed that he would make them buy from him—or never sell milk any more. Changing his tactics, he pleaded, "Consider Babuji. Would I cheat a kindly, angelic gentleman like you or this Maiji here who is the very image of Mahalakshmi? How could I ever give watered milk to those sweet children of yours?"

It is said of even Gods that if prayer does not avail flattery does. Small wonder, therefore, that a gentle softness fell on the faces of Vasant and Jayanti. They relented, although, on principle they continued to appear unbending.

"That is all very well," said Jayanti, "any milkman can say nice things, but what we want is really good milk."

"Buy not from me, Maiji, if you do not find the quality of my words in the milk I give you."

"If you are as good as that," cleverly interposed Vasant, "why don't you milk the cows in front of our house?"

"Sir, you take me for a *mamooli* (ordinary) milkman and in

340

this you do me an injustice. I own a dozen cows. They have calves and I have servants to milk them. Fifty houses buy their milk from me. If I milk the cow before your door they all will want me to do the same for them. Tell me Babuji, can I take my circus round fifty houses twice a day?"

"But," he added, "if you are keen you can send your servant to watch. I milk the cows in that *maidan* (open ground) yonder across the main road."

Jayanti could not spare the servant in the morning. Nor could they take the milkman on his own testimony. Vasant had a bright idea. Why, Romesh could be sent, little Romesh who was clever for his age and whose vigil would leave no room for doubt.

"Certainly, Babuji, but it may be hard on the little boy. I milk the cows at five in the morning and he has to be there by then."

"Oh, my son wakes up every day at four to read, or else how could he be so clever?" explained Jayanti. "He will be there by five all right."

Romesh was very clever at school. He was wonderful at English composition and expert in British history. Full of curiosity, he had found out all about Feudalism, Crusades, King Arthur of the Round Table and the beautiful ladies for whom men of valour fought. But he had not paid much attention to cows. His mother had warned him off those vulgar four-legged things. They had sharp horns which they would at any moment thrust into his belly. Besides, they were a dirty lot and had the habit of dropping cowdung just as you went near them.

In fact, it was on the consideration of vanity rather than of wisdom that Jayanti agreed to let Romesh go to watch the milk-man. Soon enough, she would revise the arrangement, for she did not wish her clever boy to stoop to such work.

Romesh passed a sleepless night. He was both eager and afraid. He was going to see the cows at close quarters. He would mingle and make friends with them. But what if they should thrust their horns into his belly? It must be early morning. He knew of his bilious father's morning temper. If cows were of the same nature he was sure they would thrust their horns into his belly. Thank God, father had no horns!

341

At half-past four, Romesh got out of bed and briskly put on his half suit of maroon and blue stripes. Then he donned his cricket cap and pulled on his socks and bright red shoes. He stood before the mirror and admired his rig, but also saw how small he looked. It seemed a good idea to carry his toy pistol— in case the cows should misbehave! As he rummaged in his little suitcase for the weapon he came upon a pair of moustaches he had pinched from the green room on the last drama day at school. Then he hit upon a bright idea. Why not wear the moustache? He would look big and the cows would be afraid of him. That is why the milkman grew such a thick moustache! Thus he set out; suit, shoes, pistol and moustache and all to see that the milkman kept his word.

Although he had set the time at five, the milkman had been nearly ten minutes on the maidan when Romesh got there at quarter to five. The cows were already there, dipping their heads in their fodder-buckets. On seeing Romesh the milkman burst into laughter. "How clever you are *behta* (youngster)," he exclaimed. "You have grown a thick moustache overnight." Delighted at his own wit, he laughed again.

"I did not grow it. It is a fake moustache I had in my box. I put it on to look big so that your cows won't hurt me."

"Ha, ha! You are great. Here you are, come to watch me milk the cow, and you are so afraid of cows that you arm yourself with a false moustache." He laughed again and louder. Indeed there seemed to be no limit to his capacity to laugh.

After laughing himself out he gently took Romesh by the hand. "Come behta," he coaxed, "take off that moustache or all my servants will laugh at you. You should not be so afraid of cows. Come, I will introduce you to them."

He led Romesh to his favourite cow. She was a spotless white and sported a necklace of coloured shells. As the milkman called out, "Ganga, Ganga" she raised her head and looked fondly at her master.

"Ganga," he said as if he could talk to the cow, and passing his hand gently along her neck, "meet this little Raja who has come to see you."

"See here, sire," he reassured Romesh. "There is nothing to fear, Ganga is my dear, dear cow. She would not harm you for

342

all the world, make friends with her while I go and look after the milking."

Romesh was happy and heartened. Ganga was soft and warm to touch. She was ever so gentle. Her soft dark eyes were so pitiful that he yearned to make her happy. She seemed to like his fondling, for as he caressed her neck she raised her face to show her dewlap. And as he curried her dewlap she turned to show the other side of her snow-white neck. He would fondle her as long as she was docile.

After a while Ganga dipped her head into the fodder-bucket. Romesh turned round and saw her tender little calf struggling with the noose of rope which held her off from where her mother's ample supply of milk was being copiously drawn for the use of man. He was sad that they should part the calf from the mother's milk it thirsted for.

"I say," he pleaded with the servant. "Why don't you please free the calf? It wants more milk."

The servant was piqued. As if he did not know his job! And what heresy—a calf to ask for more! But looking up he saw the sadness in Romesh's eyes and merely smiled like those who suffer fools gladly.

Then Romesh went about from cow to cow and to the calves, caressing and making friends with all. How serene they looked, clothed in the eager red of early dawn! Why did mother think them ugly, fierce and dirty? Sure, he would bring her one day to see for herself.

What with musing, caressing and wondering, Romesh forgot all about watching the milkman. But it turned out that the milkman did not mix water in the milk for the first two or three days. Pa and Ma were greatly pleased with their son's supervision and Romesh marched off to school with a merry heart. But his mind was full of cows and more than once he was caught mooning away while the lessons were on.

The next morning Romesh was at the maidan by half-past four so that he might miss nothing. Watching the servants fill a number of buckets with varying quantities of water he enquired why. Getting no answer from the servants he went to the master.

Of course the milkman laughed. "That is no secret," he explained after a pause, "for those who pay more, there is less water in the milking-bucket. For those who pay less, there is more. For your house, of course, there is no water at all—I have promised your parents that."

"Who takes the milk with more water?"

"So many people, why your neighbours take it."

"Surely, you are not giving this kind of milk to Raghoo and Jahnavi—they are my friends."

"I don't but their parents do."

"Why should they? It is such a pity that they should drink such poor milk."

"That is for their parents to arrange."

"But how should their parents know? You don't tell them it is such poor milk."

"Tell them! Why anyone, wanting milk at twelve annas (1s. 6d.) a *seer* (about 2 lb.) these days, should know better."

"Then why don't they tell you to give them good milk the same as you gave us yesterday."

"Because they are not rich enough. Your father is a Sahib earning a thousand rupees a month. But theirs earns only a couple of hundred."

"Oh, but why can't you give them good milk at twelve annas a seer? You know Raghoo, Ramoo and Jahnavi are such nice children."

"Behta Raghoo, Ramoo and Jahnavi make three. But my children add up to fourteen and the fifteenth will soon arrive. How am I to cater for them if I sell such good milk at twelve annas a seer? Consider the servants I have to pay. Look at my hefty cows. They have to be fed, and fodder is dear."

"But how can you think of your children alone? How can they or you be happy while such nice kids as Raghoo or Ramoo have to drink such poor milk?"

The milkman laughed. In fact he was laughing all the time, as was his wont. But the little child talked with such love and compassion, that the milkman became uneasy and rather thoughtful.

Romesh turned away to hold concourse with cows and calves. That was dearer to his heart than all the good milk that was foaming. Once again he saw the calves chafing at the leash and his heart smote him. He pleaded with the servants, but they

344

turned a deaf, and even hostile ear, to his pleas. He argued with the milkman. How could he let his servants deny the calves their own mother's milk? How could he find it in his heart to take the milk away from the calves to dilute and sell? The milkman had the same answer; fourteen children in stock and the fifteenth invoiced.

"In any case milkman, please, please do something for Raghoo, Ramoo and Jahnavi. They are nice children and should not have to drink such poor milk." With this final entreaty, he set the milkman thinking hard, and turned away.

On reaching home, instead of getting ready for school, he started an argument with his mother. He could not bear his little pals being put on such poor milk while he fattened on the special quality they got for him.

"Then it is for the milkman and Raghoo's parents to arrange."

"Yes ma, but they cannot so arrange. The milkman says he has fourteen children and the fifteenth is coming from somewhere, so he cannot afford to sell good milk at twelve annas a seer; and Raghoo's father does not get a big enough pay to buy at one rupee (2s.) a seer as you do."

"Well my dear, it is clever of you to have found out so much. But what can we do?"

"Oh, please, ma, something has to be done. Why can't father, who gets a big salary, give a part of it to Raghoo's father who gets a small one? Then we can all have good milk and Raghoo and Ramoo and Jahnavi will be stronger. You will be happy too, ma, to see them so healthy."

"Don't be silly, Romesh. Take care not to talk to other people like this; they will think you mad."

"What does it matter, ma, so long as all of us can have good milk?"

"Now Romesh, is there a thing called school or is there not? You are already late."

"All right, ma, I will run to school. But please do coax father. Only for some time, you know. When I grow up a little I will keep my own cows so I can give the best milk to every kid." He bounced off to school and left his mother musing. "He wants salaries to be shared—and he will keep cows. He is shaping nicely, indeed!"

345

All along the way Romesh pondered over his pals and the calves and cows whose beauty haunted him. The teacher was wroth that he was late. Romesh was the brightest boy in the class. Fancy him being one hour late on the very day the Inspector was visiting! Fortunately, the Inspector had not begun his rounds else what a let-down it would be!

It made little impression on Romesh, however, for his mind was all caught up in a maze of cows and calves and their docility.

When the dreaded Inspector arrived, the teacher called Romesh and showed him up to the Inspector.

"He is our brightest boy, sir, Romesh is. He is a marvel at English and amazing at British History. The Crusade, the Magna Charta, the Reformation, or whatever it be, he knows the answer."

"This is nice to hear, Romesh," said the Inspector. "Now let me see who was England's greatest queen?"

Romesh faltered for a moment and then as if talking in a dream, replied, "Ah-er-Queen Victoria, sir."

The teacher felt relieved and the Inspector was about to smile out his satisfaction when Romesh cut in. "And ooh, sir," he gratuitously added with great excitement, "What a beautiful tail she had."

The class roared with laughter. The teacher blushed and the Inspector glared. Nothing could be done at the moment. But the next evening the distressed teacher called at Vasant's place and detailed the entire story.

"I am sorry to seem to complain about him," he concluded, "but I have come to regard Romesh as my own son. We should set him right at once."

"We are most grateful to you, sir," acknowledged Vasant.

"Of course, I knew some such thing would happen," came off Jayanti, "I always warned him off cows and such vulgar things. It was his father's brain-wave, sending him out to watch the milkman and all that.

"Of course," she corrected herself, seeing the flash in Vasant's eye, "I acquiesced, but was never happy about it. It will never do to mix up boys like Romesh with cows and milkmen and the like. Why, he has been there but two days, and already he preaches me to coax his father to share his hard-earned salary with Raghoo's father! And then, he says when he grows up a little, he will keep cows!"

Vasant gently turned the talk to what they should do about it. Father, mother and teacher took deep counsel and decided that the first step, in any case, was to stop buying from that particular milkman—they were all quite sure he was influencing Romesh. The next morning when Jayanti came out to give the message to the milkman's servant, she found the milkman himself at the door. "Maiji," he began without giving her a chance to speak, "I have come to ask your forgiveness, for I cannot sell you milk any longer, no, not with your son watching."

"What is wrong with my son?" Jayanti fiercely demanded.

"Nothing at all, Maiji, he is an angel of a boy and speaks with the voice of God. But I cannot afford to do business with angels. He has been telling the servants to be kind to the calves and let them have all the milk. He has been urging me to be kind to all children and to sell pure milk to every one at twelve annas a seer. If we go on like this I am sure some day he will talk us all into becoming saints. But then, we'll all be broke! No Maiji, forgive me, I can't sell you milk any more!"

India

Adi K. Sett

MORNING PRAYER

THIS hour I love the best, this hour of cold, steel-grey dawn
The hour of maidens' waking dreams, of mists and fresh dew
When the birds break into song.

This hour I love the best, this hour of cold, steel-grey dawn
When I seem to feel Thy presence at every turn I take,
When I seem to breathe Thy breath, to clasp Thy hand, to touch
    Thy Holy feet,
Oh, Thou Immaculate Spirit, to see Thy very face.

This hour I love the best, this hour of cold, steel-grey dawn
When the sleeping are like the dead.
Nothing stirs, nothing can be heard save the wistful song of
    birds
And Thy celestial peace falls on me for a few fleeting moments
And I am purged of all my sins and am at complete peace.

This hour I love the best, this hour of cold, steel-grey dawn
When, slowly, life quivers into consciousness and an ecstasy
    divine,
When, quietly, men turn their thoughts to Thee
And begin their daily life with a hymn of praise to Thee.

This hour I love the best, this hour of cold, steel-grey dawn
When night turns and wakes from her sleep
And day dawns anew for us
When I seem to clasp Thy hand, to touch Thy Holy feet,
Oh, Thou Immaculate Spirit, to see Thy very face.

This hour I love the best, this hour of cold, steel-grey dawn
When I realise that nothing moves nor fades nor dies without Thy
    slightest command
That not even a little leaf from a tree falls without Thy knowledge,
And then, the Spirit moves
And the dawn deepens into a golden, opal day.

Samar Sen

ALAKA

IN whose blue eyes
the still sea-depths shiver,
where the tramlines terminate
and the grey city comes to an end.
Even now in the desert of the sky
night comes stalking like a lonely beast,
where the tramlines terminate
and the grey city comes to an end.

At night, the empty desert burns
in the moon
like the eye of a tiger.

Dal Stivens

THE PEPPER-TREE

MY father often spoke about the pepper-tree when we were kids, and it was clear it meant a lot to him. It stood for something—like the Rolls Royce he was always going to buy. It wasn't what he said about the pepper-tree—my father had no great gift for words—but how he said it that counted. When he spoke of the pepper-tree at Tullama where he had been brought up you saw it clearly; a monster of a tree with long shawls of olive-green leaves in a big generous country-town backyard. "A decent backyard—none of your city pocket-handkerchief lots," my father said. There were berries on the tree that turned from green to pink with waxlike covers which you could unpick and get the sticky smell of them all over your fingers. In this spanking tree there was always, too, a noisy traffic of sparrows and starlings fluttering and hopping from branch to branch.

When we lived at Newtown, Sydney, I used to look for pepper-trees when my father took me for a walk on Sunday afternoons. "Look, there's a pepper-tree," I'd say to him when I saw one with its herring-bone leaves.

"By golly, boy, that's only a little runt of a tree," my old man would say. "They don't do so well in the city. Too much smoke, by golly. You ought to see them out west where I come from."

My father was a tall, thin man with melancholy brown eyes and the soul of a poet. It was the poet in him that wanted to own a Rolls Royce one day.

"First our own house and then some day, when my ship comes home, I'll buy a Rolls Royce," he'd say.

Some of his friends thought my old man was a little crazy to have such an ambition.

350

"What would you do with one of those flash cars, Peter?" they'd tease him. "Go and live among the swells?"

My father would stroke his long brown moustache, which had only a few bits of white in it, and try to explain, but he couldn't make them understand. He couldn't even get his ideas across to my mother. Only now do I think I understand what a Rolls Royce meant to him.

"I don't want to swank it, as you put it, Emily," he'd say to my mother. "No, by golly. I want to own a Rolls Royce because it is the most perfect piece of machinery made in this world. Why, a Rolls Royce—"

And then he'd stop and you could feel him groping for the right words to describe what he felt, and then go on blunderingly with the caress of a lover in his voice, talking about how beautiful the engine was. . . .

"What would a garage mechanic do with a Rolls Royce, I ask you!" my mother would say. "I'd feel silly sitting up in it."

At such times my mother would give the wood stove in the kitchen a good shove with the poker, or swish her broom vigorously. My mother was a small plump woman with brown hair which she wore drawn tight back from her forehead.

Like the pepper-tree, the Rolls Royce symbolized something for my father. He had been born in Tullama in the mallee. His father was a bricklayer and wanted his son to follow him. But my father had had his mind set on becoming an engineer. When he was eighteen he had left Tullama and come to the city and got himself apprenticed to a mechanical engineer. He went to technical classes in the evening. After two years his eyes had given out on him.

"If I had had some money things might have been different, by golly," my father told me once. "I could have gone to the university and learnt things properly. I could have become a civil engineer. I didn't give my eyes a fair go—I went to classes five nights a week and studied after I came home."

After his eyes went, my father had to take unskilled jobs but always near machinery. "I like tinkering but I had no proper schooling," he said once.

He knew a lot and in spite of his eyes he could only have learnt most of it from books. He knew all about rocks and

351

Y

how they were formed. He could talk for hours, if you got him started, about fossils and the story of evolution. My mother didn't like to hear him talking about such things because she thought such talk was irreligious. Looking back now I'd say that in spite of his lack of orthodox schooling my father was a learned man. He taught me more than all the teachers I ever had at high school. He was a keen naturalist, too.

Just before the depression came when we were living at Newtown, my father had paid one hundred pounds off the house. He was forty-seven years old then. I was twelve.

"By golly, we'll own the house before we know where we are," he said.

"Will we?" said my mother. "At a pound a week we have twelve years to go—unless we win Tatts."

"You never know what may turn up," said my old man cheerfully.

"I have a good idea what with people losing their jobs every day."

"I haven't lost mine," my father said, "and what's more, if I do, I have a way of making some money."

"I suppose it's another of your inventions, Peter? What is it this time, I ask you?"

"Never you mind," said my father. But he said it gently.

One of my mother's complaints was that my father was always losing money on the things he tried to invent. Another was that he was always filling the backyard up with junk.

"What can you do with these pocket-handkerchief lots?" my father would say. "Now, when I was a nipper at Tullama we had a decent backyard—why it was immense—it was as big—"

He'd stop there not being able to get the right word.

Auction sales, according to my mother, were one of my father's weaknesses. He could never resist anything if it looked cheap, even if he had no use for it, she'd say. Soon after my old man had told my mother he had something in mind to make some money, he went away early one Sunday morning. He came back about lunch-time in a motor lorry. On the back of the Ford was a two-stroke kerosene engine. I came running out.

"I've bought it, Joe, by golly," he told me.

He had, too. Both engine and lorry.

"Dirt cheap. Forty quid the lot," he said. "Ten quid down, boy, and ten bob a week."

My mother cut up when she heard.

"Wasting money when it could have gone into the house, Peter."

"This'll pay the house off in no time, by golly," my father said. "And buy a lot of other things, too."

I knew by the way he looked up and over my mother's head he was thinking of the Rolls Royce which to him was like a fine poem or a great symphony of Beethoven.

All that day he was very excited, walking round the engine, standing back to admire it, and then peering closely at it. He started it running and stopped it continually all the afternoon. Every night when he came home from the garage during the next week, he'd go first thing and look at the engine. He had some plan in his mind but wouldn't say what it was at first.

"Wait and see, Joe," he'd said. "You'll see all right."

He didn't let me into his secret for over a week, although I knew he was bursting to tell someone. In the end, he drew me aside mysteriously in the kitchen one night, when my mother was in the bedroom, and whispered, "It's an invention for cleaning out underground wells, boy."

"For cleaning out wells?"

"Underground wells."

He listened to hear if my mother was coming back.

"I'm rigging a light out there tonight, boy," he whispered. "Come out later and I'll show you."

My father's idea, he explained later, was to clean underground wells in country towns by suction. You pushed a stiff brush on the end of the pipe down the sides and along the bottom of underground wells. The pipe sucked up the silt and you didn't lose much water from the well.

"Every country town has half a dozen underground wells, boy," he said. "The banks and one or two of the wealthier blokes in the town. Just like it was in Tullama. There's money in it because you can clean the well out without losing too much water. It's a gold-mine."

It sounded good to me.

"When do you start?" I asked.

"Soon, by golly," he said. "The job at the garage won't spin out much longer."

He was right about that, but until the day she died my mother always had a sneaking idea that the old man had helped to give himself the sack. It was early in 1930 when the old man set out in the lorry, heading out west.

"You've got to go to the low-rainfall districts," he said.

"Like Tullama?" I said.

"Yes, like Tullama, by golly."

I started thinking of the pepper-tree then.

"Will you go to Tullama and see the pepper-tree?"

My father stroked his long straggling moustache. Into his eyes came that look like when he was thinking or talking about the Rolls. He didn't answer me for a bit.

"By golly, yes, boy, if I go there."

Soon after this he started off. Every week brought a letter from him. He did well too. He was heading almost due west from Sydney and I followed the towns he spoke of in my school atlas. It took him nearly a day on a well, so in the larger towns he might stay over a week, in the smaller a day or a day and a half.

After he had been away for two months he still had a good few wells to go before he reached Tullama. You could see that he was heading that way.

"Him and that silly pepper-tree!" said my mother, but she didn't say it angrily. My father was sending her as much money as he used to bring home when he worked at the garage.

But in spite of what my mother said about the pepper-tree, she became a bit keen as my father got only two weeks off Tullama. She made a small pin-flag for me to stick on the map. About this time a change came in the old man's letters home. At first they had been elated, but now they were quieter. He didn't boast so much about the money he was making, or say anything about the Rolls. Perhaps excitement was making him quieter as he got nearer to the pepper-tree, I thought.

"I know what it is," my mother said. "He's not getting his proper meals. He's too old to be gallivanting off on his own. I bet he's not cooking proper meals for himself. And without a decent bed to sleep in—only the back of that lorry."

I thought the day would never come, but soon enough my

dad had only one town to do before he would reach Tullama. His letters usually arrived on a Tuesday—he wrote home on the Sundays—but round this time I watched for the mail every day and was late for school three mornings running. When a letter did come I grabbed it from the postman's hand and hurried inside with it, reading the postmark on the run. It was from Tullama.

"All right, all right, don't rush me, Joe," my mother said. "You and your pepper-tree."

I read over her elbow. There was only one page. There was nothing about the pepper-tree. Dad was well and making money, but he was thinking of returning soon. Only a few lines.

I couldn't understand it.

On the next Tuesday there was no letter. Nor on the Wednesday. On the Thursday my father came home. He turned up at breakfast-time. He gave us a surprise walking in like that. He said that he had sold the truck and engine and come home by train. He looked tired and shamefaced and somehow a lot older. I saw a lot more white in his moustache.

"The engine was no good," he said. "It kept breaking down. It cost me nearly all I earned and it was hungry on petrol. I had to sell it to pay back what I borrowed and get my fare home."

"Oh, Peter," my mother said, putting her arms round him. "You poor darling. I knew something was wrong."

"Mother reckoned it was the food," I said. "She reckoned you weren't getting your proper meals."

"I'll make you a cup of tea, Peter," my mother said, bustling over to the stove and pushing another piece of wood into it. "Then I'll get you some breakfast."

"By golly, that sounds a bit of all right," my father said then. This was the first time since he had walked in that he had sounded like his old self.

My mother hurried about the kitchen and my father talked a bit more. "I thought I was going to do well at first," he said. "But the engine was too old. It was always spare parts. It ate up all I earned."

He talked on about the trip. I had got over my surprise at seeing him walk in and now wanted to know all about the pepper-tree.

"Did you see the pepper-tree, dad?"

"Yes, I saw it all right."

I stood directly in front of him as he sat at the table, but he was not looking at me but at something far away. He didn't answer for what seemed a long time.

"It was a little runt of a tree, boy—and a little backyard."

He wouldn't say any more than that and he never spoke of the pepper-tree—or the Rolls—again.

Australia

Ray Mathew

PRESENT

OCTOBER and uncertain spring
Trims the park to English green.
Daisies open on the grass
Lovers have absorbing eyes.
Somewhere heaven's all the time.
We have heaven just for now.
Sing, birds, sing.

November and the very spring
Moves the streets with soft white rain.
Sunlight doubles in their glass.
Lovers share umbrella'd light.
Somewhere heaven's all the time.
We have heaven just for now.
Sing, birds, sing.

December and its summered spring
Dyes the sea to surfing green.
Picnics flower on the grass.
Lovers face their love to smile.
Somewhere heaven's all the time.
We have heaven just for now.
Sing, birds, sing.

Robert D. FitzGerald

EMBARKATION

THE land filled; and the people
had nothing to eat and no room.
They pushed each other into death as into
    a dark river.

Indeed there was no standing
and no lying down for the living.
Those nearest the cold edge
faced fear and wild water.

Drag the great double canoe
into the fear which is water,
the water which is the other death,
the death by waves of those dead by hunger.

Countries were hauled in the old time
from the sea's hollows
at the world's fence of distance
by hunger that went fishing;

yet to live past drowning is elsewhere
a dying from this place:
the death by parting.
They are dead men in the canoe.

And the young women
who will not endure being left
at the back half of parting
go too to drink salt wandering.

The last of the food and a little water
is not begrudged the lost folk.
New land or a path towards night
is in front of them; nothing behind them

but us who remain
with a little more room to die in
and one less canoe to be buried in
on this bank of the death by parting.

Krishna Baldev Vaid

A MAN OF MOODS

*E*ARLIER, Lachman Singh was with my friend, Anil. Prior to that he worked as a sort of bearer in a modest eating-shop. And before that he used to sit outside India Coffee House, polishing shoes.

Lachman Singh is a master of North-Indian cuisine; he knows how to give a fairly deceptive appearance to the house without much cost; he washes clothes with the cleverness of a dhobi; he can handle children better than a mother; but his forte is shoe-polishing where, perhaps, he is a master. Shoes polished by him shine with the transparence of a mirror and wear for years without a crack or crease. While at this work, Lachman Singh forgets himself. After applying a layer of polish on the shoes he brushes them awhile with the tenderness reminiscent of a warm old lady caressing a child's head. Then he takes a shoe and, fixing it on his right knee, rubs its toe with a piece of rag, beginning with slow movements, climaxing them with breathtaking speed. While rubbing, sometimes his tongue comes out, sometimes his teeth are fast set, and sometimes a film song escapes his lips with the speed of a fast-running train.

Lachman Singh claims that polishing a pair of shoes requires no less skill and labour than making one.

Once my friend, Anil, asked him, "Lachman Singh, why at all did you give up shoe-polishing? Why, you're an artist in this, a real one. . . ." Lachman Singh had answered with a smile—a smile envelopes all he says—"Well, *Bhai Sahib*, an idea arose in my mind one day; I said to myself, 'Lachman Singh, shouldn't you stop touching everyone's shoes?' And there and then I gave it up and went over to that eating-shop. Lachman Singh, you see, is a man of moods."

Then Lachman Singh told Anil that before polishing shoes he used to work in a garage, where he had to wash all sorts of automobiles. It was there he made friends with a white man, one John something. His car used to come in frequently for overhauling, etc. One day this gentleman gave him an unexpectedly large tip—a ten-rupee note—that brought Lachman Singh immediately down on his knees.

"I said, '*Sahib*, if I have to serve I'll serve you.' He was puzzled a trifle at first, but being green of heart, he said yes and I bade good-bye to the garage. John took me home in his car. On the way he advised me to complete the month at the garage lest I should lose my pay. But I said, '*Sahib*, Lachman Singh is a man of sudden moods, he doesn't care for money.'"

At this Anil naturally remarked, "Perhaps you quarrelled with him later." Lachman Singh smiled, "Not at all, *Bhai Sahib*. I've never quarrelled with anyone, and may I never do! Reasons were different. He was a great drunkard, you see. One day he abused me. Besides I didn't fancy his wife much. She was so hard to please. So one day I folded my hands before him and offered my resignation. He said, 'Why, Lachman Singh? Do you want more?' I said, 'No, Sahib, Lachman Singh is a moody man and he cares not for money but he can't stay for a day more.' The *Sahib* realised he was dealing with a strong man. With a laugh he said, 'All right, settle your accounts with *Mem Sahib* and here is your tip.' I took the two ten-rupee notes he was offering me. After some time that very day when the *Mem* heard about this she started murmuring. I could see that she wasn't happy about the tip. I may not know a word of English but I can understand it when it concerns me. So I immediately rushed to the bazaar and purchased a tricycle worth thirty-five rupees. I got the shopkeeper to write on a chit these words: *From Lachman Singh to Gimmy*. I tagged that on to the machine, came home and presented it to their youngest kid. The *Sahib* and his *Mem* were speechless. Even now if they see me on the roadside they stop their car to ask me how I am doing. *Bhai Sahib*, no one can say this of Lachman Singh that he is a mercenary. . . ."

Anil told me that his own contact with Lachman Singh developed rather fast into intimacy. Before his marriage Anil often went to Lachman Singh's eating-shop for meals and tea.

One day he had just sat down when Lachman Singh approached him and whispered that the meat dish was rather stale and he should take something else. This gesture pleased Anil much. After meals that day he tried to give Lachman Singh a tip which he refused with a polite smile. That was the beginning of their friendship. And soon after that Anil was married. Lachman Singh was one of the wedding party.

A few days later Anil took Shakuntala to that place while showing her round his pre-marital haunts. Lachman Singh greeted them with great exuberance and said rather loudly, "*Bhai Sahib*, the bride is a real beauty." Shakuntala felt embarrassed. Lachman Singh saw through it and said to Anil in an audible whisper, "Haven't you told her that I am an old friend." Shakuntala frowned at this.

After they had eaten Anil put his hand in his pocket for payment but Lachman Singh instantly caught his hand saying with an appeal in his voice, "Today's fare was from me." Shakuntala resented this but Anil was not able to pay for the meals despite her insistence.

And, perhaps, that very day Lachman Singh said to Anil, "*Bhai Sahib*, if you don't mind, I have an offer to make; in fact, it's a request. You see, I am fed up with the owner of this dirty place. The bastard is dishonest, every inch of him. Now, how can Lachman Singh pull on with a rogue and a cheat? If *Bhabi* has no objection, I may as well start living with you."

When Anil hesitated a little, Lachman Singh remarked, "There's not much to think about, *Bhai Sahib*. It means both times meals in exchange for faithful service. You needn't worry about pay for I'll accept anything you can easily spare. I don't need money. . . ."

When I met Lachman Singh, he had already put in a year or so with Anil and Shakuntala. And, if he was to be believed, this period, brief though it was, had wrought certain basic changes in Anil. Changes for which he held Shakuntala responsible, largely, if not entirely. For instance in the beginning he used to address Anil as *Bhai Sahib* and Shakuntala as *Bhabi*. Anil never took it ill. But Shakuntala did. So he had to change his mode of address to *Sahib* for Anil and *Bibiji* for Shakuntala.

"I know that servants are expected to address the master and mistress like that, but our relations, you see, are slightly different. Even then I wouldn't have taken it ill had Anil *Bhai Sahib* shown some disagreement with *Bhabi*. It is true people are generally obedient to their wives but. . . ."

Behind their back even now he stuck to his earlier mode of address for Shakuntala and Anil.

I was then putting up with Anil for I had no home of my own. Lachman Singh and I had taken to each other like the proverbial bedfellows in adversity. So he often took some time off his domestic chores and took me into confidence about many things that bothered him.

"The rest is all right but I just can't stand this bad habit of *Bhabi*. Every morning when I return from the market, she wants me to account for every pie [coin of small value]. I naturally take it ill and when I take anything ill I lose my temper. The matter goes to Anil *Bhai Sahib*. Now, tell me is it fair to suspect an honest man. . . ."

Sometimes he said:

"I don't know why Anil *Bhai Sahib* is going from bad to worse with regard to me. Yesterday you weren't in. I was in the kitchen cooking. And as is my habit I was humming too. You know me and my moods. Well in comes Anil *Bhai Sahib*. 'Lachman Singh, this is a home, not a brothel. Stop your humming, are you listening?' Now, I leave it to you: If a man hums while cooking just to lighten his work, does a home get changed into a brothel? Hasn't *Bhabi* herself ever hummed? And no one can say my voice is bad, at least it isn't worse than *Bhabi's*. . . ."

What a naïve man this Lachman Singh, I thought.

One day he came up to me with Meeto in his arms, and pointing to his frock said, "Look here, *Bhai Sahib*, is this colour bad? No, no, please do say if it is so. Just because it is my purchase *Bhabi* dislikes it. And even Anil *Bhai Sahib* says he doesn't like it, though, I'm sure, it is just to please *Bhabi*. . . ."

Lachman Singh has a keen insight into character, I thought.

Another day I was looking at the newspaper when Lachman Singh thumped up to my room and said: "Please come down for a moment. They are quarrelling over something and poor Meeto is crying like mad. When I intervened, *Bhabi* said, 'Mind your own business, Lachu.' And Anil says, 'Are you our servant or our father?' Now I leave it to you. . . ."

When I advised him not to poke his nose into their private affairs, he retorted, "Why not, I say. A member of the family has to intervene in everything. . . ."

How could I tell him that he was not a member of that family. With a view to putting him off I said, "This isn't your affair, Lachman Singh. Let them be. You should mind your own work."

"I'm surprised that you also talk like *Bhabi*. Then I should be reduced to a mere servant's status. But Lachman Singh is not a servant. As long as he is here everything is as much his concern as any other member's. . . ."

It took me some time to change the topic and nip the misunderstanding in the bud. We were still talking when we heard Shakuntala shouting from below, "Lachman Seeeengh, where are you? Don't you have anything to do?" And Lachman Singh went downstairs, drawing my attention with his smile to the resentment in his mistress's tone.

Anil and Shakuntala too had many complaints against Lachman Singh, though the nature of their complaints was rather different.

One of Shakuntala's chief suspicions was that Lachman Singh secretly drank a part of the milk himself, adding some water to the rest to fill it up. That's why, she said, Meeto is losing colour and Anil finds the milk so insipid.

Another of her complaints was that Lachman Singh shirked work. If an old acquaintance of Lachman Singh came to meet him, her effort was always to send the man away. Of course Lachman Singh didn't like it. Sometimes he would refuse to take meals or some such thing.

"I am fed up with his sulks. Every trifle displeases him. He behaves as if he were our master. I don't know why we are keeping him. If I had my own way I would have turned him out long ago. We'd be much better off without such an impertinent servant. And the lot he eats, my . . . !"

Mercifully these things were never said within Lachman Singh's hearing.

"I don't know why he delights in useless argument. Ask him to cook potato-and-peas; pat comes the reply, 'But we had potatoes yesterday.' Tell him to bring less milk and he'll ask, 'Why, are you dining out?' You come back from a late night show, tired, to find him waiting to hear the story of the film. . . . He'll sometimes go on chattering even if you don't as much as nod in his direction. And sometimes he is deaf to whatever you shout. If you are invited to some marriage, he'll expect to be taken along. And if you take him along, he'll go and sit idle, as if he were the chief guest. . . .

"In the beginning he got on our nerves, believe me. He would keep on eating even as he served us on the table. And if we wanted more of anything, his reply would be 'But I had kept back just enough for myself. . . .' "

While Shakuntala narrated all this, Anil generally kept quiet, though his silence seemed to be an indication of his agreement with her. I, of course, had to keep quiet out of sheer self-interest.

"When some guest drops in he becomes insufferable. He tries to outdo us in everything. He will put all sorts of questions to the visitor. Regardless of anybody's intimacy with us he'll extend a general invitation for lunch and dinner. In any case he must give a cup of tea to anyone that drops in, without our asking him to do so, and, to be frank, quite often, without even our wanting him to. You should see him when some guest is leaving. He'll run out of the kitchen to say, 'Leaving already? Why, where is the hurry? Please stay awhile. I couldn't even sit with you . . .' Now you tell us, are these the ways of a servant?"

And I thought that these may not be the ways of a servant, but they were certainly those of a wonderful man.

One of Anil's chief complaints was that Lachman Singh never asked him for money; he just made straight for the coat or for the drawer where Shakuntala kept the household money.

"And what will you say to this?" she said. "When I'm in the bathroom, he'll stand outside the closed door and keep on saying something or other. . . . 'Shall I do this? Shall I do that? Have you taken the towel in? How shall I wipe Meeto's mouth? What are you bathing with? There wasn't any soap left, or was there any?' Now, how disgraceful it is!

"And the care he takes of his appearance, my!

"One day his audacity was the limit. We had gone out; Meeto too was with us. When we returned we found the flat all locked. We thought he must be nearabouts, so we shouted for him. And, believe me, he returned after full two hours. You should have seen him as he came, his face beaming with his stupid smiles, and, what's more, he was wearing that gaberdine suit of Anil's which Anil himself uses only on special occasions! I was on fire and so was Anil. But he wouldn't let me say anything to him. Those days he used to be 'my friend' of Anil. . . ."

"To cut it short, the credit for controlling him goes to Shakuntala," said Anil. "You know, after that incident when we started putting everything under lock and key, he took it ill, grumbling that we mistrusted him.

"And so we do. Why shouldn't we? He is after all a servant."

After that, I remember, Shakuntala related how one of her parents' trusted servants had once pilfered her mother's ring and how he had not confessed his crime even under serious threats. Of course, the ring was later found on her mother's little finger.

"The rogue must have slipped it on while mother was asleep—despite her age, she always slept soundly."

After all this, when one day Lachman Singh came and told me something shocking I wasn't shocked.

Those days I was caught in an engrossing dilemma. I had to make a momentous decision: Should I propose to Anjana, or should I postpone it? So most of my time in the evening was spent in my room, pacing up and down like a fool. One evening I was engaged in this futile movement in an effort to choose the better alternative when Lachman Singh looked in.

"Well, how goes Lachman Singh?"

"*Bhai Sahib*, it is something serious. In fact, I don't know. . . ."

"Please speak out."

"On one condition."

"What?"

"That you'll put me no questions."

"Out with it, Lachman Singh."

"*Bhai Sahib*, better make your own arrangements now."

"I don't understand you."

"I suggest you shouldn't try to. I don't want to see two friends parted but . . . but . . . better look for a house before. . . ."

What Lachman Singh told me that day, on my insistence on

a full account of what Shakuntala had said about me to Anil, decided my next step. I immediately proposed to Anjana. My fears turned out to be baseless, and we were soon married.

Within a few days of my marriage Lachman Singh left Anil and came over to us.

This happened nearly six months ago. Lachman Singh is now our servant. He is extremely efficient. We ought to have no complaints against him. But surprisingly my wife, Anjana, has almost all those complaints that Shakuntala had. Lachman Singh had to discard *Bhai Sahib* and *Bhabi* for *Sahib* and *Bibiji*. Behind our back he still sticks to his own mode of address. When he hums in the kitchen, Anjana frowns and I shout at him. When he shows excessive familiarity with our guests we take it ill. When some acquaintance of his comes to see him, our effort is to send him away. Whenever he sulks we feel like threatening him with dismissal.

And, when, after some time he'll bring a frock for the child we expect, I am sure we won't like its shade. But as far as I know Lachman Singh, he'll leave us before that.

India

K. T. Krishnaswami

LIBERATION

LIBERATION
Is neither being
Nor becoming
But fulfilment.

Liberation
Is neither life
Nor death
But immortality.

Liberation
    Is neither divine
    Nor human
But transcendence.

Liberation
    Is neither renunciation
    Nor self-indulgence
But self-unfolding.

Liberation
    Is neither movement
    Nor rest
But poise.

Pakistan

Abdul Rashid Khan

RAIL-LINES

BESIDE these rail-lines
You and I face to face,
Girded by water:
To green paddy-stalks restless winds
Bring some message,
Some I understand
The rest dies with the wind.

Beside these rail-lines
You and I:
Many trains go and come,
Come and go,
The moon touches the water and drowns;
The water has received the lunar touch,
Yet I see the moon reach for the waters.

367

z

The rail-lines stretch to a distance
Very far and yet farther on,
Equidistant lines,
Have not met at any point.
Yet it seems perhaps at the horizon's end
They meet,
Become united as one.

You and I are close even now,
Look here:
On my hands your soft hands rest
Lightly now;
We are parted by a million miles.
Trains go, trains come:
Rail-lines: equidistance:
Now I am mirrored in someone's eyes,
Now I am not,
Yet we are close
Like these railway lines.

WHO'S WHO IN "SPAN"

These brief biographies are as complete and up-to-date as possible; but at the time of going to press three biographies had still not arrived. Additional information is welcomed, for incorporation in future editions.

ABBAS, Khawaja Ahmad

Born Panipat, India, 1914; educated at Aligarh University; has travelled widely and directed several films; has been journalist, columnist, short-story writer, novelist and scenarist; member of Indian National Book Trust.

ABDULLA, Mena Kashmiri

Born Bundarra, New South Wales; is a Commonwealth of Australia public servant whose principal hobby is "arguing with Ray Mathew"; has published short stories and verse in the *Bulletin*, and verse in *Australian Poetry*, 1955 and 1957.

ALI, Ahmed

Short story writer in Urdu; author of novel in English, *Twilight in Delhi*; translator of Urdu, Chinese and Indonesian poetry into English (editor and co-translator of *The Flaming Earth*, a volume of Indonesian poems from which some are included in *Span*).

ANAND, Mulk Raj

Born Peshawar, 1905; educated in the Punjab and at London and Cambridge Universities; studied philosophy in England; editor of *Marg*; organised Asian Writers' Conference in Delhi, 1956; recreations are travelling, mountaineering and friendship; has written fiction, essays and drama, and philosophy and art criticisms; publications include: *Coolie, Untouchable, Two Leaves and a Bud, The Village across the Black Waters, The Sword and the Sickle, The Banker's Trade Union and Other Stories, The Big Heart, The Tractor and the Corn Goddess, Seven Summers,* and *Private Life of an Indian Prince.*

ANWAR, Chairil

Born Medan, Sumatra, 1922; died aged 27; he began writing poetry at school, and his work began appearing in print when he was 21; his name

369

is associated with the so-called "generation of 1945" which burst into print after experiencing the hardships of wartime occupation, and broke away from the traditional form and content of Indonesian literature; his works appear principally in *Kerikil Tadjam* and *Deru Tjampur Debu*. See also Apin, Rivai.

APIN, Rivai

Born Padang Pandjang, 1927; graduated from Senior High School and became law student in Djakarta; then editor of the periodicals *Nusentara*, *Gema Suasana*, *Gelonggang* and *Zenith*; is editor-in-chief of *Zaman Baru*. Rivai Apin, Asrul Sani and Chairil Anwar were leaders of the revolutionary "Generation of '45", and the three of them published a volume of verse of their own composition, *Tiga Menguak Takdir*.

BANDARANAIKE, S. W. R. D.

Born Ceylon, 1899; educated St Thomas' College, Mount Lavinia and Christ Church College, Oxford; called to Bar in England; returned to Ceylon, 1925, to practise law and enter politics; member of State Council 1936-46; member House of Representatives and Cabinet Minister 1947; went into opposition till 1956, then became fourth Prime Minister of Ceylon.

BHATTACHARYA, Bhabani

Born India, 1906; educated in India and at University of London; assistant editor *Illustrated Weekly of India*; for a time Press Attaché to the Indian Embassy in Washington, now devotes time to writing, with travel as his recreation. Has published three novels: *So Many Hungers* (1948), *Music for Mohini* (1952), *He who Rides a Tiger* (1954); has written a fourth, *A Goddess named Gold*.

CAMPBELL, David

Born Adelong, Australia, 1915, educated King's School, Sydney, and Cambridge University; was prominent footballer; served as Wing-Commander in Royal Australian Air Force (D.F.C. and Bar); poet, short story writer and farmer near Canberra; published *Speak with the Sun* (1949) and *Miracle of Mullion Hill* (1956).

CHANYONG, Manas ("Rung Nampet", "Rudi Janyong", etc.)

Born Petchburi, Thailand, 1907; recreation, Thai classical music; author by profession, has written over 200 stories; publications include *Slave Lover* (1935), *Three Savages* (1937), and *Fighting the Monsoon* (1944).

CHATTERJEE, Margaret

Born London, 1925; educated at Oxford; lecturer in Philosophy at the University of Delhi; married with three children; interested in the composition and criticism of music, and in pianoforte and lieder recitals; music critic for *The Statesman*; has published a number of stories, articles and poems in *The Statesman, Sainik Samoehar*, and the *Illustrated Weekly of India*.

CHAYA, Prem (His Highness Prince Prem Purachatra)

Born Bangkok, 1915; educated in England; professor at Chulalongkorn and Thammasat (Political Sciences) Universities; recreation, writing; has published *Magic Lotus* (1937), *World Tour* (1952), *Khun Chang Khun Phaen* (1955) and *Scandinavian Journey* (1956).

DALAL, Nergis J.

Born Panchgani, India, 1920; a housewife with three young children; hobbies, reading, cooking and chess; has written a large number of articles and short stories, one of which, "The Sacrifice" won the All-India Short Story Competition in 1954 and has been published in *World's Prize Short Stories*.

DAS, Jibananda

Born East Bengal, 1899; died Calcutta, 1954; graduated M.A. in English at Calcutta University; became professor at City College, Calcutta, and several other educational institutions; published works include *Jhara Palak* (1928), *Dhushar Pandulipi* (1936), *Banalata Sen* (1942), *Mahaprithivi* (1944), *Sat-ti tarar timir* (1948), *Banalata Sen* (1952), *Jivananda Daser Shreshtha Kavita* (1954), *Kavitar Katha* (essays, 1956).

DEMETILLO, Ricaredo

Born Panay, Philippines, 1920; M.A. (Iowa State Univ., U.S.A.), lecturer in comparative literature and the humanities at the University of the Philippines; art critic for Manila journals. Has published verse in the United States, Italy and the Philippines, including *No Certain Weather* (1955).

DOBSON, Rosemary

Born Sydney, 1920; educated Frensham School and University of Sydney; studied and taught art; travelled abroad and worked in London publishing house; married; has published three books of verse: *In a Convex Mirror* (1944), *The Ship of Ice* (1948), and *Child with a Cockatoo* (1955).

DUTTON, Geoffrey Piers H.

Born Kapunda, Australia, 1922; educated Geelong Grammar and Oxford University. Served as Flight-Lieut. in R.A.A.F. Lecturer in English literature at Adelaide University; published two books of verse: *Night Flight and Sunrise* (1944), *Antipodes in Shoes* (1958); one novel:

The Mortal and the Marble (1950); and three travel books: *A Long Way South* (1953), *Africa in Black and White* (1955), and *States of the Union* (1958).

EASWARAN, Eknath

Born Palghat, S. India, 1914; educated at Madras and Nagpur universities. Professor of English at Morris College, Nagpur; recreations, gardening, hiking and playing on the sitar; broadcasts light talks on All-India Radio, and has published a series of sketches of rural life in Malabar, entitled *Village Vignettes*; working on full-length novel, *The Rope and the Snake*.

"FAIZ" (Faiz Ahmed Khan)

Born Sialkot, 1912, educated there and at Government College, Lahore (M.A. in English and Arabic), lecturer at M.A.O. College, Amritsar, and editor of *Adab-e-Latif*; lecturer at Hadley College; worked in War Department of Government of India during World War II; became editor of *Pakistan Times* in 1947 and subsequently chief editor of *Imroze*; active in Labour movement in Pakistan; imprisoned under Pakistan Safety Ordinance for some time; published three collections of lyrics: *Naqsh-e-Fariyadi*, *Dast-e-Saba* and *Zindannama*.

FITZGERALD, R. D.

Born Sydney, 1902; educated Sydney Grammar School and Sydney University; spent five years in Fiji as surveyor; now with Australian Department of the Interior; published four books of verse: *To Meet the Sun* (1929), *Moonlight Acre* (1938), *Heemskerck Shoals* (1949), *Between Two Tides* (1952).

FORREST, David

Born Maryborough, Queensland, lives in Brisbane; bank officer; hobbies, writing and shooting; has had several short stories published and has written a novel now being considered by a publisher.

GILMORE, Mary, D.B.E.

Born near Goulburn, Australia, 1865; taught for some years; went with William Lane group to Paraguay; returned to Australia 1902, and conducted women's page of Sydney *Worker*. Created Dame of the British Empire, 1936, in recognition of her contribution to literature. Has published twelve books of verse: *Married and Other Verses* (1911), *The Tale of Tiddley Winks* (1917), *The Passionate Heart* (1918), *The Tilted Cart* (1925), *The Wild Swan* (1930), *The Rose Tree* (1931), *Under the Wilgas* (1932), *Battlefields* (1939), *The Disinherited* (1941), *Selected Verse* (1948), *Fourteen Men* (1954), and *Verses for Children* (1955); and several books of prose including *Old Days: Old Ways* (1934), and *More Recollections* (1935).

GONZALEZ, N. V. M.

Born Remblon, Philippines, 1915, a teacher at University of the Philippines; recreation, fishing; has published four books: *The Winds of April* (1941), *Seven Hills Away* (1949), *Children of the Ash-Covered Loam and Other Stories* (1954), and *A Season of Grace* (1956).

HALL, Maxwell

Former government official; now farming near Jesselton, North Borneo, where he is well known among the indigenous people; has published three books: *Makan Siap, Kinabalu Guerillas,* and *Labuan Story*; also several short stories.

HOPE, Alec Derwent

Born Cooma, Australia, 1907; educated Hobart and Sydney; B.A. (Syd. and Oxon.); has been teacher, vocational psychologist and lecturer, and is now Professor of English at Canberra University College; well-known critic and reviewer, and has published one book of verse: *The Wandering Islands* (1955).

JOAQUIN, Nick

Born 1917, Manila; journalist (*Philippines Free Press*); recreation, music; has published *Prose and Poems* (1953).

JOSÉ, Francisco Sionil

Born Pangasinan 1924; attended University of Santo Tomas; became a journalist; managing editor since 1949 of the *Sunday Times Magazine*, editor since 1956 of *Comment* (quarterly dealing with Philippine affairs); editor from 1958 of *Progress* (annual publication of *Manila Times*); is national secretary of Philippine Centre of International P.E.N.; hobby: photography; has published two novels: *The Chief Mourner* (1953), *The Balete Tree* (1956); is preparing *A Cultural History of the Ilocanos* and a tetralogy *The Pretenders* (of which "The Ancestor" is a chapter).

JOSHI, Umashankar Jethalal

Born Bombay, 1911; Professor at Gujarat University, editor of *Sanskriti* (Culture), and a member of the National Academy of Letters; recreation, conversation; has published verse, short stories and essays: *Vishva Shanti* (1931), *Gangotri* (1934), *Nisheeth* (1939), *Prachina* (1944), *Atithya* (1946), *Vasant-Varsha* (1954); one-act plays: *Sapnna Bhora* (1936); short stories: *Shravani Melo* (1937); criticism: *Akho* (1941); essays: *Goshthi* (1951).

KHIEM, Pham Duy

Born Hanoi, 1908; educated in France; taught for some years at Lycee Albert Sarraut, Hanoi; became Secretary of State in first Ngo Dinh Diem government, High Commissioner in Paris, 1954, Ambassador in Paris 1956.

KRISHNASWAMI, Kurichi Tiruvenkata Ayyangar

Born Serankulam, India 1891; formerly Professor of English, now engaged in study and research into philosophical, mystic and occult literature; has published critical articles, essays and poems.

LAL, P.

Born Punjab, 1929; lives in Calcutta; principal occupation "being human"; has published *The Art of the Essay* (1951) and *Six Sanskrit Plays* (1958).

LEONG, Margaret

Born St Louis, Missouri; graduated B.A. in History, M.A. in Education and Psychology, Columbia University; is a teacher, living in Singapore; has published *The Coral Sands* (1957), *My First Poetry Book, The Air Above the Tamerinds* and *Rivers to Senang* (1958). Lyrics for *Songs of Malaya* are in production.

LUBIS, Mochtar

Born Central Sumatra 1922; journalist and editor-in-chief of *Indonesia Raya*; translates from English and Chinese; interested in painting, growing orchids, tennis, carpentry and flying; has published two novels: *Tak Ada Esok* (There is no Tomorrow) (1950) and *Djalan Tak Ada Udjung* (Road Without End) (1956); one book of short stories: *Si Djhmal* (1950); three other books, *Tjatatan Korea* (Korean Notebook) (1951), *Perkenalan Di Asia Tenggara* (Journalist's Report on South-east Asia, 1952), *Perlawatan Ke Amerika* (A Visit to America) (1953) and *Pers Dan Wartawan* (The Press and Pressman) (1954).

McAULEY, James

Born Lakemba, Australia, 1917; M.A., Dip.Ed., Sydney University; during World War II was in Australian Army Directorate of Research and Civil Affairs; now Senior Lecturer in Government at the Australian School of Pacific Administration. Is editor of *Quadrant*, and well-known critic and reviewer; has published two books of verse: *Under Aldebaran* (1946) and *A Vision of Ceremony* (1956).

MANTO, Saadat Hasan

Born 1912 in East Panjab, educated in Amritsar and at Aligarh Muslim University. Joined Urdu-language newspaper and began translating

French and Russian fiction; soon developed creative short story talent. Edited Urdu film journal at Bombay, and wrote script for several films; published collections of radio plays written for All-India Radio at Delhi during World War II. After partition lived in Lahore and wrote 300 stories, sketches, radio plays and essays in sixteen years; died 1955. Better-known titles include *Dhuan* (Smoke), *Nimrood ki Khudai* (Kingdom of Nimrood), *Gunje Farishte* (Bald Angels), *Khalee Botalen Khalee Dibea* (Empty Bottles, Empty Tins) and *Sarkandoan ke Peeche* (Behind the Reeds).

MARSHALL, Alan

Born Noorat, Australia, 1902. A writer by profession, he gathers material—Australiana, folk stories and bush songs—caravanning round Australia; has published nine books: *These are my People* (New edition 1957), *Tell us about the Turkey, Joe* (1946), *Ourselves Writ Strange* (1948), *Pull down the Blind* (1949), *How Beautiful are Thy Feet* (1948), *Bumping into Friends* (1950), *People of the Dream Time* (1952), *I Can Jump Puddles* (1955), and *How's Andy Going?* (1956).

MATHEW, Ray

Born Sydney, 1929. Regards tutoring as his principal occupation, but writing as his recreation and hobby; has written four one-act and two full-length plays, and has published two books of verse: *With Cypress Pine* (1951), and *Song and Dance* (1956).

MIHARDJA, Achdiat Karta

Born Western Java, 1911; head of Editorial Board of Mass Education at Ministry of Education; president of the Indonesian P.E.N. Club; vice-president of Association of Indonesian Writers; member of Board of Indonesian Cultural Body and of Advisory Board of Indonesian Broadcasting Commission. Interested in literature and politics; published one novel: *The Atheist* (1948); two plays: *Raden Sastro's Family* (1952) and *Dress and Falsehood* (1953); and one book of short stories: *Cracks and Tensions* (1956).

MOELJONO, Jake

Born Bandung, Java, 1925; attended school in Bandung; spent several years studying medicine in Djarkata, and continued these studies in Amsterdam.

MOORE, Tom Inglis

Born Camden, Australia, 1901, educated Sydney Grammar School; B.A. (Syd.), M.A. (Oxon.); Associate Professor of English, University of Philippines, Manila, 1928-31; leader-writer on *Sydney Morning*

Herald 1934-40; served in A.I.F. 1940-5; now Senior Lecturer in Australian Literature, Canberra University College; member of Commonwealth Literary Fund Board; has published two plays: *Love's Revenge* (1930) and *We're Going Through* (1944); one novel: *The Half Way Sun* (1935); three books of verse: *Adagio in Blue* (1938), *Emu Parade* (1942), *Bayonet and Grass* (1957); has written critical studies, including one book: *Six Australian Poets* (1942); and has edited *Best Australian One-Act Plays* (1938), *Australian Poetry* (1947), *Australia Writes* (1953), and *Kendall's Selected Poems* (1957).

MORRISON, John

Born England, 1906, reached Australia in 1928; has worked as station hand and on waterfront; published two books of short stories: *Sailors Belong to Ships* (1947) and *Black Cargo* (1955), and two novels: *The Creeping City* (1949) and *Port of Call* (1950).

ONN, Patrick Kah Ng

Born Kuala Lumpur, 1932; he is a teacher with a wide variety of interests, including stage-craft, night-club entertaining (non-professional), exotic cooking, Eastern (especially Balinese and Malayan) ballet, dress designing and collecting paintings; has written various scripts for Radio Malaya, and has had a number of short stories published in *Youth* and *The Young Malayan*.

PALMER, Vance E.

Born Bundaberg, Australia, 1885; educated Ipswich Grammar School; journalist in Brisbane, then freelance writer in England; visited Russia and Asia; spent time outback; served in first A.I.F.; member of Advisory Board of Commonwealth Literary Fund; publications include two critical studies on A. G. Stephens and Frank Wilmot; two dramas: *The Black Horse* (1924) and *Hail Tomorrow* (1947); two books on Australian history: *National Portraits* (1940) and *The Legend of the Nineties* (1954); two books of verse: *The Forerunners* (1915) and *The Camp* (1920); and sixteen books of fiction, including *Sea and Spinifex* (short stories, 1942), *Cyclone* (1947), *Golconda* (1948), *Let the Birds Fly* (short stories, 1955), *The Swayne Family* (1957), *The Rainbow Bird* (short stories, 1957), *Seedtime* (1957), and *The Passage* (New edition 1957).

RAJARATNAM, S.

Born Ceylon, 1915; lived in Malaya from infancy and was educated there and at London University; studied law at the Middle Temple, but left law for journalism; became editor of *Singapore Standard*, then leader and feature writer for the *Straits Times*; radio scriptwriter and broadcaster; recreations are keeping tropical fish, badminton, reading and dreaming. Has had articles published in U.K., U.S.A., Germany and Switzerland, and short stories published in U.S.A. and U.K.

ROBINSON, Roland E.

Born Belbriggan, Co. Clare, Ireland, 1912; has been in Australia since age of nine. Worked in western New South Wales and in Northern Territory, where he lived with the aborigines and gathered the material on myths and legends on which his book *Legend and Dreaming* (1952) is based; collaborated on script for prize-winning film *Back of Beyond*; won Commonwealth Literary Fund Award for *Tumult of the Swans* (1953), and was awarded Commonwealth Literary Fund Fellowship in 1954, which enabled him to gather the material for *The Feathered Serpent* (1956); has also published *Beyond the Grass-tall Spears* (1945), and *Language of the Sand* (1949).

ROCES, Alejandro R.

Born Manila 1924; is Bachelor of Fine Arts, Dean of Institute of Arts and Sciences, Far Eastern University; hobbies: reading and writing; has published in the *New Mexico Quarterly*, U.S.A.

SAHA, Proshanto Kumar

Born Calcutta, 1932; teacher of English in Cleveland, Ohio; formerly associate editor of *The Orient Review*; hobbies, billiards and table tennis; has published a number of reviews, short stories and poems, and one novel: *After the Sunlit Hour*.

SANTOS, Bienvenido N.

Born Manila, 1911; educated universities of Philippines, Illinois, Columbia and Harvard U.S.A.; edited *Philippines* (government magazine pub. Washington, D.C.); lecturer for American Association of Teachers' Colleges; actively interested in teachers' associations; President of Legazpi College; has won a number of prizes for short stories and holds a Rockefeller Foundation fellowship in Creative Writing; has published one book of short stories: *You Lovely People* (1955); and one of verse: *The Wounded Stag* (1956).

SEN, Samarendra Nath

Born Calcutta 1916; graduated as Gold Medallist in English, Calcutta University; became successively lecturer, Commercial College, Delhi; assistant editor, Publications Division, Ministry of Information and Broadcasting, New Delhi; sub-editor *The Statesman*, Calcutta; Bengali translator, Foreign Languages Publishing House, Moscow; has published *Samar Sener Kavita* (poems, 1954).

SETT, Adi K. (Ardeshir Kavasji Sett)

Born Bombay 1904; writer by profession; Fellow of Royal Geographical and Royal Art Societies; recreations, walking, meeting people and Western classical music; has published *A Trip to Ootacamundi* (1920), *Chameleon* (1928), *The Emperor Shah Jahan: Man and Artist* (1937), *The Light Above the Clouds: Thirty-nine Poems* (1948), and *Rain in my Heart: Forty Poems* (1954).

SHIREEN, Mumtaz

Born Mysore, 1924, educated Universities of Mysore, Karachi and Oxford; travelled in Europe; published Urdu literary journal, *Nya Daur*, in collaboration with her husband (Dr Samad Shaheen); has written cultural study of Emily Brontë, compiled an anthology of American short stories, translated Steinbeck's *The Pearl* into Urdu, has a collection of cultural articles and one of short stories, *Dipak Rag Nagarya* due for publication shortly, and has published a book of short stories, *Apni Nagaria.*

SHRIDHARANI, Krishnalal

Born Umrala, India, 1911; columnist for *Amrita Bazar Patrika* and an author; recreations, gardening and birds; has written and published both in Gujarati and English: *Vadalo* (1931), *Insan Mita Dunga* (1932), *Pilan Palash* (1933), *Padmini* (1934), *Morna Inda* (1934), *Kodiya* (1934), *By Piyo, Gori!* (1946), *Insan Mita Dunga ane Biji Vato* (1950), and *War without Violence* (1939), *My India, My America* (1941), *Warning to the West* (1942), *The Mahatma and the World* (1946), *The Big Four of India* (1951), *Story of the Indian Telegraph* (1953), *An Adventure of the Upside-Down Tree* (1956), and *The Journalist in India* (1956).

SIBUNRUANG, Jit-Kasem

Born Bangkok, 1915; is a professor at Chulalongkorn and Political Sciences Universities; recreation, writing; has published a number of works in English, French and Thai: *Le Français par la Radio* (1951), *Siamese Folk Tales* (1954), *Le Théâtre Français* (1954), *La Littérature Siamoise* (1955), *Le Roi Rama IV et le Théâtre Siamois* (1957), *Manuel de Français* (1957).

SITUMORANG, Sitor

Born Central Sumatra, 1924; received secondary school education in Djakarta just before the Japanese occupation; worked during the revolution against Dutch rule as a freelance journalist in Medan and Java; later spent several years in Europe and one in U.S.A.; member of the National Council of the Republic of Indonesia; has written critical essays on modern Indonesian literature; author of volumes of plays, poems and short stories.

378

SMITH, Vivian Brian

Born Hobart, Tasmania, 1933; educated Hobart High School and University of Tasmania; lecturer in French at the University of Tasmania; published one book: *The Other Meaning* (1956).

"SOD, Dok Mai" (Mom Luang Bubpa Sukich Nimmanheminda)

Born 1906; educated at a French convent; is a housewife whose principal hobby is sewing; has published six books: *Satroo Kong Choa Lon* (Her Enemy) (1929), *Kwarm Pid Krang Rag* (The First Mistake) (1930), *Karm Koa* (The Nemesis) (1935), *Chai Chana Kong Luang Narupal* (The Victory of Luang Narupal) (1956), *Nee Lae Lok* (This World of Ours) (1935), *Poo Dee* (The Nobles) (1937).

SOEBROTO, Oentoeng

Born Tegal, Java, 1928; an economist, obtained Master of Commerce degree in Australia; recreations, hiking, beaches, cards and writing; has published a number of freelance articles in Indonesia, Ceylon, Canberra and Sydney.

STEWART, Douglas

Born Eltham, New Zealand, 1913; educated at New Plymouth Boys' High School and Victoria University College; on staff of New Zealand newspapers, then worked passage to England; has lived in Australia since 1938 and now edits "Red Page" of the *Bulletin*; has published seven books of verse: *Green Lions* (1936), *The White Cry* (1938), *Elegy for an Airman* (1940), *The Dosser in Springtime* (1946), *Glencoe* (1947), *Sun Orchids* (1952) and *The Birdsville Track* (1956); four plays: *Ned Kelly* (1943), *Fire on the Snow* and *The Golden Lover* (1943), and *Shipwreck* (1946); one book of criticism: *The Flesh and the Spirit* (1947); and, with Nancy Keesing, has edited *Australian Bush Ballads* (1955) and *Old Bush Songs* (1957).

STIVENS, Dal

Born Blayney, Australia, 1911; author and journalist; recreations, travel, music, natural history and theatre; has returned from eight years abroad; publications include *The Tramp and Other Stories* (1936), *The Courtship of Uncle Henry and Other Tales* (1946), *Jimmy Brockett* (novel, 1951), *The Gambling Ghost and Other Tales* (1953), *Ironbark Bill* (1955), *The Scholarly Mouse and Other Tales* (1957), *The Wide Arch* (novel, 1958). Has edited *Coast to Coast* (1957-8).

"SUYIN, Han", (Elizabeth K. Chow, Mrs E. Comber)

Born Peking, China, 1917; graduated in medicine from London University, 1948; hobbies and recreations, writing, Siamese cats and water skiing; has published four books: *Destination Chungking* (1942), *A Many-Splendoured Thing* (1952), . . . *and the rain my drink* (1955) and *The Mountain is Young* (1958).

"TAMBIMUTTU" (Thurairajah Tambimuttu)

Born Jaffna, Ceylon, 1916; spent early life in Ceylon; went to London in 1937; subsequently launched *Poetry in London*; is now in New York publishing *Poetry London—New York*; has compiled *Anthology of Poetry in Wartime*, and is working on an anthology of Indian verse; has written a number of short stories, poems, and critical articles.

THANDAVESWARA, Sri

Born Hassan, S. India, 1910; M.A., University of Mysore, studied law at University of Bombay; worked in Government Service for eighteen years; became a business executive and vice-president of the Indian Drama League; recreations, writing and public speaking; has published a number of short stories.

TIEMPO, Edith L. (Mrs)

Born Nueva Vizcaya, Philippines, 1919; Professor of English at the Silliman University, where she has recently returned from the United States; has published verse, a number of essays, short stories and critical articles, and one novel: *A Blade of Fern* (1956).

TOER, Pramoedya Ananta

Born Java, 1925; war correspondent during Independence campaign; author by profession; many of his works have been translated into Spanish, Dutch, English, German, Chinese and Russian; has published seven novels: *Keluarga Gerilja* (The Guerilla Family) (1950), *Perburuan* (Pursuit) (1950), *Mereka Jang Dilumpuhkan* (The Paralysed) (1951), *Ditepi Kali Bekasi* (On the Bank of the Bekasi River) (1951), *Gulat* (The Struggle) (1953), *Si Midah Borgigi Emas* (Midela, the Girl with a Golden Tooth) (1954), *Korupsi* (Corruption) (1955), and four books of short stories: *Subuh* (Dawn) (1950), *Pertjikan Revolusi* (Spatters of the Revolution) (1950), *Tjerita Dari Blora* (Stories from Blora) (1952), and *Tjerita Dari Djakarta* (Stories from Djakarta) (1957).

VAID, Krishna Baldev

Born 1927; a teacher of English language and literature in the Hans Raj College, Delhi University; recreations, reading fiction and meeting people; writes in Hindi and translates into English, has had a number of stories published, including some in New York and London, and has published a novel: *Us Ka Bachpan* (His Childhood) (1957).

VILLA, José Garcia

Born Manila; poet and short story writer; attaché to the Philippine Mission to the United Nations; has published *Footnote to Youth* (1933), *Have Come, Am Here* (1942), *Volume Two* (1949), *Selected Poems and New* (1958).

WEBB, Francis

Born Adelaide 1925, but lived mainly in Sydney; educated Christian Brothers School and Sydney University; served in R.A.A.F. during World War II; went to Canada after war; returned to Australia then went to England; Commonwealth Literary Fund Fellowship, 1957; published two books of verse: *A Drum for Ben Boyd* (1948), and *Leichhardt in Theatre* (1952).

WRIGHT, Judith Arundell (Mrs J. McKinney)

Born Armidale, 1915; educated by correspondence and at New England Girls' School and Sydney University; spent a year in Europe, and worked for University Commission and University of Queensland. Now devotes herself to writing and domestic duties; hobbies, surfing and gardening; has published four books of verse: *The Moving Image* (1946), *Woman to Man* (1949), *The Gateway* (1953), *The Two Fires* (1955); one of biography: *The Generations of Men* (1958); one children's story: *The Kings of the Dingoes* (1958); and has edited two anthologies: *A Book of Australian Verse* (1956) and *New Land New Language* (1957).

"ZAWGYI" (U Thein Han)

Born Pyapon, India, 1908; educated at the Rangoon University and the universities of London and Dublin; librarian, University of Rangoon; member of the Burma Research Society and of the Executive Council of the Burma Translation Society; translated *The Cloister and the Hearth* (Charles Reade), *The Would-be Gentleman* (Molière) and *Shakuntala* (Kalidasa); has published collections of essays, short stories and poems, including *New Year Blossoms* (poems, 1950) and *U Lun: Man and Poet* (1955).